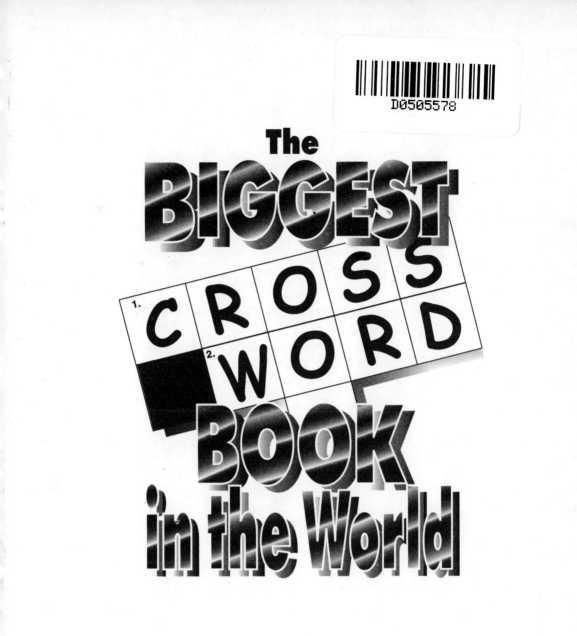

The
BIGGEST
CROSS
WORD
BOOK
in the World

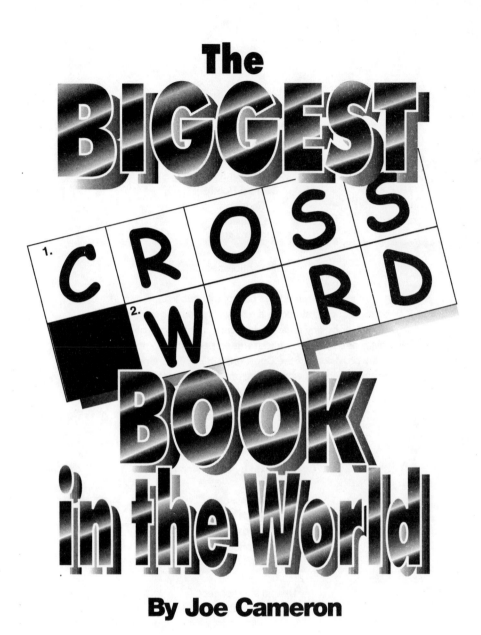

The BIGGEST CROSSWORD BOOK in the World

By Joe Cameron

Capella

Published by Arcturus Publishing Limited
for Bookmart Limited
Registered Number 2372865
Trading as Bookmart Limited
Desford Road
Enderby
Leicester
LE19 4AD

This edition published 2003

Printed and bound in India

Cover design by Chris Smith

Crosswords:
© Dilemma Puzzles
PO Box 200
Tonbridge
Kent TN11 0XX

Design and concept:
© Arcturus Publishing Ltd
26/27 Bickels Yard, 151–153 Bermondsey Street, London SE1 3HA

ISBN 1-84193-032-6

CONTENTS

PUZZLES

SOLUTIONS

THE

PUZZLES

The Biggest Crossword Book In The World

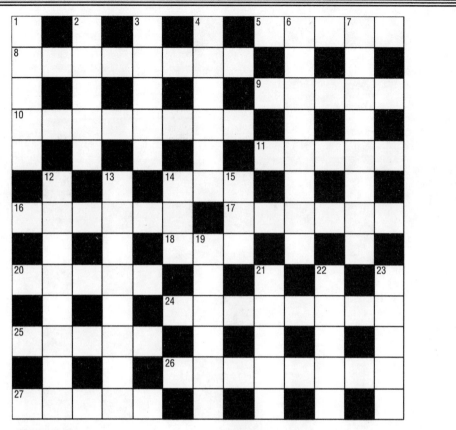

ACROSS

5 Amidst (5)
8 Former name for Zimbabwe (8)
9 Concede the truth (5)
10 Cable message (8)
11 Body of water (5)
14 Meadow, pasture (3)
16 Husky (6)
17 German city (6)
18 Rugby score (3)
20 Scope (5)
24 Queue of traffic (8)
25 French novelist (5)
26 Escape clause? (8)
27 Cut (5)

DOWN

1 Speak publicly (5)
2 Money (slang) (5)
3 Squeeze into narrow space (5)
4 Fierce verbal attack (6)
6 Remedy (8)
7 Trouble-maker (8)
12 Character from Mad Hatter's Tea Party (8)
13 Annoy, pester (8)
14 Allow (3)
15 Aviator, - - - Johnson (3)
19 Debate logically (6)
21 Run away with a lover (5)
22 Early conqueror of parts of England (5)
23 Winter sportsman (5)

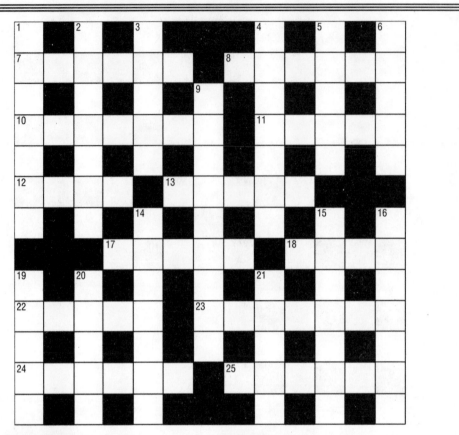

ACROSS

7 International agreement (6)
8 Knife (6)
10 Deeds (7)
11 Live (5)
12 Dinosaur (1-3)
13 Inflexible (5)
17 Permitted amount (5)
18 Water vapour (4)
22 Needless (5)
23 Rear, nourish (7)
24 Comfortable bar (6)
25 Serious (6)

DOWN

1 Secrecy (7)
2 Cured hide (7)
3 One of the Three Musketeers (5)
4 Tearfully sentimental (7)
5 Think alike (5)
6 Honestly (5)
9 Helper (9)
14 Coin-operated record-player (7)
15 Mixed with water (7)
16 Spoke (7)
19 Tend (5)
20 Mature person (5)
21 Welcome (5)

The Biggest Crossword Book In The World

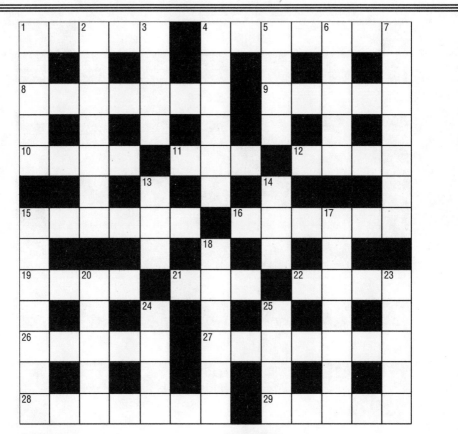

ACROSS

1 Throw out, expel (5)
4 Land measure (7)
8 Pantomime hero (7)
9 Picture surround (5)
10 Twofold (4)
11 Hard knock (3)
12 Orange peel (4)
15 Girl's name (6)
16 Ready for action (6)
19 Man (4)
21 Soft roll (3)
22 Golf stroke (4)
26 Shatter (5)
27 Hard and fragile (7)
28 Layman (7)
29 Linger (5)

DOWN

1 African antelope (5)
2 Proceed from a source (7)
3 Neat (4)
4 Tim - - -, British tennis player (6)
5 Wristband (4)
6 Humiliate (5)
7 Built (7)
13 Dance (3)
14 Distress call (1, 1, 1)
15 Branch of mathematics (7)
17 Stammer (7)
18 Hairdresser (6)
20 John Major's wife (5)
23 Minute (5)
24 Eyelid sore (4)
25 Slight colour (4)

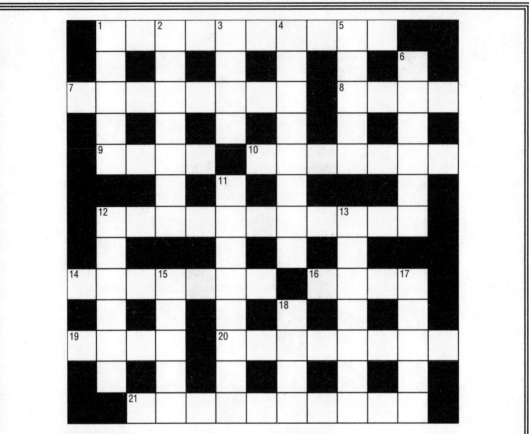

ACROSS

1 Favourable circumstances (10)
7 Healing cream (8)
8 Twisted (4)
9 Make money (4)
10 Remark (7)
12 Finishing line (7, 4)
14 Jewellery item (7)
16 Mature (4)
19 Thaw (4)
20 Coal mine (8)
21 Ruling politicians (10)

DOWN

1 Blazing (5)
2 Old-timer (7)
3 Want (4)
4 Notwithstanding (8)
5 Famous racecourse (5)
6 Small basket for fruit (6)
11 Highest point (8)
12 Sigourney - - -, actress (6)
13 Opening (7)
15 Proportion (5)
17 Lesser white heron (5)
18 Tribe bearing the same surname (4)

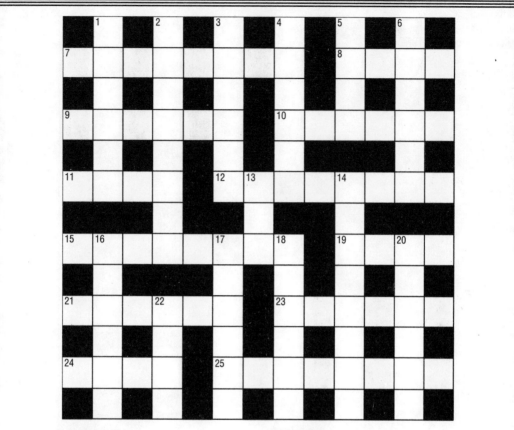

ACROSS

7 Revolted (8)
8 Location (4)
9 Divide in two (6)
10 Writer (6)
11 Bye-bye! (2-2)
12 Distinguished (8)
15 Criminal (8)
19 Apply paint (4)
21 Hire payment (6)
23 Old gold coin (6)
24 Prison room (4)
25 Blend of tea (4, 4)

DOWN

1 Queen's title (6)
2 Send as a deputy (8)
3 Heavy overcoat (6)
4 Electric lamp inventor (6)
5 Russian ruler (4)
6 Steady, firm (6)
13 Sooner than (3)
14 Film, *Four - - - and a Funeral* (8)
16 Probe, antenna (6)
17 Pleasant (sound) (6)
18 Consider (6)
20 One-sided (6)
22 Lean (4)

The Biggest Crossword Book In The World

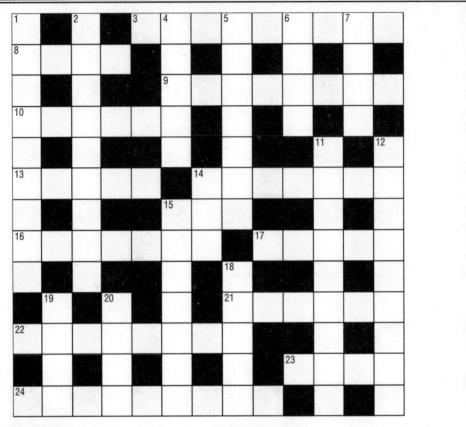

ACROSS

3 Hair colour (3, 6)
8 Wrestling match (4)
9 Made bigger (8)
10 Consolation (6)
13 Tusk material (5)
14 Underground cave (7)
15 Wrong-doing (3)
16 False (7)
17 Proficient (5)
21 Large collection
of foreign colonies (6)
22 American state (8)
23 Greek goat's-milk
cheese (4)
24 Pleasure, satisfaction (9)

DOWN

1 Former name for
Ethiopia (9)
2 Earth-moving
machine (9)
4 Melodious (5)
5 Inflatable toy (7)
6 Fairy-tale giant (4)
7 Sketched (4)
11 Occasionally (9)
12 Cultured bloke! (9)
14 Match (3)
15 Miser (7)
18 Sticky sap (5)
19 Medicinal herb,
- - - vera (4)
20 Liquid measure (4)

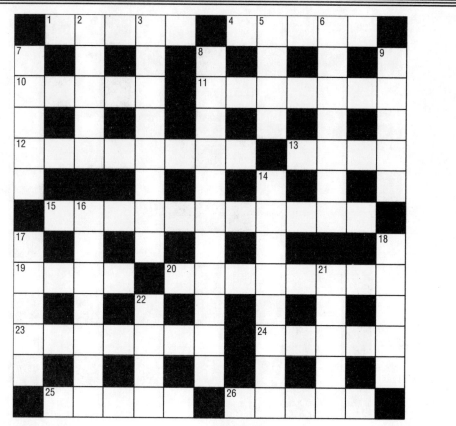

ACROSS

1 Train driver's union (5)
4 Fragile (5)
10 Floor support (5)
11 Either side of (7)
12 Earn vast amounts of money! (4, 2, 2)
13 Ship's officer (4)
15 Balanced and reliable (5-6)
19 Move (a muscle) (4)
20 Alluring (8)
23 Ungrateful person (7)
24 City in Nebraska (5)
25 Improvised (2, 3)
26 Sharp ringing sound (5)

DOWN

2 Smug grin (5)
3 Plaited (8)
5 Religious ceremony (4)
6 Copy (7)
7 Narrow inlet of the sea (5)
8 American singer (6, 5)
9 Carouse (5)
14 Reddish brown bird (5, 3)
16 Came into view (7)
17 Fasten (5)
18 Dazzling effect (5)
21 Mark - - -, *Tom Sawyer* author (5)
22 Stodgy pudding (4)

ACROSS

1 Traffic barricade (9)
8 Forehead (4)
9 Continuous (9)
10 Hard-winged insect (6)
13 Agreement (6)
15 Very angry (5)
16 Perform, play out (5)
17 Sound of a clock's bell (5)
18 Capital of Vietnam (5)
21 Spoiled (6)
22 Popular 'whodunit' board game (6)
25 Burden, drawback (9)
26 List of duties (4)
27 Roman soldier (9)

DOWN

2 Corpulent (5)
3 Supplies store (5)
4 Second of two (6)
5 Man's scarf (6)
6 Tropical amphibian (9)
7 Cheat (7)
11 Wipe out (9)
12 Supple (5)
14 Politician, - - - Parkinson (5)
16 Put aside for a specific purpose (7)
19 Regard highly (6)
20 Wild American cat (6)
23 Make a sound (5)
24 Wild dog (5)

ACROSS

1 Hotel worker (12)
9 Increase in pay (5)
10 Undressed kid (5)
11 Welfare body (1, 1, 1)
12 Military shop (inits)
13 Insane (7)
15 Sledge (6)
17 Accounts dossier (6)
20 Cravat (7)
23 Destruction, damage (5)
25 Hawaiian garland (3)
26 Slight tint (5)
27 Game of chance (5)
28 Operating theatre worker (12)

DOWN

2 Heather (5)
3 Night-time (7)
4 Scuffle (6)
5 Film legend, - - - Welles (5)
6 Inactive (5)
7 Wizard of Oz character (3, 9)
8 Ol' Blue Eyes (5, 7)
14 Combine (3)
16 Irritate (3)
18 Display (7)
19 Look forward to (6)
21 Single-file Cuban dance (5)
22 Lock of hair (5)
24 Roman goddess of love (5)

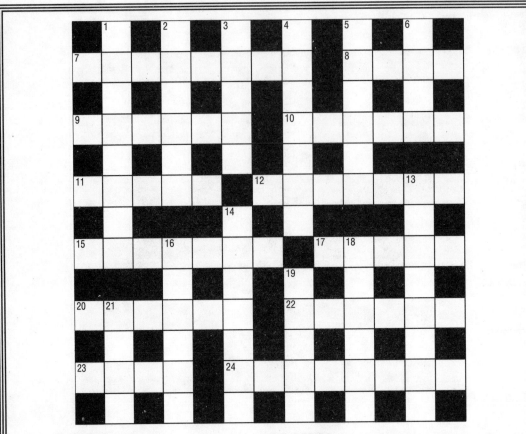

ACROSS

7 Spanish plantation (8)
8 Which thing? (4)
9 Manage, control (6)
10 Horse harness (6)
11 Unclothed (5)
12 Flightless bird (7)
15 Collection of books or records (7)
17 Tom - - -, singer (5)
20 Bully (6)
22 Specialist (6)
23 Leap in water (4)
24 In a different country (8)

DOWN

1 Squid (8)
2 Pierce with many holes (6)
3 List of subjects (5)
4 Walker (7)
5 Canvas shelter (6)
6 Clear water from a boat (4)
13 Cold sweet (3-5)
14 Personal liberty (7)
16 Bookworm (6)
18 Object (6)
19 Delay (5)
21 Give forth (4)

The Biggest Crossword Book In The World

ACROSS

1 *Coronation Street* star (7, 6)
7 Warm jacket (5)
8 Railway car (7)
9 Oriental (7)
10 Occurred (5)
11 Clothing (7)
17 Golf clubs (5)
18 Plunge into liquid (7)
20 Violent storm (7)
21 Period of development (5)
22 Conker tree (5, 8)

DOWN

1 Kermit the Frog, eg (6)
2 Cherry red (6)
3 Diminish (5)
4 Raise (7)
5 Use (6)
6 Place where food is kept (6)
8 Grand Prix venue (3, 6)
12 Extract from a book (7)
13 Spasmodic jerk (6)
14 Frightening movie (6)
15 Initiate into the priesthood (6)
16 Reiterate (6)
19 Biblical character (5)

ACROSS

1 Revolting (4)
4 Sample of cloth (6)
8 Large cylindrical airship (8)
9 Type of bean (4)
10 Of the kidneys (5)
11 Character (7)
13 Knitting rod (6)
15 Chain of police (6)
17 Shetland Isles town (7)
19 General truth (5)
22 Recipient from a will (4)
23 Absurd (8)
24 Chaos (6)
25 Greek god (4)

DOWN

2 Flowery plant (5)
3 Land of the Midnight Sun (7)
4 Bottom part of a door (4)
5 Declare in public (8)
6 Hereditary Hindu class (5)
7 Electricity generating machine (6)
12 Compassionate (8)
14 Cricket team (6)
16 Accept as fact (7)
18 More adverse (5)
20 US state (5)
21 Small tipple (4)

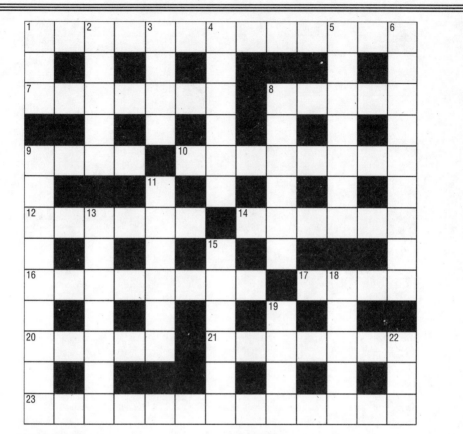

ACROSS

1 Lazy, idle (13)
7 Tasteful in dress (7)
8 Fleshy fruit (5)
9 Glaswegian? (4)
10 Refuse vehicle (8)
12 Tell (6)
14 Buy back (6)
16 Magician (8)
17 Flow (4)
20 Express a personal belief (5)
21 Coach (7)
23 Tiny European principality (13)

DOWN

1 Tell fibs (3)
2 Statement of faith (5)
3 Eve's partner (4)
4 Man's name (6)
5 Curving inwards (7)
6 Circus performer (4, 5)
8 Multicoloured (6)
9 Sponge cake (5, 4)
11 Wallpaper border (6)
13 Secretive (7)
15 Irish PM, - - - Ahern (6)
18 Snow leopard (5)
19 Cereal (4)
22 Dashed (3)

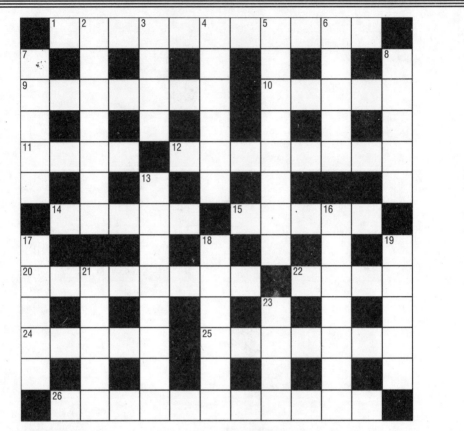

ACROSS

1 Patron saint of travellers (11)
9 Overseas letters (3, 4)
10 Soldier's fur hat (5)
11 Fine port (4)
12 Rule imperiously (8)
14 Small hill (5)
15 Father Christmas (5)
20 Hinder (8)
22 Jetty (4)
24 Bedeck (5)
25 Overhaul of a vehicle (7)
26 Chance (11)

DOWN

2 Whaler's barbed spear (7)
3 Saddam Hussein's country (4)
4 Hard animal fat (6)
5 Innkeeper (8)
6 Occur next (5)
7 Volley of shots (5)
8 Wales (5)
13 Large pink wading bird (8)
16 Foreign traveller (7)
17 Rot (5)
18 Fast social group? (3, 3)
19 Winona - - -, film star (5)
21 Chew noisily (5)
23 Smile (4)

The Biggest Crossword Book In The World

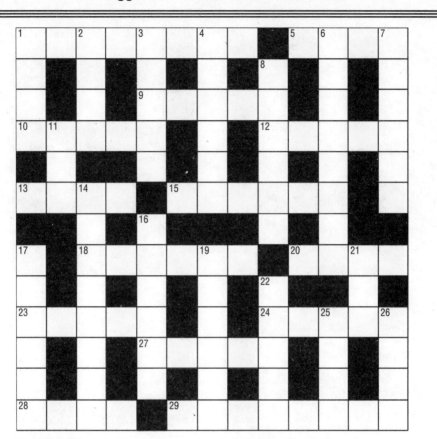

ACROSS

1 French policeman (8)
5 Cut with acid (4)
9 Leg bone (5)
10 Kind, sort (5)
12 Earlier (5)
13 Face cover (4)
15 Servile (6)
18 Close-up feature (6)
20 Pack tightly (4)
23 Ground grain (5)
24 Item of value (5)
27 One of Snow
White's friends? (5)
28 Child's toy (2-2) (4)
29 Legendary dragon
slayer (2, 6)

DOWN

1 Criminal group (4)
2 A gas (4)
3 Change (5)
4 Movable (6)
6 Suspense novel (8)
7 Every sixty minutes (6)
8 Small piece of cloth (6)
11 Hitler's mistress,
- - - Braun (3)
14 Unfortunately (3, 2, 3)
16 Strongly built (6)
17 Brawl (6)
19 Strong impression (6)
21 Traditional beer (3)
22 Indiscreet remark (5)
25 Rider's goad (4)
26 Newcastle's river (4)

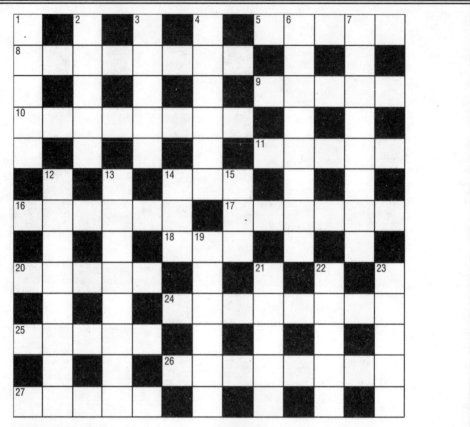

ACROSS
5 Flower part (5)
8 Wonderful (8)
9 Meat for roasting (5)
10 Item of clothing (8)
11 Discard (5)
14 TV entertainer,
- - - O'Connor (3)
16 Type of pancake (6)
17 Jostle (6)
18 Humorous (3)
20 Unused playing card (5)
24 Dish of eggs,
beaten and fried (8)
25 Wide (5)
26 Hairstyle (8)
27 Quaintly amusing (5)

DOWN
1 Animal charity (inits)
2 Fierce look (5)
3 Garden mollusc (5)
4 Desert illusion (6)
6 Drive out (evil spirits) (8)
7 Every twelve months (8)
12 Manual worker (8)
13 However (5, 3)
14 Morning moisture (3)
15 Bashful (3)
19 Rifle cleaner (6)
21 Deceive (5)
22 Support, prop (5)
23 Gauge (5)

The Biggest Crossword Book In The World

ACROSS

7 Confuse (6)
8 Row of arches (6)
10 Soft shoe (7)
11 Stripy African animal (5)
12 Yemen port (4)
13 Acute pain (5)
17 Small earrings (5)
18 Pack of cards (4)
22 Challenger (5)
23 Amelia - - -,
US aviator (7)
24 Ice cream topped
with fruit etc. (6)
25 Young woman (6)

DOWN

1 Extremely bad (7)
2 Policeman (7)
3 Go furtively (5)
4 American state (7)
5 Taxi driver (5)
6 Asian country (5)
9 Army officer (9)
14 From Milan or Rome? (7)
15 Fall back into
bad habits (7)
16 Bowling pin (7)
19 Obliterate (5)
20 Sporting contest (5)
21 Of a city (5)

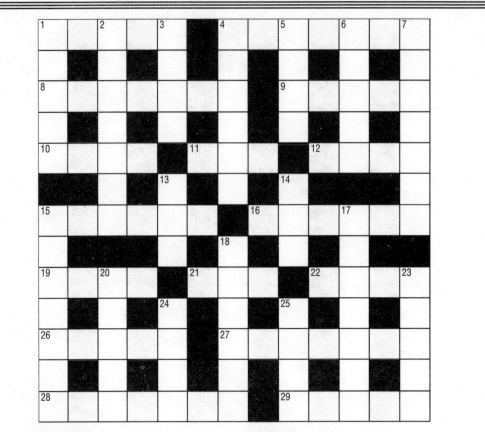

ACROSS

1 Crazy (5)
4 Rotted (7)
8 Permit (7)
9 Tough cotton fabric (5)
10 Mend with a needle (4)
11 London soccer
  club (inits)
12 Level (4)
15 Royal prince (6)
16 Pal, chum (6)
19 Rock star, - - - Jagger (4)
21 Clumsy person (3)
22 Gentle (4)
26 Card game (5)
27 Instruction (7)
28 Selfish driver (4-3)
29 Pungent (5)

DOWN

1 Mix ingredients (5)
2 Given up work (7)
3 Abominable
  snowman (4)
4 French ferry port (6)
5 Buffalo Bill's surname (4)
6 Barbra Streisand film (5)
7 Relegated (7)
13 Precious stone (3)
14 Snoop (3)
15 Fan (7)
17 Issue (7)
18 Common people (6)
20 Pause mark (5)
23 Neat and attractive (5)
24 Imaginary person
  or object (4)
25 Abandon (4)

The Biggest Crossword Book In The World

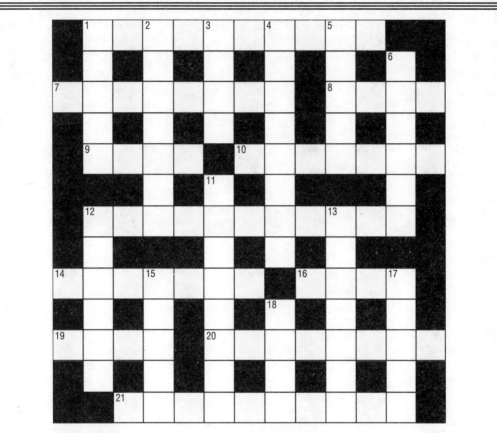

ACROSS

1 School principal (10)
7 TV newscaster (4, 4)
8 Part of a yacht (4)
9 Cunning (4)
10 Hermit (7)
12 Fortune telling aid (7, 4)
14 Difficulty (7)
16 Girl's name (4)
19 Sicilian volcano (4)
20 Daphne Du Maurier novel (3, 5)
21 Fawlty Towers owner (4, 6)

DOWN

1 Hair dye (5)
2 General disorder (7)
3 Cat's cry (4)
4 Without warning (8)
5 Artist's support (5)
6 Glittering decoration (6)
11 Michael - - -, cricketer (8)
12 Clergyman (6)
13 Worry greatly (7)
15 Child's comic (5)
17 Gentle poke with the elbow (5)
18 Ring out (4)

The Biggest Crossword Book In The World

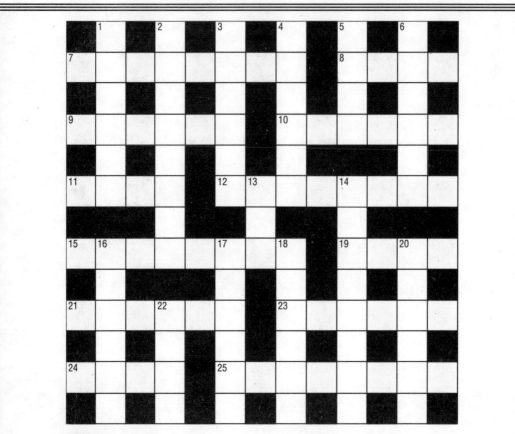

ACROSS

7 Elaborate (8)
8 Biting insect (4)
9 Overindulge (6)
10 Helpful, practical (6)
11 Baptism bowl (4)
12 Informed (8)
15 Mayor's office (4, 4)
19 Exlamation of wonder (4)
21 Nook, niche (6)
23 Buccaneer (6)
24 Life-saving
charity (1, 1, 1, 1)
25 Kept from flying (8)

DOWN

1 Small pleasure boat (6)
2 The 'Mad Monk' (8)
3 Old British coin (6)
4 Alter (6)
5 Stare, gape at (4)
6 Military greeting (6)
13 North Sea fuel (3)
14 Statuette (8)
16 Four-sided shape (6)
17 Take retaliation (6)
18 Portable computer (6)
20 Irish dog (6)
22 Leave out (4)

The Biggest Crossword Book In The World

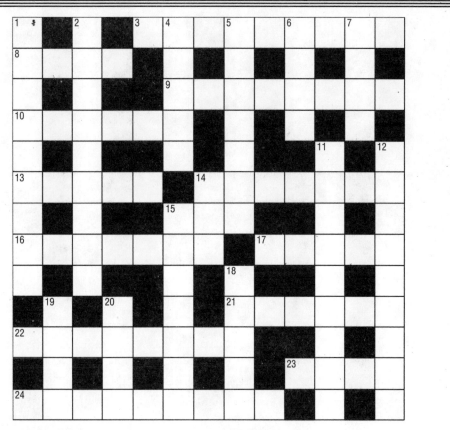

ACROSS

3 Painful inflamation of the joints (9)
8 Look after (4)
9 Obtained temporarily (8)
10 A group of acrobats (6)
13 Song of lament (5)
14 Sally - - -, British athlete (7)
15 Adult elver (3)
16 Distinguished (7)
17 W.G. - - -, famous cricketer (5)
21 Large power-driven boat (6)
22 Put in storage (8)
23 Sign of crying (4)
24 Prohibition bar featured in The Untouchables (9)

DOWN

1 Ready to wear (clothing) (3-3-3)
2 The world's fourth largest nation (9)
4 Revolt against those in power (5)
5 Detrimental (7)
6 Flatten clothing (4)
7 Notion (4)
11 Rest (9)
12 In another place (9)
14 Fetch (3)
15 Compel (7)
18 Praise (5)
19 Cultivated produce (4)
20 Japan's continent (4)

The Biggest Crossword Book In The World

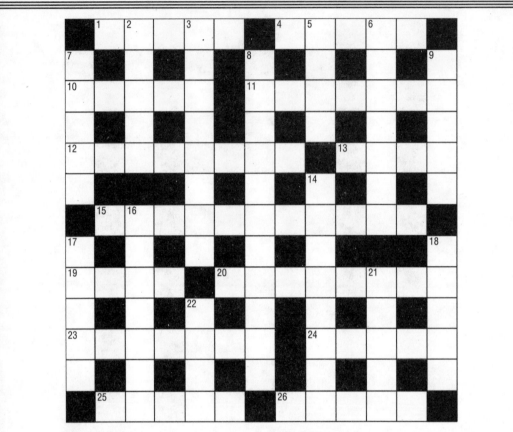

ACROSS
1 Ecclesiastical council (5)
4 Anticipate with terror (5)
10 Turn away (5)
11 Fried meat dish (7)
12 Give up (the throne) (8)
13 Woman (4)
15 Mild analgesic drug (11)
19 Glassy gemstone (4)
20 Beauty product (8)
23 Desert (7)
24 Malicious (5)
25 Falter (5)
26 Utter fool (5)

DOWN
2 Produce, bear (5)
3 Eye doctor (8)
5 Coarse file (4)
6 Pear-shaped tropical fruit (7)
7 Of the nose (5)
8 Swedish-born actress (5, 6)
9 English diary writer (5)
14 Harried (8)
16 Southern US state (7)
17 Terry - - -, Irish-born TV star (5)
18 Raise, bring up (5)
21 Irish county (5)
22 Margin (4)

ACROSS

1 Put into operation (9)
8 Hindu meditation (4)
9 Pub feature (9)
10 Wreckage (6)
13 Cunning (6)
15 New - - -, capital of India (5)
16 Exploratory spacecraft (5)
17 Snapshot (5)
18 Plentiful (5)
21 Actually (6)
22 Vigour, vim (6)
25 Long pasta strands (9)
26 Not as much (4)
27 Physics expert (9)

DOWN

2 Strong desire (?) (5)
3 Bury (5)
4 Awaken (6)
5 Enhance (6)
6 Baking ingredient (9)
7 Huntsman's cry (5-2)
11 Lose one's temper (4, 1, 4)
12 Perfect (5)
14 Mature (5)
16 Henry - - -, British composer (7)
19 Short-sighted (6)
20 Federation of clubs (6)
23 Vote into office (5)
24 Movable barriers (5)

The Biggest Crossword Book In The World

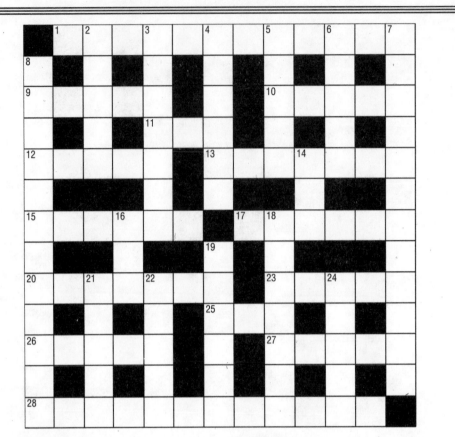

ACROSS

1 Pass through the Mendip Hills (7, 5)
9 Pig food (5)
10 Harmony (5)
11 Historical epoch (3)
12 Drug from a poppy (5)
13 Enigmatic (7)
15 South African city (6)
17 Ball game (6)
20 Coloniser (7)
23 Palpitate (5)
25 Hatchet (3)
26 Pungent bulb vegetable (5)
27 Cut of meat (5)
28 Treat unfairly (12)

DOWN

2 Caribbean country (5)
3 Quandary (7)
4 Peruvian llama (6)
5 Romany (5)
6 Respond (5)
7 Gym equipment (8, 4)
8 Well-behaved (2, 4, 2, 4)
14 Metal peg (3)
16 Contrary to expectation (3)
18 Gloria - - -, singer (7)
19 Cricketer, - - - Gooch (6)
21 Shadows (5)
22 Of the moon (5)
24 Cook in the oven (5)

The Biggest Crossword Book In The World

ACROSS

7 Punctuation mark (4, 4)
8 Suspended (4)
9 Set of stairs (6)
10 Choice (6)
11 Convent (5)
12 Salty fish (7)
15 Novice driver (7)
17 Trench (5)
20 Sea journey (6)
22 Figure with a human head and body of a lion (6)
23 One's span of years (4)
24 Grow, increase (8)

DOWN

1 Easily fooled (8)
2 Deadly disease (6)
3 Condition (5)
4 Determine (7)
5 Roofing material (6)
6 Unravel (4)
13 Surrounding area (8)
14 Shameless woman (7)
16 Bellowed (6)
18 Breathe in (6)
19 Children's charity (5)
21 American state (4)

The Biggest Crossword Book In The World

ACROSS

1 Welsh mountain range (6, 7)
7 Pebble (5)
8 Queen singer, - - - Mercury (7)
9 Swerve (7)
10 Flabbergast (5)
11 Sly laugh (7)
17 Travel, estate or secret? (5)
18 Submarine's missile (7)
20 Personal belongings (7)
21 Three-wheeled cycle (5)
22 Set of matching crockery (6, 7)

DOWN

1 Next to (6)
2 Adapt over a long period (6)
3 Last Greek letter (5)
4 Typical amount (7)
5 Terrible trial (6)
6 Currency of Israel (6)
8 Cargo ship (9)
12 Remarkable (7)
13 Stale (6)
14 Good reputation (6)
15 Sign of the zodiac (6)
16 Stick together (6)
19 Helicopter blade (5)

The Biggest Crossword Book In The World

ACROSS
1 Thick, stiff paper (4)
4 Set out (6)
8 Small animal (8)
9 Indian bird (4)
10 Bear? (5)
11 Circus performer (7)
13 Wall built to stop
   beach erosion (6)
15 Protective coating (6)
17 Sudden industrial
   action (4-3)
19 Distribute (5)
22 Slim (4)
23 Framework of bones (8)
24 Capital of England (6)
25 Ripped (4)

DOWN
2 Love (5)
3 Stately, formal (7)
4 Way in or out (4)
5 Religious speaker (8)
6 Ladies' man (5)
7 Incite (6)
12 Appalled (8)
14 William - - -, *Coronation
   Street* star (6)
16 Illness (7)
18 Martial art
   using sticks (5)
20 Smell (5)
21 James - - -,
   Giant actor (4)

The Biggest Crossword Book In The World

ACROSS

1 Martin Sheen's son (6, 7)
7 Scottish football club (7)
8 Absurd behaviour (5)
9 Wave added to hair (4)
10 Casino worker (8)
12 Medicine (6)
14 Pertain (6)
16 Large animal (8)
17 Sporting match (4)
20 Oily fruit (5)
21 Exact (7)
23 Tax collectors (6, 7)

DOWN

1 Stray (3)
2 Interior (5)
3 Separate article (4)
4 Make certain (6)
5 Dizziness (7)
6 Belgian port (9)
8 American name for a tap (6)
9 Spicy sausage (9)
11 Prince Edward's wife (6)
13 Popular police series (3, 4)
15 Hidden gunman (6)
18 Straighten up (5)
19 Diesel oil (4)
22 Trevor - - -, actor (3)

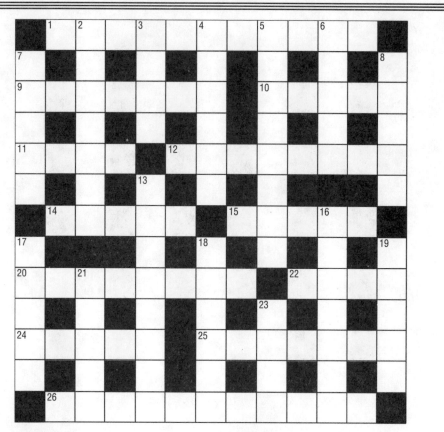

ACROSS

1 Absolute chaos (11)
9 Insect's feeler (7)
10 Prisoner's excuse (5)
11 Highest point (4)
12 Explore for gold (8)
14 Reel (5)
15 Colour (5)
20 Become greater in size (8)
22 King's title (4)
24 Protective garment (5)
25 Imaginary line around the middle of a planet (7)
26 Told off (11)

DOWN

2 Belgian port (7)
3 Refute (4)
4 Insufficient (6)
5 Biblical ship (5, 3)
6 Join as one (5)
7 Indian prince (5)
8 Noble descent (5)
13 Prison chief (8)
16 Jet engine inventor (7)
17 Backless sofa (5)
18 High respect (6)
19 Listened to (5)
21 Slice (meat) (5)
23 Scorch, char (4)

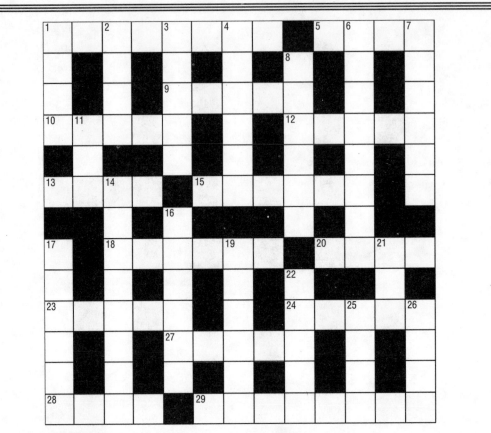

ACROSS

1 Prize often won at fun fairs (8)
5 Large black bird (4)
9 Elastic fabric (5)
10 Larceny (5)
12 Uncanny (5)
13 Animal of the cat family (4)
15 Rely entirely (6)
18 Express sorrow (6)
20 Seize (4)
23 Be ready for (5)
24 Circular disc (5)
27 Row of bushes (5)
28 Wind instrument (4)
29 Celestial body (8)

DOWN

1 Rough particles of sand (4)
2 Tardy (4)
3 Disgusting dirt (5)
4 Reaping hook (6)
6 Indication (8)
7 Meander (6)
8 *Tom - - -*, Mark Twain novel (6)
11 Cut grass (3)
14 Story teller (8)
16 Thriller writer, Dame - - - Christie (6)
17 Riches (6)
19 Old Testament book (6)
21 Devoured (3)
22 Type of turnip (5)
25 Sound reflection (4)
26 Master (4)

The Biggest Crossword Book In The World

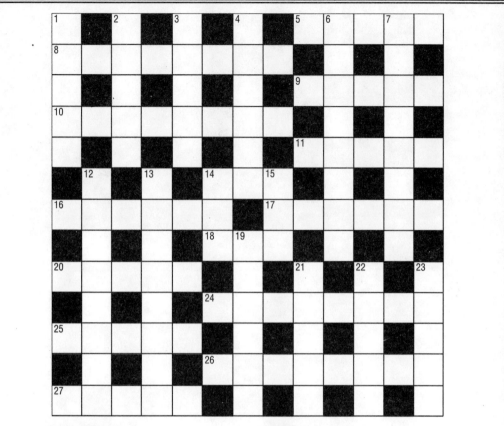

ACROSS
5 Savoury Indian dish (5)
8 Idle (8)
9 Dummy cartridge (5)
10 Tennis court boundary (8)
11 Verse (5)
14 Collection of crockery (3)
16 Anti-aircraft fire (3-3)
17 Dreamland (6)
18 Snappish bark (3)
20 Intended (5)
24 Handbills (8)
25 Glory (5)
26 American gangster (2, 6)
27 Money owed (5)

DOWN
1 Greek bread (5)
2 Fleshy fruit (5)
3 Stable compartment (5)
4 Street (6)
6 Child's toy (4-4)
7 Unsolicited correspondence (4, 4)
12 Timetable (8)
13 Mackintosh (8)
14 Upper atmosphere (3)
15 Ram (3)
19 Time-honoured (3-3)
21 Less valuable parts of the carcass (5)
22 Interior paintwork and furnishing (5)
23 Crooked (5)

ACROSS

7 Alfred Hitchcock film (6)
8 Alarm (6)
10 Nickname for Louis XIV of France (3, 4)
11 End prematurely (5)
12 Mislaid (4)
13 Compassion (5)
17 Fold in material (5)
18 Rise upwards (4)
22 Grass cutter (5)
23 Free time (7)
24 Boil very gently (6)
25 Indian religious teacher (6)

DOWN

1 Leader of reform (7)
2 Olga Korbut, eg (7)
3 Seat (5)
4 Improve (7)
5 John - - -, British prime minister (5)
6 English poet (5)
9 Pleasant (9)
14 Flattering talk (7)
15 Circular room (7)
16 Fred - - -, cricket legend (7)
19 Wrong (5)
20 Waterlogged ground (5)
21 Confused situation (3-2)

The Biggest Crossword Book In The World

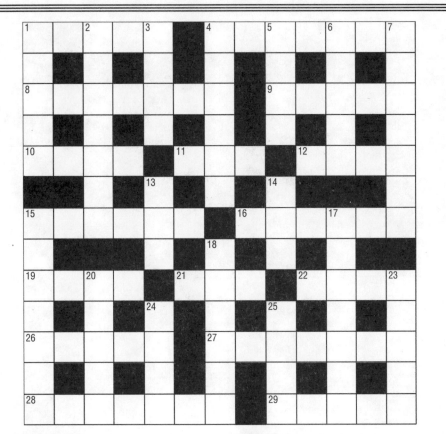

ACROSS

1 Romantic flowers (5)
4 Irrelevant (7)
8 Housebreaker (7)
9 Indian warrior (5)
10 Unfermented soya bean curd (4)
11 Relatives (3)
12 Calf meat (4)
15 Violent destruction (6)
16 Deceived (6)
19 Swing to and fro (4)
21 Karate grade (3)
22 Large bag (4)
26 Under way (5)
27 One of three babies (7)
28 Technical drawing (7)
29 Indentation (5)

DOWN

1 Mechanical person (5)
2 Unkempt (7)
3 Sodium chloride (4)
4 Nickname for Sarah or Alex (6)
5 Red gemstone (4)
6 Senseless (5)
7 Provoked (7)
13 Japanese currency (3)
14 Write briefly (3)
15 Lost (7)
17 Handbill (7)
18 Small domestic fowl (6)
20 Fragrance (5)
23 Sailing boat (5)
24 Distant sun (4)
25 Symbol (4)

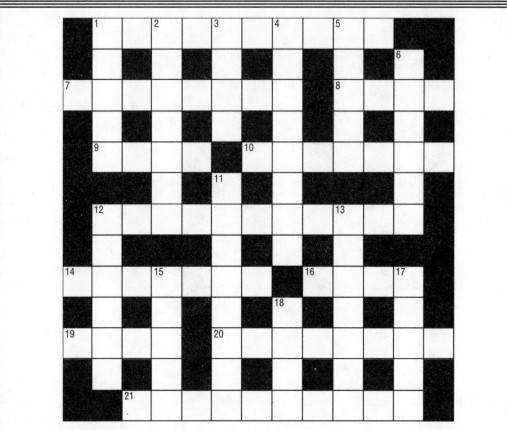

ACROSS

1 Australian state (10)
7 Wind instrument (8)
8 Partiality (4)
9 Bound (4)
10 Wealthy (7)
12 Expert (11)
14 Absence of noise (7)
16 Hospital snap (1-3)
19 Cash penalty (4)
20 Mexican resort (8)
21 Estimation, analysis (10)

DOWN

1 Game bird (5)
2 Make clear (7)
3 Back of the neck (4)
4 Funeral bugle-call (4, 4)
5 Peace Prize founder (5)
6 Flag (6)
11 Secret meeting (8)
12 Specialist hospital, sometimes for outpatients (6)
13 On the way (2, 5)
15 Level odds! (5)
17 Fast-sailing vessel (5)
18 Yorkshire girl! (4)

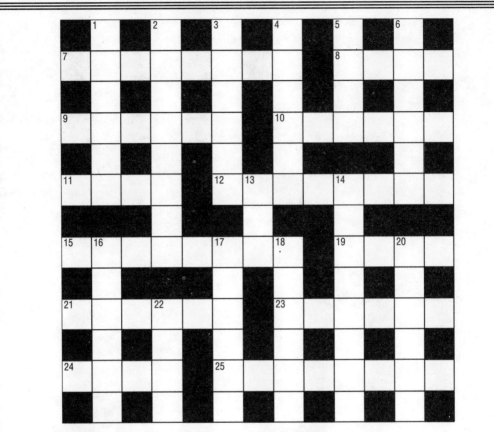

ACROSS
7 Film processing place (8)
8 Learned, sagacious (4)
9 Medicinal pill (6)
10 Large, slim hound with long hair (6)
11 Card game (4)
12 Politician, - - - Thatcher (8)
15 Difficulty to overcome (8)
19 Wet (4)
21 Flavoursome herb (6)
23 Painter (6)
24 Following (4)
25 North American Indian tribe (8)

DOWN
1 Oriental market (6)
2 Roof window (8)
3 Lowest part (6)
4 Harm (6)
5 Burglar's booty (4)
6 Get free (6)
13 The lot (3)
14 Test of a performer's suitability (8)
16 Agent (6)
17 Grasp firmly (6)
18 Art rubber (6)
20 School teacher (6)
22 Italian wine (4)

The Biggest Crossword Book In The World

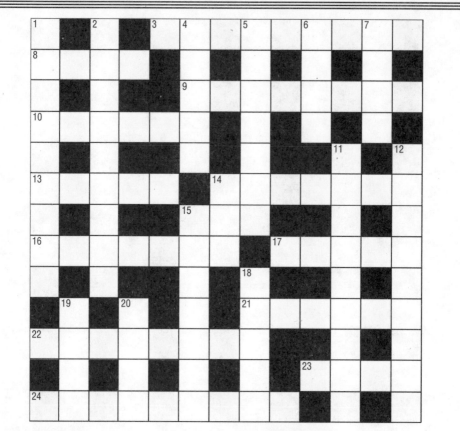

ACROSS

3 Cryptic (9)
8 Large gap (4)
9 Definite (8)
10 Exultant cry (6)
13 Council head (5)
14 Roman god of water (7)
15 Trouble (3)
16 Tidiest (7)
17 Playing card (5)
21 Craving for a drink (6)
22 Geniality (8)
23 Clan (4)
24 Certain, sure (9)

DOWN

1 Contract (9)
2 Vicar, eg (9)
4 Connected with childbirth (5)
5 Stylish (7)
6 In the middle of (4)
7 Lazy (4)
11 Daphne - - -, novelist (2, 7)
12 Private conversation between two people (4-1-4)
14 Louse egg (3)
15 Embarrassed (7)
18 Earthenware beer mug (5)
19 Game played on horseback (4)
20 Head cook (4)

The Biggest Crossword Book In The World

ACROSS

1 Illicitly distilled spirit (5)
4 Call on (5)
10 Precocious girl (5)
11 Charm (7)
12 Popular board game (8)
13 Annihilate (4)
15 Mixed, combined (11)
19 Level, balanced (4)
20 Kept woman (8)
23 Place of safety (7)
24 Slide (5)
25 Word of apology (5)
26 Extent (5)

DOWN

2 Methodical arrangement (5)
3 Naomi - - -, model (8)
5 Jot (4)
6 Picture in the mind (7)
7 Entertain (5)
8 TV magician (4, 7)
9 Coral island (5)
14 A very tiny amount (8)
16 Distinguished musician (7)
17 For this reason (5)
18 Attendant (5)
21 Explode, as a volcano (5)
22 Sussex river (4)

The Biggest Crossword Book In The World

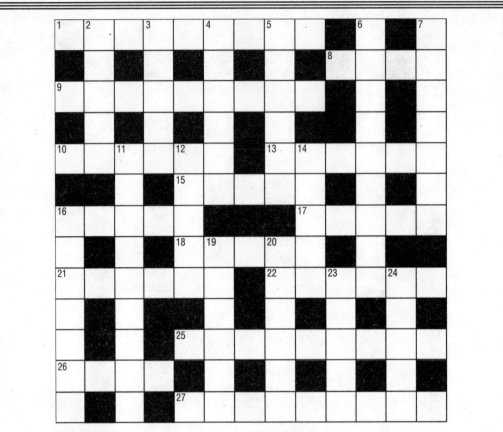

ACROSS
1 Venetian traveller (5, 4)
8 Tidings (4)
9 Irish county (9)
10 Nonchalant (2, 4)
13 Capital of Turkey (6)
15 Affectionate greeting (5)
16 Depth finder (5)
17 Self-respect (5)
18 Summarise (5)
21 Kind of Swiss
   wooden house (6)
22 Road built around
   a town (6)
25 Diligently (9)
26 Frozen vapour flakes (4)
27 Retired person (9)

DOWN
2 Foster permanently (5)
3 Bedtime drink? (5)
4 Strike repeatedly (6)
5 Asian plant (6)
6 For each person (3, 6)
7 Quarantine,
   segregate (7)
11 Culture (9)
12 Cavalry sword (5)
14 Diaper (5)
16 Spanish painter (7)
19 Odourless gas (6)
20 Nun in charge of
   a convent (6)
23 Farthest planet (5)
24 Healing ointment (5)

The Biggest Crossword Book In The World

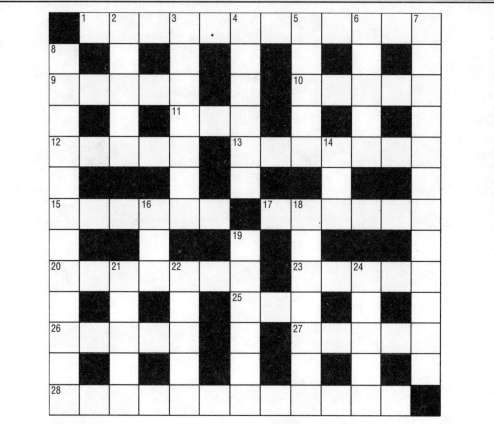

ACROSS

1 Popular TV
programme (10, 1, 1)
9 Battle (5)
10 Singer, - - - Wynette (5)
11 Bother (3)
12 Passing fashion (5)
13 Sweet red pepper (7)
15 Mrs Simpson's
royal lover (6)
17 Plumber's spanner (6)
20 Chose (7)
23 Fencing weapon (5)
25 Self worth (3)
26 Should (5)
27 Game of chance (5)
28 Lonely hearts club (6, 6)

DOWN

2 Dishonest person (5)
3 Bullfighter (7)
4 Ghost actress,
- - - Goldberg (6)
5 American Indian's
symbolic pole (5)
6 Of people (5)
7 Number 21 in
bingo (3, 2, 3, 4)
8 Unofficially (3, 3, 6)
14 Lengthen (3)
16 Sweeping curve (3)
18 Conclude (7)
19 Black Sea port (6)
21 Rowing team (5)
22 Powerful person (5)
24 Of the eyes (5)

The Biggest Crossword Book In The World

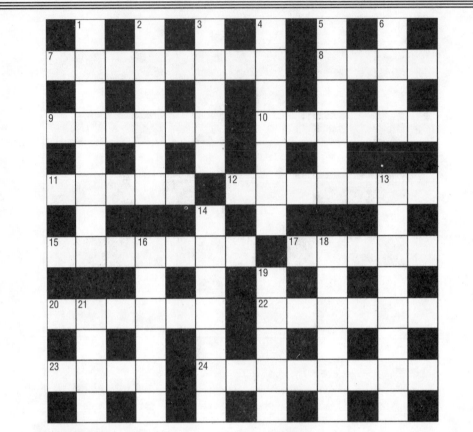

ACROSS

7 Sufficient (8)
8 Iron spike (4)
9 Radio or television antenna (6)
10 Russian soup (6)
11 Extensive view (5)
12 Not worthy of (7)
15 Scent (7)
17 Currency unit of Denmark (5)
20 Scold (6)
22 Dozing (6)
23 Spun fibre (4)
24 Fused together (8)

DOWN

1 Sticky substance (8)
2 Peer with half-closed eyes (6)
3 Tale of Aesop (5)
4 England's football stadium (7)
5 False (6)
6 Record (4)
13 Meddled (8)
14 Huge (7)
16 Easy, graceful (6)
18 Hard revolving cylinder (6)
19 Dawdle (5)
21 Style and vigour (4)

ACROSS

1 Worldwide travellers (13)
7 Unfasten (5)
8 Style of cooking (7)
9 Artist (7)
10 Survey (5)
11 Attribute, character (7)
17 Open (5)
18 Erratic (7)
20 Gift, donation (7)
21 To the left or right (5)
22 Welsh rarebit ? (6, 2, 5)

DOWN

1 One of Snow White's dwarfs (6)
2 Rig, get-up (6)
3 Exercise (5)
4 Matching jumper and cardigan (7)
5 Newspaperman (6)
6 Slender (6)
8 American athlete (4, 5)
12 Having no purpose (7)
13 Traditional language of the Scottish Highlands (6)
14 Stephen King novel (6)
15 Yachting station (6)
16 Commercial (6)
19 Raising agent (5)

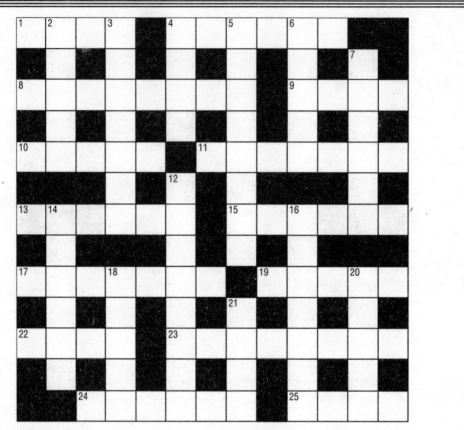

ACROSS

1 Become weary (4)
4 Sir - - - Hillary, mountaineer (6)
8 Senior councillor (8)
9 Admirer (4)
10 Book of maps (5)
11 Picks (7)
13 Day of the week (6)
15 Jewish state (6)
17 Short stalks of cut grain (7)
19 Beautiful woman (5)
22 Responsibility (4)
23 Wine-producing region of France (8)
24 Most senior (6)
25 US space control centre (4)

DOWN

2 Narrow bay (5)
3 Green gemstone (7)
4 US television award (4)
5 Christmas pastry (5, 3)
6 Person of high rank (5)
7 Aimless chatter (6)
12 Part of a word (8)
14 Part of the eye (6)
16 Girl's public school (7)
18 Aromatic herb (5)
20 Jazz band leader, - - - Armstrong (5)
21 Worry over nothing (4)

The Biggest Crossword Book In The World

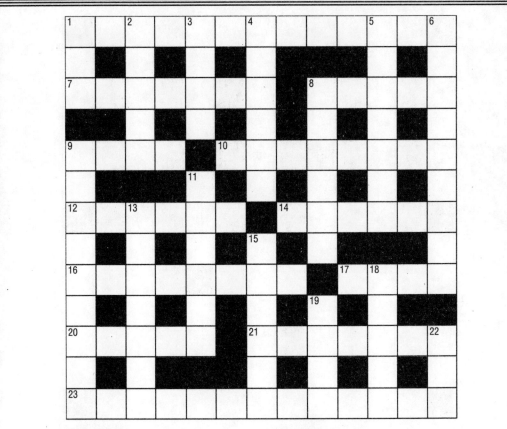

ACROSS

1 *Blackadder* star (5, 8)
7 South African conflict (4, 3)
8 Local authority regulation (5)
9 Greek letter (4)
10 Army officer (8)
12 Delicate (6)
14 Show of respect (6)
16 Rude, disrespectful (8)
17 Stop (4)
20 Musical phrase (5)
21 Infuriated (7)
23 Explosive liquid (13)

DOWN

1 Actor, - - - Lowe (3)
2 Corn crop (5)
3 Nothing! (4)
4 Small tower (6)
5 Seedless raisin (7)
6 Birmingham railway station (3, 6)
8 Circus tent (3, 3)
9 Game (9)
11 Former British PM (6)
13 Look closely at (7)
15 Ill, sick (6)
18 Wrath (5)
19 Ernie's partner (4)
22 Animal's lair (3)

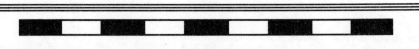

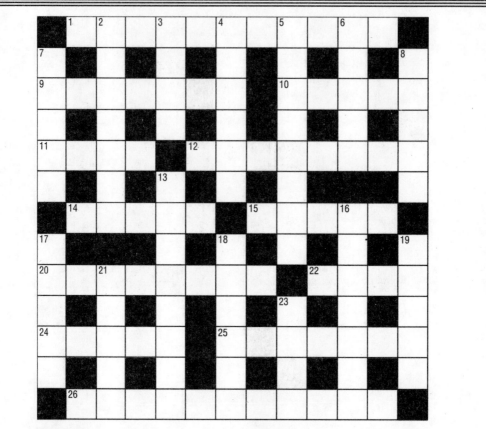

ACROSS

1 Means of communication (6, 5)
9 Newspaper item (7)
10 In front (5)
11 Actress, - - - Bryan (4)
12 Rescue (8)
14 Twelve in number (5)
15 Find an answer to (5)
20 Infinite time (8)
22 Increase sharply (4)
24 Smother, stifle (5)
25 Plunder (7)
26 Inspector Wexford actor (6, 5)

DOWN

2 Canadian province (7)
3 Irritation (4)
4 Devon town (6)
5 Height under a bridge (8)
6 Female relative (5)
7 Smart man (5)
8 Poisonous British snake (5)
13 Antlered animal (8)
16 Break (law) (7)
17 Blood-sucking worm (5)
18 Metal clip (6)
19 Urge forward (5)
21 Wear away (5)
23 Arm bone (4)

The Biggest Crossword Book In The World

ACROSS

1 Jumpers, eg (8)
5 Kiss quickly (4)
9 Horrify (5)
10 White bear (5)
12 Beginning (5)
13 Edging stone (4)
15 Twist (6)
18 Foil, frustrate (6)
20 Children's author,
  - - - Blyton (4)
23 British athlete,
  - - - Jackson (5)
24 Nearly (5)
27 Scatter-brained (5)
28 Hurry (4)
29 Portable rain
  protector (8)

DOWN

1 Seaweed (4)
2 False god (4)
3 Harbour platform (5)
4 Live-in home help (2, 4)
6 German-born genius (8)
7 Loose garment (6)
8 Extremely drunk! (6)
11 Mineral bearing rock (3)
14 Merciless (8)
16 Pang (6)
17 Business agent (6)
19 In any order (6)
21 Debtor's note (1, 1, 1)
22 Stratum (5)
25 Spoken exam (4)
26 *Brassed Off* star,
  - - - Fitzgerald (4)

The Biggest Crossword Book In The World

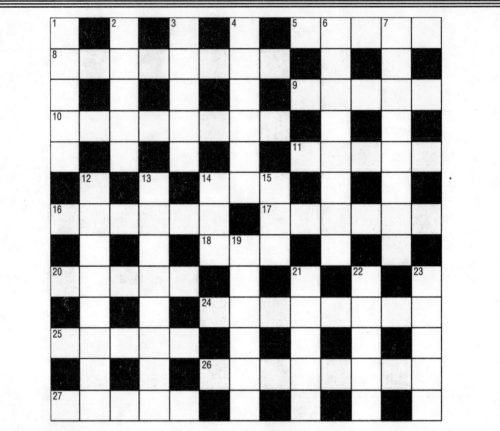

ACROSS

5 Dirty (5)
8 Folklore creature (8)
9 Oak fruit (5)
10 Final piece of work (4, 4)
11 Estimate (5)
14 Stitch (3)
16 Lucky toy or animal (6)
17 Land encircled
by water (6)
18 Nevertheless (3)
20 Portly (5)
24 Metric unit of weight (8)
25 Black bird (5)
26 Able to read and write (8)
27 Poem (5)

DOWN

1 Distort (5)
2 Test (5)
3 Fashionable, smart (5)
4 Submerge (6)
6 Disconnect (8)
7 Aircraft fuel (8)
12 Foolproof (4-4)
13 Runs away (8)
14 Farm enclosure
for pigs (3)
15 Cleverly humorous
person (3)
19 Medicine (6)
21 Interlaced (5)
22 Dairy product (5)
23 Glowing coal (5)

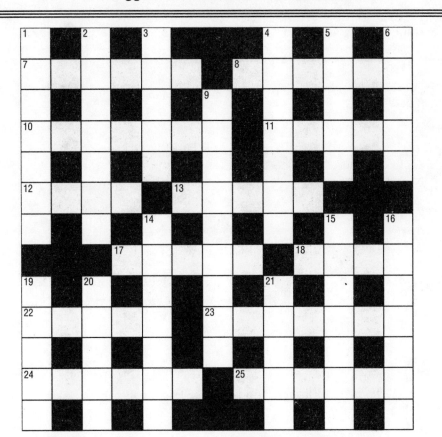

ACROSS

7 TV personality,
- - - Turner (6)
8 Breathe out (6)
10 Hair cleaner (7)
11 Court announcer (5)
12 Noisy (4)
13 Animal (5)
17 Frequently (5)
18 Four-wheeled bike (4)
22 Marie - - -,
French physicist (5)
23 Make use of (7)
24 Feature, element (6)
25 Flemish painter (6)

DOWN

1 Small container (7)
2 Layer of rock (7)
3 Combed, tidy (5)
4 Carry out sentence
of death (7)
5 Sorcery (5)
6 Former boxer,
- - - Cooper (5)
9 Polite (9)
14 Transgression (7)
15 Gin-making berry (7)
16 Contrary (7)
19 Go away (5)
20 Chart (5)
21 N American
Indian tribe (5)

The Biggest Crossword Book In The World

ACROSS

1 Gloomy (5)
4 Quotation (7)
8 Team game (7)
9 Freshwater fish (5)
10 Outer layer of bacon (4)
11 Trendy (3)
12 Song of praise (4)
15 American state (6)
16 Canadian province (6)
19 Cartoon locomotive, - - - the Engine (4)
21 Favourite (3)
22 Weed with large leaves (4)
26 Walk slowly (5)
27 Saved property (7)
28 Time between (7)
29 Sigmund - - -, psychiatrist (5)

DOWN

1 Nobleman's land (5)
2 Body of aides (7)
3 Fifty-two weeks (4)
4 Cream-filled cake (6)
5 Appealing (4)
6 Spacious (5)
7 Ill-fated passenger liner (7)
13 Crib (3)
14 Double entendre (3)
15 Paper-folding art (7)
17 Patterned fabric (7)
18 Cargo thrown overboard (6)
20 Planet's circular path (5)
23 Work (dough) (5)
24 Forest animal (4)
25 Patron saint of Norway (4)

The Biggest Crossword Book In The World

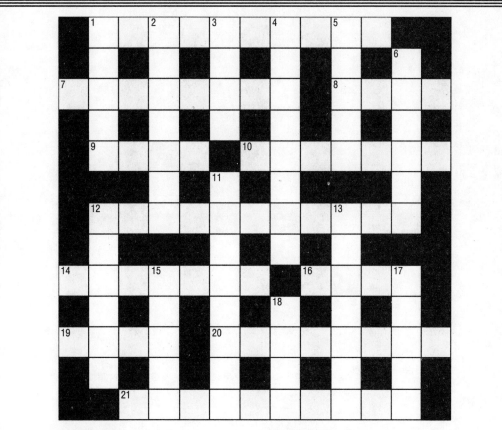

ACROSS

1 US Presidents home (5, 5)
7 Noblewoman (8)
8 Curse (4)
9 Practical joke (4)
10 Looked briefly (7)
12 US Defense headquarters (11)
14 Puzzle, bewilder (7)
16 Average level of achievement (4)
19 As a result of birth (4)
20 John - - -, *Pulp Fiction* actor (8)
21 Prestigious car (5, 5)

DOWN

1 Anger (5)
2 Metallic period of history (4, 3)
3 Biblical garden (4)
4 Out-of-date (8)
5 Promised on oath (5)
6 Scattered (6)
11 Column support (8)
12 Shudder (6)
13 The study of rocks (7)
15 Theatrical performance for children (5)
17 Metric measurement (5)
18 Travelling entertainment with sideshows (4)

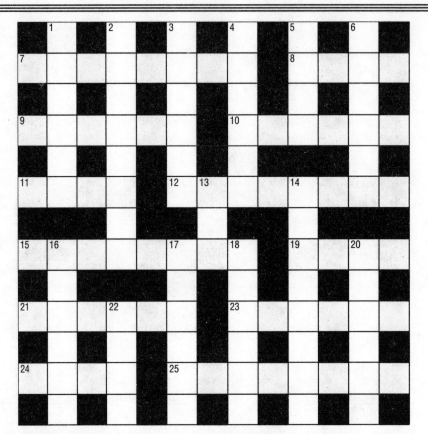

ACROSS

7 Vegetable strips (8)
8 Wish, trust (4)
9 Move from side to side (6)
10 Spanish Mrs (6)
11 Cried (4)
12 From corner to corner (8)
15 Norwegian explorer (8)
19 Currency of Italy (4)
21 Turn down, decline (6)
23 Crushed up (6)
24 Slipped (4)
25 Moved unsteadily (8)

DOWN

1 Pointless (6)
2 Capital of Jamaica (8)
3 Mean, plan (6)
4 Old name for Iran (6)
5 Former Chinese ruler (4)
6 Ancient Greek city (6)
13 Skating surface (3)
14 Observer (8)
16 Swiss breakfast food (6)
17 Close-fitting cover (6)
18 Lump of gold (6)
20 Declaimed (6)
22 Official language of Pakistan (4)

The Biggest Crossword Book In The World

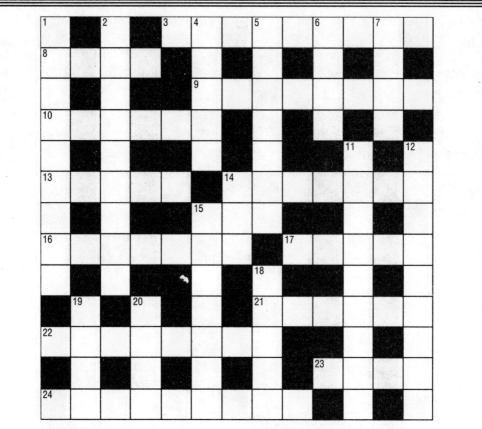

ACROSS

3 One of Robin Hood's merry men (5, 4)
8 Skivvy (4)
9 Appreciative (8)
10 Support (6)
13 Inspect accounts (5)
14 English seaside resort (7)
15 Dry (of wine) (3)
16 Cube of toasted bread served in soup (7)
17 Bone in the leg (5)
21 Young swan (6)
22 Powerful weedkiller (8)
23 Disfigurement (4)
24 Lucky (9)

DOWN

1 Guarantee (9)
2 Sherlock Holmes's housekeeper (3, 6)
4 Raring to go (5)
5 Annual calendar (7)
6 Become sour (4)
7 Rabbit fur (4)
11 Mouth organ (9)
12 Office worker (9)
14 Adult males (3)
15 Stay for a time (7)
18 Group of eight (5)
19 Mexican dish in a folded tortilla (4)
20 Way of walking (4)

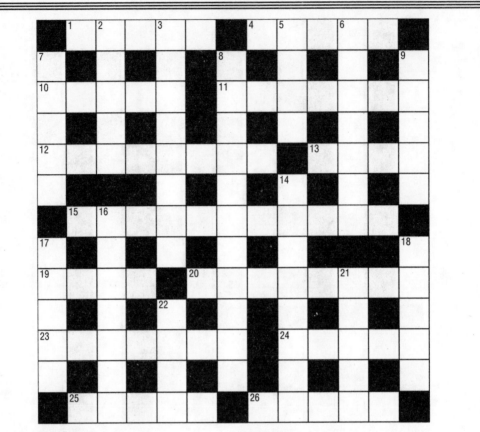

ACROSS

1 US cowboy state (5)
4 Entrance hall (5)
10 Bid (5)
11 Greed (7)
12 Formal discussion meeting (8)
13 Writer of verse (4)
15 Sylvester Stallone film (11)
19 Grass (4)
20 Unconditional (8)
23 Cynic, doubter (7)
24 Novelist, - - - Bronte (5)
25 Reversal of political policy (1-4)
26 Impede the growth of (5)

DOWN

2 Pixie-like, delicate (5)
3 Flying machine (8)
5 Actor, - - - Sharif (4)
6 Instalment (7)
7 Loaf, slouch (5)
8 Blame someone else (4, 3, 4)
9 Fangs (5)
14 Naive (8)
16 Biggest (7)
17 Put away (5)
18 *Out of Africa actress*, - - - Streep (5)
21 Alliance (5)
22 Commotion (4)

The Biggest Crossword Book In The World

ACROSS

1 Proper attention (9)
8 Chip shop fish (4)
9 Town in NE England (9)
10 Trouble (6)
13 A puzzle (6)
15 Fixed look (5)
16 Ronald - - -, train robber (5)
17 Accurate (5)
18 Plant-louse (5)
21 Cheerio! (3-3)
22 Method (6)
25 Tennis venue (9)
26 Estimate (4)
27 Greatly frightened (9)

DOWN

2 Likeness (5)
3 Incompetent (5)
4 Urge (6)
5 Shellhole (6)
6 *Four Weddings and a Funeral* actor (4, 5)
7 Tarmac (7)
11 Isolate (9)
12 Written composition (5)
14 Poor (5)
16 All-in-one outfit for a young child (7)
19 Small and dainty (6)
20 Line on a weather map (6)
23 Ledge (5)
24 Summon up (5)

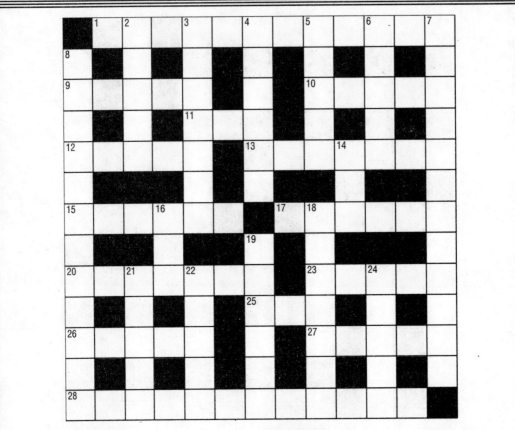

ACROSS
1 Additional comment (12)
9 Ward (off) (5)
10 Swimming style (5)
11 Feel sorrow (3)
12 Muddle (5)
13 Operation (7)
15 Sailor's song (6)
17 Rotten and foul-smelling (6)
20 Centre (7)
23 Short-legged sturdy dog (5)
25 Also (3)
26 Pollute (5)
27 Servant (5)
28 Silly (4, 2, 1, 5)

DOWN
2 Swindle (5)
3 World's highest mountain (7)
4 Mother - - -, nun (6)
5 Happen (5)
6 Feed on grass (5)
7 Noel's TV show (5, 7)
8 Murdered (12)
14 Obtained (3)
16 Nothing (3)
18 Reveal (7)
19 Illness causing difficulty in breathing (6)
21 Steep rock face (5)
22 Additional (5)
24 Governs (5)

The Biggest Crossword Book In The World

ACROSS

7 Totalled (8)
8 Undying spirit (4)
9 Capital of Lebanon (6)
10 Small exclusive group (6)
11 Algeria's currency unit (5)
12 Low-padded seat (7)
15 Pudding (7)
17 Tell off (5)
20 Greg - - -, golfer (6)
22 Andy - - -, pop artist (6)
23 Look of lust (4)
24 Novelist, - - - Steel (8)

DOWN

1 Young person (8)
2 Ancient name for the country now comprising Spain and Portugal (6)
3 Shred (cheese) (5)
4 Teach (7)
5 Inhabitant of Greenland (6)
6 Desmond - - -, S African clergyman (4)
13 Oxford college (3, 5)
14 Small bomb (7)
16 Dark, gloomy (6)
18 Group of companies (6)
19 Strong string (5)
21 Undo (4)

The Biggest Crossword Book In The World

ACROSS

1 Carnivorous dinosaur (13)
7 Conductor's wand (5)
8 Convinced (7)
9 Cattle farmer (7)
10 Large lorry (5)
11 Racetrack obstacle (7)
17 Sullen (5)
18 Neat (7)
20 Send away (7)
21 Block of metal (5)
22 Schwarzenegger film (3, 10)

DOWN

1 Herald's coat (6)
2 Round (6)
3 Beethoven's last symphony (5)
4 Choose not to vote (7)
5 Uncommon thing (6)
6 Allure, attract (6)
8 Extremely wicked (9)
12 Crazy (7)
13 In the middle of (6)
14 Hair styling preparation (6)
15 Sudden fear (6)
16 Shellfish (6)
19 Think fit (5)

The Biggest Crossword Book In The World

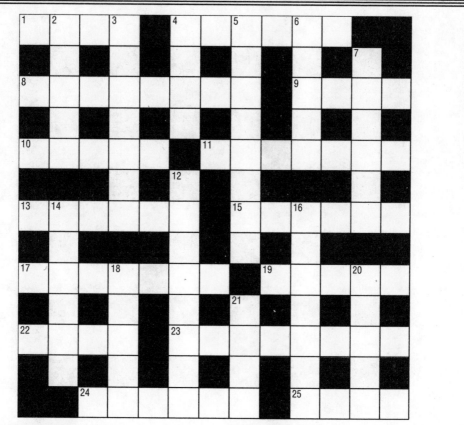

ACROSS
1 Kind of leather (4)
4 Stefan - - -,
  tennis player (6)
8 Rebellious person (8)
9 Low cart (4)
10 Carl - - -, American
  athlete (5)
11 French cartoon hero (7)
13 Small, sturdy
  breed of hound (6)
15 Crossed out (6)
17 Brand of vermouth (7)
19 Divine messenger (5)
22 Plunge (4)
23 Enrolled (8)
24 Container (6)
25 Helper (4)

DOWN
2 Perceptive (5)
3 Blind spot (7)
4 Fencing foil (4)
5 Yorkshire town (8)
6 Narrow hilltop (5)
7 Literary send-up (6)
12 Wanders aimlessly (8)
14 Grant authority to (6)
16 Loss of memory (7)
18 Conical tent (5)
20 Correct (5)
21 National airline
  of Israel (2-2)

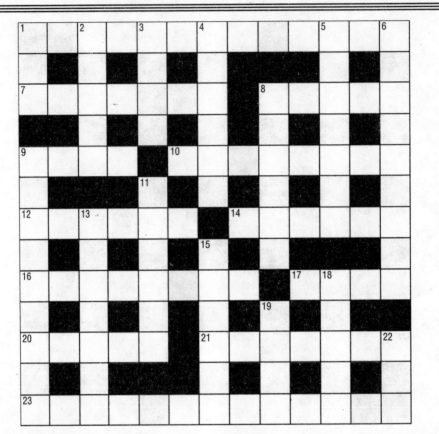

ACROSS

1 Arrogant (4, 3, 6)
7 Socialist newspaper (7)
8 Group of singers (5)
9 Social insects (4)
10 Judith Krantz novel (8)
12 Traffic diversion (6)
14 Small lobster (6)
16 Item of furniture
  with a door (8)
17 Indication (4)
20 Aquatic mammal (5)
21 Small wood (7)
23 Furtive (13)

DOWN

1 Small house (3)
2 Blame (5)
3 Stand next to (4)
4 Soak (6)
5 Petty gangster (7)
6 English county (9)
8 Invalid's stick (6)
9 Bold (9)
11 Unverified statement (6)
13 Result forecaster (7)
15 German drinking
  toast (6)
18 Language (slang) (5)
19 Slimming regime (4)
22 Positive answer (3)

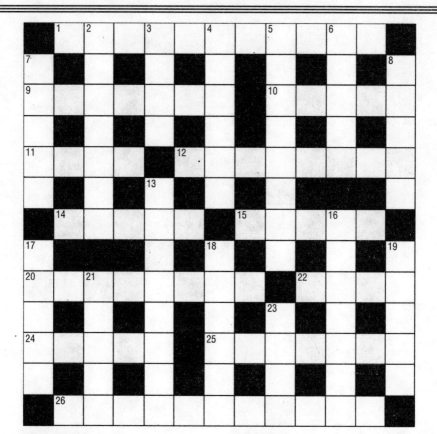

ACROSS

1 Fortune teller (11)
9 Prisoner on the run (7)
10 Irish police force (5)
11 Small nail (4)
12 Teeth? (8)
14 Search for water (5)
15 Bet (5)
20 Make up item (3, 5)
22 Wrath, anger (4)
24 Woo (5)
25 Multi-socket plug (7)
26 Grudge contest (6, 5)

DOWN

2 Opera singer,
- - - Pavarotti (7)
3 Simple game (1-3)
4 Capital of Austria (6)
5 Native of Belgrade (8)
6 Ancient Scandinavian
language (5)
7 Medicinal plants (5)
8 Bogus (5)
13 Placed apart (8)
16 Stretchy material (7)
17 Remove feathers (5)
18 Extensive private
property (6)
19 Nick - - -, actor (5)
21 Dried plum (5)
23 Father (4)

The Biggest Crossword Book In The World

ACROSS

1 African country (8)
5 Action word (4)
9 Young eel (5)
10 Transparent (5)
12 Pilgrim city (5)
13 Cow meat (4)
15 Car's bumper (6)
18 Grass with large white feathery flowers (6)
20 Throwing line in a game of darts (4)
23 Trick (5)
24 Yachting resort (5)
27 Ted - - -, former PM (5)
28 Exhibit (4)
29 Loathed (8)

DOWN

1 Long story or poem (4)
2 Ramble (4)
3 Obvious (5)
4 Ask (6)
6 Exciting, tense (8)
7 Conduct oneself (6)
8 Large fleet of ships (6)
11 Film star, - - - Marvin (3)
14 Frothy coffee (8)
16 Forge (6)
17 Alcove (6)
19 Burning violently (6)
21 Gardener's tool (3)
22 Yellow-orange colour (5)
25 Kill time (4)
26 Slide sideways (4)

The Biggest Crossword Book In The World

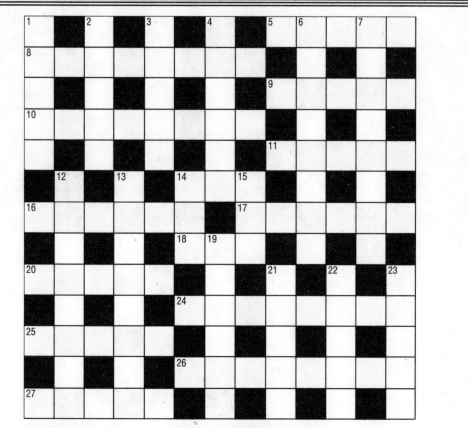

ACROSS

5 Acute glandular disease (5)
8 Deduct (4, 4)
9 English county (5)
10 Earmarked (8)
11 Poisonous (5)
14 Label (3)
16 Small falcon (6)
17 Attractiveness (6)
18 Tawdry articles (3)
20 Get up (5)
24 Minister's house (8)
25 Carried chair (5)
26 Point out, show (8)
27 Joyous (5)

DOWN

1 Vapour (5)
2 Craft (5)
3 Meat and vegetable pie (5)
4 Picture-taker (6)
6 Not damaged (8)
7 First performance (8)
12 Stay of execution (8)
13 Author, - - - Maclean (8)
14 Explosive (1, 1, 1)
15 Nocturnal flying mammal (3)
19 Foreigners? (6)
21 Automatic reaction (5)
22 Manmade waterway (5)
23 Frenzy (5)

The Biggest Crossword Book In The World

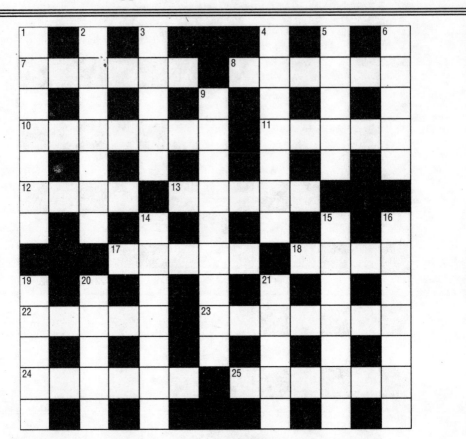

ACROSS

7 Sharp-tasting (6)
8 Gwen - - -, actress (6)
10 Inconsequential talk (7)
11 Italian explorer,
  - - - Polo (5)
12 Deal out sparingly (4)
13 Beatles' song,
  - - - *Lane* (5)
17 Savoury jelly (5)
18 Window frame (4)
22 Make fun of (5)
23 Down wind (7)
24 Sleepy (6)
25 Reason for a
  course of action (6)

DOWN

1 Waterfall (7)
2 Essentially (7)
3 Breadth (5)
4 Reward (7)
5 Signal light (5)
6 Bride's partner (5)
9 Film about a whale (4, 5)
14 Blacken (7)
15 Tropical fever (7)
16 Shake, tremble (7)
19 Academic workroom (5)
20 Variety of cabbage (5)
21 Under (5)

The Biggest Crossword Book In The World

ACROSS

1 Piece of bread (5)
4 Lorry driver (7)
8 Deficiency (7)
9 Spring month (5)
10 Fight (4)
11 Insect (3)
12 Garden barrier (4)
15 Component (6)
16 Royal house (6)
19 Mesh (4)
21 Scull (3)
22 Closed (4)
26 Chime (5)
27 Free from germs (7)
28 Permit (7)
29 Old (5)

DOWN

1 Place in an upright position (5)
2 As a substitute (7)
3 Fish-eating bird (4)
4 Threefold (6)
5 America's Beehive state (4)
6 Indian dish (5)
7 Give relief (7)
13 Ernie - - -, golfer (3)
14 Rock projection (3)
15 Enchanting (7)
17 Godless person (7)
18 Trouble (6)
20 Scientist, Sir - - - Newton (5)
23 Walk (5)
24 Outer layer (4)
25 Lustful (4)

The Biggest Crossword Book In The World

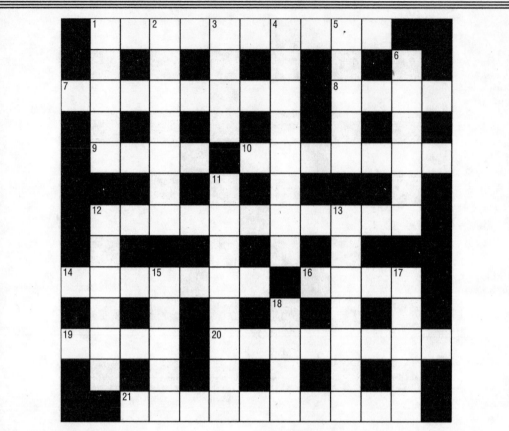

ACROSS

1 Unstained (10)
7 Calm, serene (8)
8 Market (4)
9 Christmas (4)
10 Record of past events (7)
12 Tom Cruise
film (1, 3, 4, 3)
14 A deadly poison (7)
16 Proper (4)
19 Inflatable rubber
mattress (4)
20 Visionary (8)
21 Remarkable object (10)

DOWN

1 Home of Glasgow
Rangers (5)
2 Official command (7)
3 Successful move (4)
4 Sweet on a stick (8)
5 Coax (5)
6 Rehearsal (3, 3)
11 Engine starter system (8)
12 Scared (6)
13 Actress, - - - Monroe (7)
15 Age (5)
17 Stone-worker (5)
18 Appear (4)

The Biggest Crossword Book In The World

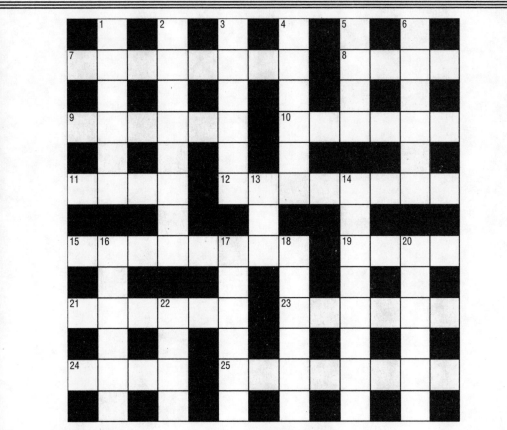

ACROSS

7 Sit on a horse (8)
8 Ballot (4)
9 Ben Kingsley film (6)
10 Fine strand (6)
11 Saintly circle (4)
12 Labour politician (4, 4)
15 Devote (8)
19 Gemstone (4)
21 Deliver a sermon (6)
23 Chris - - -, boxer (6)
24 Shoe cover (4)
25 A to Z (8)

DOWN

1 Canadian city (6)
2 Indian cooking style (8)
3 Without a clear purpose (6)
4 Overcome (6)
5 Always (4)
6 Accomplish (6)
13 On many occasions (3)
14 Intimidate (8)
16 Northern continent (6)
17 Religious retreat (6)
18 Free from obligation (6)
20 Over there (6)
22 Pretends (4)

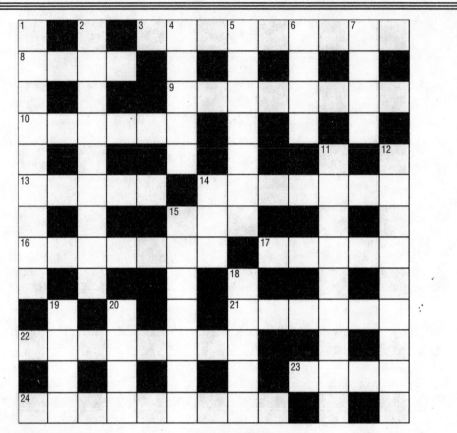

ACROSS

3 Wiltshire city (9)
8 Link, union (4)
9 Three-sided shape (8)
10 Large lizard (6)
13 To such time as (5)
14 Debate, discuss (7)
15 Legendary bird (3)
16 Sentry (4, 3)
17 First-rate (5)
21 Agree to (6)
22 Large pile of cut grass (8)
23 Greyish-yellow (4)
24 Soft fruit (9)

DOWN

1 Clearly (9)
2 Instinct (9)
4 Communion table (5)
5 Utterly stupid (7)
6 Flex (4)
7 Depend (4)
11 Award-winning actress (4, 5)
12 Crafty, cunning (9)
14 Full stop (3)
15 Search through, ransack (7)
18 Bread maker (5)
19 Molten matter (4)
20 Please reply (1, 1, 1, 1)

The Biggest Crossword Book In The World

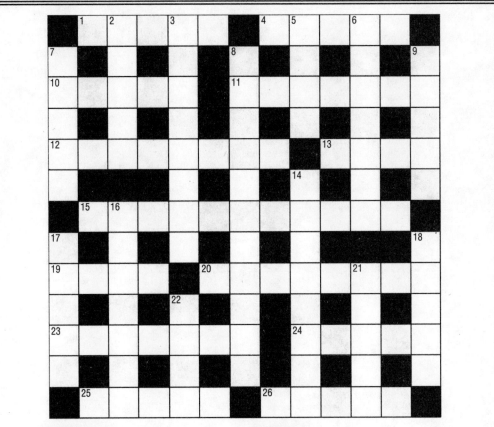

ACROSS

1 Provide permanent support for (5)
4 Vision seen in sleep (5)
10 Make a false replica (5)
11 Pantomime character (3, 4)
12 Use, employ (8)
13 Walk in water (4)
15 Ugly object (11)
19 Prison in a navy ship (4)
20 Attachment (8)
23 Of the hip (7)
24 Conscious (5)
25 Vulgar (5)
26 Big and strong (5)

DOWN

2 Daring (5)
3 Cloudy (8)
5 Bridle strap (4)
6 Utterly determined (7)
7 Behind (5)
8 Make in large quantities (11)
9 Brooch with a head carved on it (5)
14 Approximate calculation (8)
16 Laurence - - -, film legend (7)
17 Bottomless pit (5)
18 South American mountain range (5)
21 Not suitable (5)
22 Small earring (4)

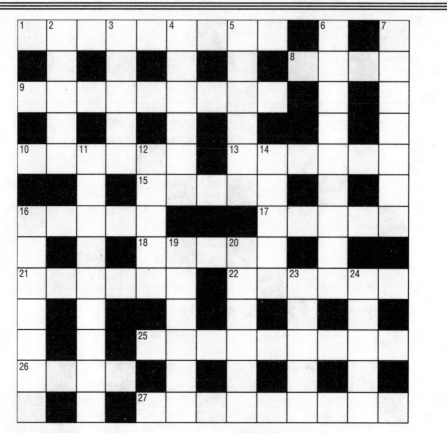

ACROSS

1 Opera singer (9)
8 Enthusiastic (4)
9 Fat (9)
10 Alcoholic drink (6)
13 Song of grief (6)
15 Main drain (5)
16 Relating to sound (5)
17 African country (5)
18 Farewell (5)
21 Public outburst (6)
22 Improve (6)
25 Pinball-like game (9)
26 Sandy - - -, golfer (4)
27 Initial advantage (4, 5)

DOWN

2 Beside the length (5)
3 Variety of poplar (5)
4 Do a favour for (6)
5 Throbbing sensation (6)
6 Reckless person (9)
7 Lack of movement (7)
11 By and large (9)
12 Film academy award (5)
14 Dispute (5)
16 English county (7)
19 Speak ill of (6)
20 Short trip to do something (6)
23 Armada (5)
24 Measuring device (5)

The Biggest Crossword Book In The World

ACROSS

1 *White Christmas* writer (6, 6)
9 Unsophisticated (5)
10 Soldier's jacket (5)
11 Actor, - - - Kingsley (3)
12 Eric Morecombe's wise partner! (5)
13 Army officer (7)
15 Succeed in doing (6)
17 Launch a physical assault on (6)
20 Tread on and crush (7)
23 Long piece of tartan cloth (5)
25 Serious crime (1, 1, 1)
26 Force out (5)
27 Seance board (5)
28 Chris de Burgh hit song (3, 4, 2, 3)

DOWN

2 Period of rule (5)
3 Huge frozen floater (7)
4 Passing look (6)
5 Praise highly (5)
6 Former Soviet Union leader (5)
7 **Ex wife of** Tom Cruise (6,6)
8 Sporadic (12)
14 Not at home (3)
16 Purpose (3)
18 Cyclone (7)
19 Gift left in a will (6)
21 Fruit (5)
22 Old-time dance (5)
24 Active (5)

The Biggest Crossword Book In The World

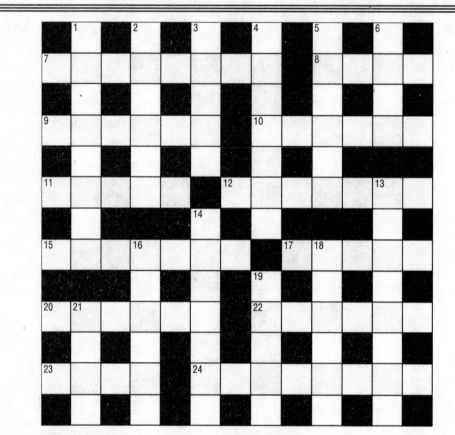

ACROSS

7 Impudence, cheek (8)
8 Wreck (4)
9 Three times (6)
10 Ring placed
under a bolt (6)
11 Point opposite South (5)
12 Perfectly cooked
pasta (2, 5)
15 First in importance (7)
17 Reasoning (5)
20 Sweet plant juice (6)
22 Angelic child (6)
23 Bamboo stick (4)
24 Abstinent from
alcohol (3-5)

DOWN

1 Peak travel period (4, 4)
2 Lasso (6)
3 Striped cat (5)
4 Isle of Man
parliament (7)
5 *Robinson - - -*, novel (6)
6 Motion of the ocean (4)
13 Court of justice (8)
14 In proportion (3, 4)
16 Child's glove (6)
18 King of the fairies (6)
19 Metal fastener (5)
21 Dutch cheese (4)

The Biggest Crossword Book In The World

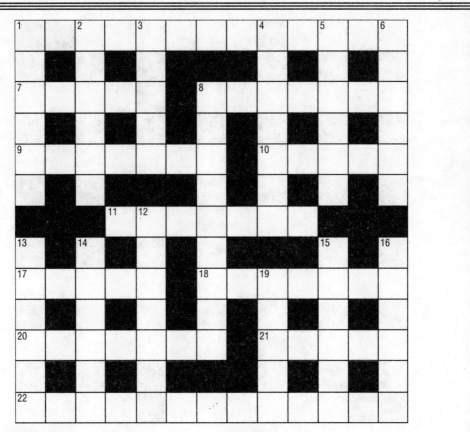

ACROSS

1 British funny man (5, 8)
7 Serving spoon (5)
8 Small embroidery frame (7)
9 Unpredictable (7)
10 Classical music show (5)
11 Prominent (7)
17 Rank (5)
18 Create feelings (7)
20 Amount of wear (7)
21 Bring upon oneself (5)
22 Crane fly (5-4-4)

DOWN

1 Dismal, dull (6)
2 Indian PM, - - - Gandhi (6)
3 Upright (5)
4 Satirical attack (7)
5 Hand warmers (6)
6 Routine (6)
8 Planner (9)
12 Useful facility (7)
13 Reached a unanimous decision (6)
14 English king (6)
15 Ring (6)
16 Red playing-card suit (6)
19 Support for a broken arm (5)

The Biggest Crossword Book In The World

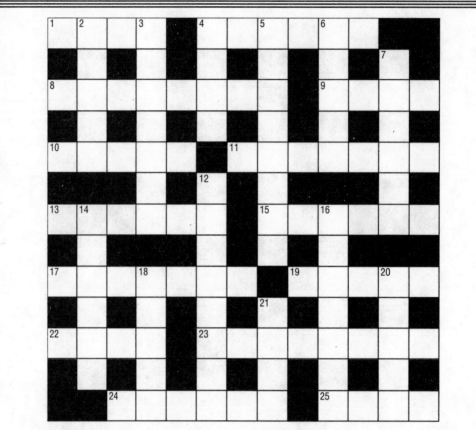

ACROSS

1 London park (4)
4 Chris - - -, Radio 1 DJ (6)
8 European country (8)
9 Became larger (4)
10 Quiver of arrows (5)
11 Receive through a will (7)
13 Light wind (6)
15 Child (6)
17 Modernised (7)
19 Leader of the Argonauts (5)
22 French cheese (4)
23 *Monty Python* star (4, 4)
24 Cloak (6)
25 Spot, detect (4)

DOWN

2 Young person (5)
3 Carve figures on a surface (7)
4 Greater in amount (4)
5 Strong desire (8)
6 Large bird of prey (5)
7 Bring back to life (6)
12 Television news and information service (8)
14 Written statement (6)
16 Nutty sweet (7)
18 Sports stadium (5)
20 Lowest deck of a ship (5)
21 Widespread (4)

The Biggest Crossword Book In The World

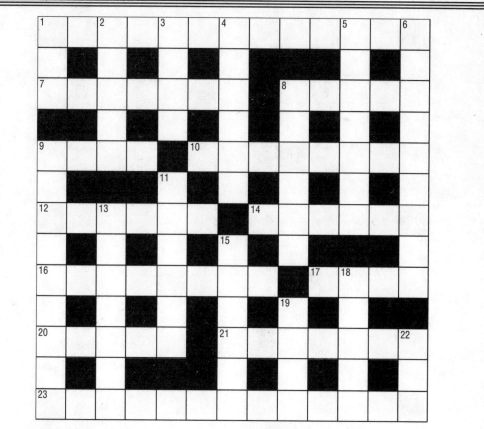

ACROSS

1 Labour MP (6, 7)
7 Normal (7)
8 Immature (5)
9 Microbe (4)
10 Final speech (8)
12 Part of the throat (6)
14 Instant (6)
16 Alienate (8)
17 Woodwind
mouthpiece (4)
20 Elude (5)
21 Radio channel (7)
23 Capital punishment
device (8, 5)

DOWN

1 Alcoholic drink (3)
2 Go inside (5)
3 Soil (4)
4 Dilapidated old car (6)
5 Cuddle (7)
6 Overlooked (9)
8 Cowardly colour (6)
9 James Bond film (9)
11 Raid (6)
13 Pitiless struggle (3, 4)
15 Andre - - -,
tennis player (6)
18 Andrew Lloyd-Webber
musical (5)
19 Soft, silvery-white
mineral (4)
22 And not (3)

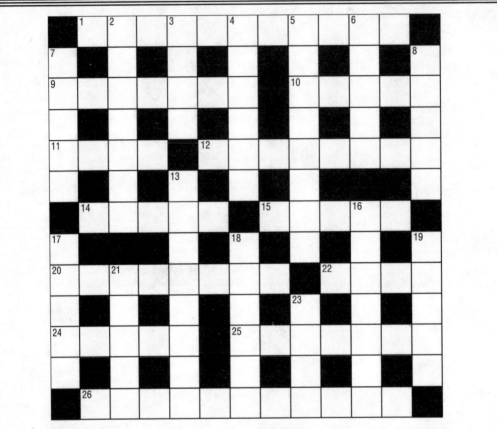

ACROSS

1 Academic cap (11)
9 Far-reaching (7)
10 American cafe (5)
11 Former name
of Thailand (4)
12 Wealthy (4-2-2)
14 Renown (5)
15 Preserve (food) (5)
20 Conquer (8)
22 Impolite (4)
24 Sumptuous meal (5)
25 Waterproof fabric (7)
26 TV presenter (4, 7)

DOWN

2 Eccentric person (7)
3 Skill in avoiding
giving offence (4)
4 Wheeled (6)
5 Previous partner (3, 5)
6 Beatles' drummer,
- - - Starr (5)
7 From Dublin? (5)
8 Evidence (5)
13 Michael - - -, author (8)
16 Finger joint (7)
17 Greek island (5)
18 Unruffled (6)
19 Female ass (5)
21 Electronic letter (1, 4)
23 Smart man! (4)

The Biggest Crossword Book In The World

ACROSS

1 Bird-watcher (8)
5 Strong aftertaste (4)
9 Amusing (5)
10 Gambling resort, - - - Carlo (5)
12 Goat's cry (5)
13 Cain's brother (4)
15 Italian city (6)
18 Correspond (6)
20 Warm and snug (4)
23 Brag (5)
24 Dog-like African animal (5)
27 Insulting comments (5)
28 Poet, - - - Pound (4)
29 Indian tourist attraction (3, 5)

DOWN

1 Rain heavily (4)
2 Iraq's neighbour (4)
3 Shrink in fear (5)
4 Whole (6)
6 Second self (5, 3)
7 Mild (6)
8 Cross-bred (6)
11 Sphere (3)
14 US lift (8)
16 Stringed instrument (6)
17 Air pocket (6)
19 Emotional shock (6)
21 Earth's star (3)
22 Domestic gas unit (5)
25 Everyone separately (4)
26 Absent without leave (inits)

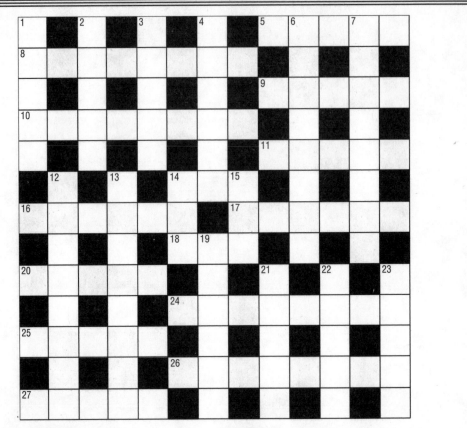

ACROSS

5 Two at cards (5)
8 Desirable (8)
9 Hold-up (5)
10 Courtesy (8)
11 Trifling (5)
14 Elite squadron (1, 1, 1)
16 Rebound (6)
17 Room for free
 movement (6)
18 Cambridgeshire city (3)
20 Leap over (5)
24 Soccer official (8)
25 Charred bread (5)
26 Precious metal foil (4, 4)
27 Soft and flexible (5)

DOWN

1 Educate, train (5)
2 All night watch (5)
3 Conclusive (5)
4 Radio presenter,
 - - - Hunniford (6)
6 Scrooge's first name (8)
7 Foolish talk (8)
12 Torpid, lethargic (8)
13 Examined critically (8)
14 Notice (3)
15 Sneaky, cunning (3)
19 Provided (4, 2)
21 Shabby (5)
22 Fix firmly (5)
23 Amalgamate (5)

The Biggest Crossword Book In The World

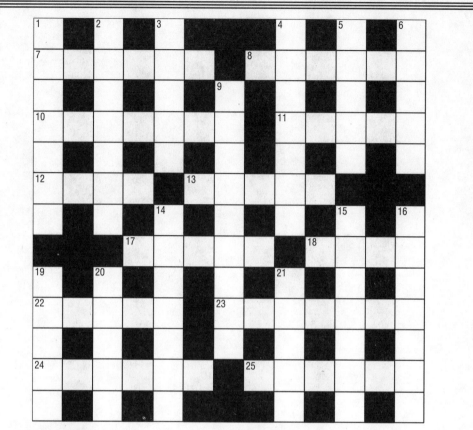

ACROSS

7 Constant (6)
8 Melted animal fat (6)
10 Stir up (7)
11 Quilt (5)
12 Grudge (4)
13 Peculiar (5)
17 Pasture land (5)
18 Over, past (4)
22 Light-purple colour (5)
23 Chris - - -, radio
   and TV star (7)
24 Jamaican music (6)
25 Well known (6)

DOWN

1 Leaked from
   a container (7)
2 Accept as true (7)
3 Novelist, - - - Wallace (5)
4 Mud-clearing boat (7)
5 Divide into two pieces (5)
6 Irish poet (5)
9 Necessary (9)
14 Vital (7)
15 Benefactor (7)
16 Tooth surgeon (7)
19 Utter quickly (5)
20 Impedes (5)
21 Part by force (5)

The Biggest Crossword Book In The World

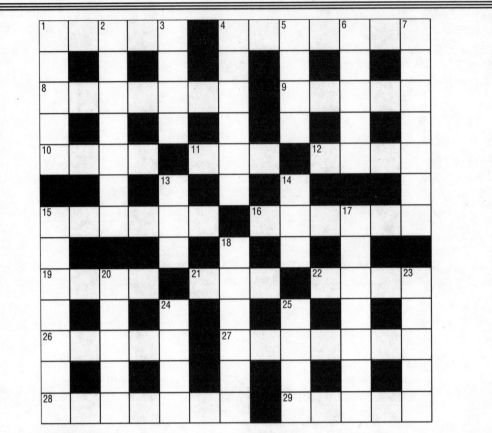

ACROSS

1 Weak and feeble (5)
4 Changed (7)
8 Tight (7)
9 Island in the
   Bristol Channel (5)
10 Spruce (4)
11 Naval spirit (3)
12 Damage caused
   by use (4)
15 European country (6)
16 Full-scale model (4-2)
19 Flexible part of a whip (4)
21 Short-winged bird (3)
22 Definite winner (4)
26 Hero (5)
27 Vacuum flask (7)
28 Day of the week (7)
29 Stomach! (5)

DOWN

1 Ladies (5)
2 Capture, trap (7)
3 English city (4)
4 Sanctuary, refuge (6)
5 Yarn (4)
6 Scope (5)
7 Short excursion? (3, 4)
13 Coat hook (3)
14 West country hill (3)
15 Seek business (7)
17 Stay silent (4, 3)
18 Cricketer,
   - - - Ambrose (6)
20 Disgrace (5)
23 Appetising (5)
24 Potato? (4)
25 Badger's burrow (4)

The Biggest Crossword Book In The World

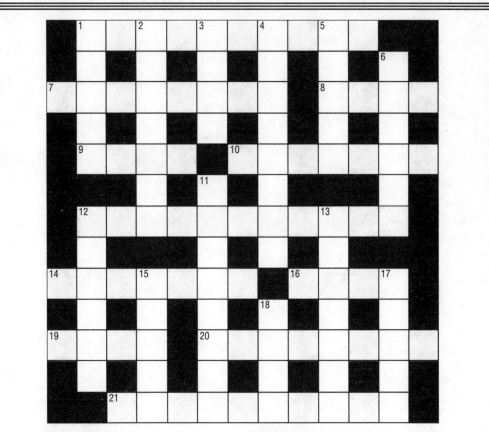

ACROSS

1 Former *Big Breakfast* presenter (4, 6)
7 Piece (8)
8 Baby carriage (4)
9 Small whirlpool (4)
10 Imitator (4-3)
12 Sanction (11)
14 Heavy iron lever (7)
16 Utter melodious sounds (4)
19 Small car (4)
20 Looked at closely (8)
21 Newly colonized place (10)

DOWN

1 Canyon (5)
2 Capital of Iraq (7)
3 Spool for cotton (4)
4 French resort (2, 6)
5 Insinuate (5)
6 Unoccupied (6)
11 Decorative object (8)
12 Small pincered insect (6)
13 Large building (7)
15 Use a pen (5)
17 Hotel resident (5)
18 Tarzan's friend (4)

The Biggest Crossword Book In The World

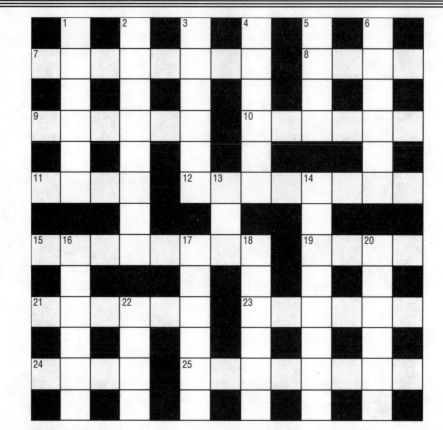

ACROSS

7 Methodical (8)
8 Martin - - -, *EastEnders'* actor (4)
9 Chatter idly (6)
10 Emblem (6)
11 Scoff (4)
12 Grappled (8)
15 Enjoyable (8)
19 Scottish loch (4)
21 Fully informed (2, 4)
23 Footballer (6)
24 Greek god (4)
25 Member of New Zealand national Rugby team (3, 5)

DOWN

1 Expression (6)
2 Standards (8)
3 Animal's hole (6)
4 Pure (6)
5 Glide smoothly over (4)
6 Enforce (6)
13 Sprint (3)
14 Octopus arm (8)
16 Foliage of the bay-tree (6)
17 Existing in reality (6)
18 Duffel coat fastener (6)
20 Sew (6)
22 Church alcove (4)

The Biggest Crossword Book In The World

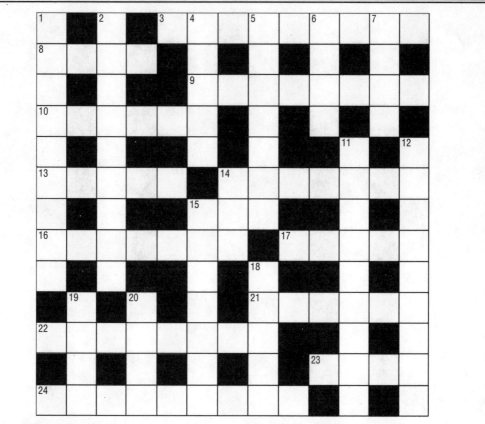

ACROSS

3 Calms (9)
8 Abel's brother (4)
9 Large social event (8)
10 Spanish currency unit (6)
13 Spherical body (5)
14 Turn the other
way round (7)
15 Toothed wheel (3)
16 Stated without proof (7)
17 Severe (5)
21 Last meal of the day (6)
22 Break up (buildings) (8)
23 Actress, - - - Moore (4)
24 Symbolise (9)

DOWN

1 Person to take
the blame (9)
2 Beauty contest (4, 5)
4 British-based charity (5)
5 Cricket position (4-3)
6 Gala, bazaar (4)
7 Food taster,
- - - Ronay (4)
11 Notorious murderer (2, 7)
12 Listless (9)
14 Angler's pole (3)
15 Temperature scale (7)
18 Pale (5)
19 Small lake (4)
20 Sixty minutes (4)

The Biggest Crossword Book In The World

ACROSS

1 Japanese rice dish (5)
4 Tree (5)
10 Royal horse-racing venue (5)
11 Peach-like fruit (7)
12 Garden plant (5, 3)
13 Solid shape with six equal square sides (4)
15 *Speed* actor (5, 6)
19 Coloured (4)
20 Edible snail (8)
23 Food associated with Shrove Tuesday (7)
24 Hang in the air (5)
25 Jargon (5)
26 Publish (5)

DOWN

2 Male relative (5)
3 Item of furniture (8)
5 Askew (4)
6 Reprimand, scold (7)
7 Pretty meadow flower (5)
8 Uninvited intruder (4-7)
9 Guide (5)
14 Figure of speech (8)
16 Everlasting (7)
17 Make suitable for a purpose (5)
18 Harsh, strict (5)
21 Boy's name (5)
22 Excessively proud (4)

The Biggest Crossword Book In The World

ACROSS

1 Benefit (9)
8 Horsefly (4)
9 Content (9)
10 Flow back (6)
13 Nearer (6)
15 Drive away (5)
16 An obsession (5)
17 Prize, trophy (5)
18 Refracting glass (5)
21 Scottish city (6)
22 Obvious (6)
25 Flippant remark (9)
26 Long-running battle (4)
27 *Tomorrow - - -*, Bond film (5, 4)

DOWN

2 Actress, - - - Keaton (5)
3 Supple (5)
4 Caramel (6)
5 Country (6)
6 Alan - - -, playwright (9)
7 Sent to Coventry (7)
11 Riddle (9)
12 Cover with material (5)
14 South American camel (5)
16 Specialist nurse (7)
19 Say from memory (6)
20 Globe (6)
23 Weary (5)
24 Suitable position (5)

The Biggest Crossword Book In The World

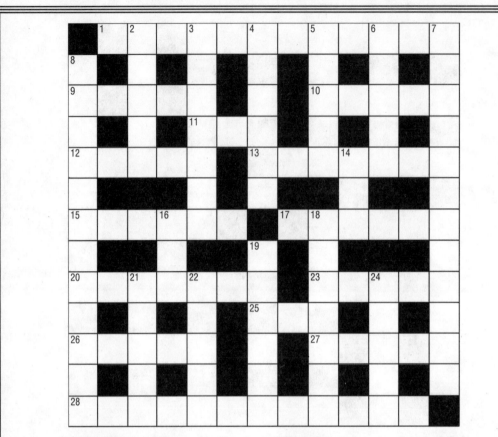

ACROSS

1 Unprincipled (12)
9 Barmy, crazy (5)
10 Ability to see (5)
11 Expanse of salt water (3)
12 Deal with (5)
13 Lockjaw (7)
15 Fit to eat (6)
17 Ballroom dance (6)
20 Mail delivery person (7)
23 Creature (5)
25 Farmhouse cooker (3)
26 Regal (5)
27 Safari animal? (5)
28 Lighthouse association (7, 5)

DOWN

2 Slip-knot (5)
3 Piece of cut glass (7)
4 Modernise (6)
5 Disturbance (5)
6 Large musical instrument (5)
7 Pleasure (12)
8 Noel Coward comedy (6, 6)
14 Pointed tool (3)
16 Have a flutter (3)
18 Trade ban (7)
19 Irritable (6)
21 Johanna - - -, *Heidi* author (5)
22 More than one (5)
24 An assumed name (5)

The Biggest Crossword Book In The World

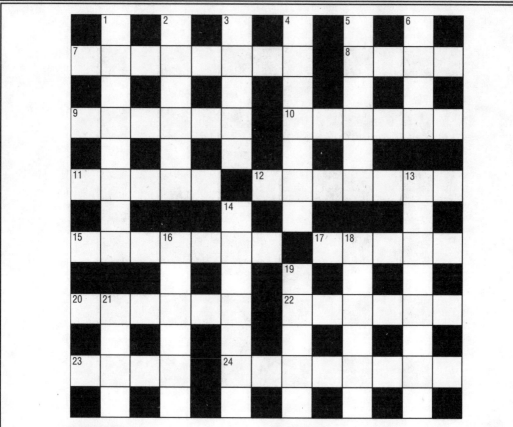

ACROSS

7 Ill-will (8)
8 Follow closely (4)
9 Entire (6)
10 Animal dung (6)
11 Religious man (5)
12 Experience (7)
15 Woman's bedroom (7)
17 Tine (5)
20 On (a ship) (6)
22 Send to Coventry (6)
23 Snack (4)
24 Determined (8)

DOWN

1 Summary of a film (8)
2 Albanian capital (6)
3 Personal strong point (5)
4 American state (7)
5 Attitude, standing (6)
6 Coffin frame (4)
13 Produce (8)
14 Irish county (7)
16 Baby's nappy (6)
18 US president,
 - - - Reagan (6)
19 Telephone box (5)
21 Method of cooking (4)

The Biggest Crossword Book In The World

ACROSS

1 Radioactivity recording device (6, 7)
7 *Peggy Sue* singer, - - - Holly (5)
8 Loyal countryman (7)
9 Precisely (7)
10 Phantom (5)
11 Performer (7)
17 Synthetic fibre (5)
18 Restrain, hinder (7)
20 Group of soldiers (7)
21 Course traversed (5)
22 Amusement (13)

DOWN

1 Drinking cup (6)
2 One from New Delhi? (6)
3 African country (5)
4 Tense, irritable (7)
5 Suit maker (6)
6 Revolve (6)
8 Doctor (9)
12 Bitterness (7)
13 Increase threefold (6)
14 Oppresive ruler (6)
15 Dull-witted (6)
16 City road (6)
19 Wading bird (5)

The Biggest Crossword Book In The World

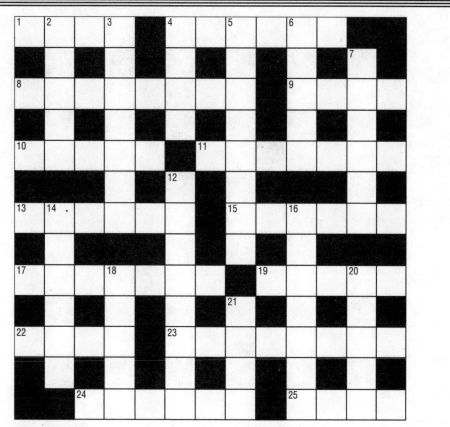

ACROSS

1 Attic (4)
4 Novelist (6)
8 Wood preservative (8)
9 Void (4)
10 Material object (5)
11 Blood-drinking
creature (7)
13 Powerful (6)
15 **Former** monetary unit
of Portugal (6)
17 Environment (7)
19 Idleness (5)
22 Not bright or clear (4)
23 West Indian island (8)
24 Bobby - - -, former
England manager (6)
25 Grievance (4)

DOWN

2 Talk show host,
- - - Winfrey (5)
3 Thrash (7)
4 Nautical shout (4)
5 Youth (8)
6 Confess (3, 2)
7 TV personality,
- - - Marks (6)
12 The lost continent (8)
14 Not transparent (6)
16 Bone ingredient? (7)
18 Eskimo's hut (5)
20 Jewelled headdress (5)
21 Oven (4)

The Biggest Crossword Book In The World

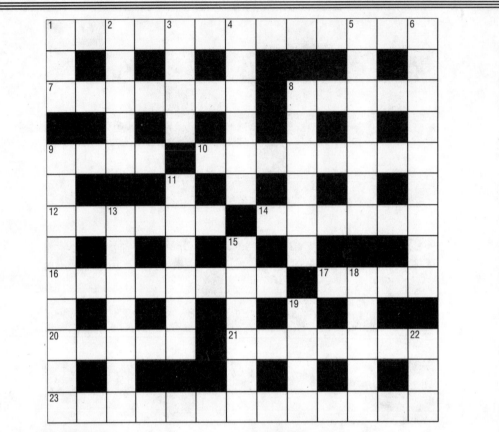

ACROSS

1 Without enthusiasm (4-9)
7 Ritzy style (7)
8 Ladder treads (5)
9 Highland valley (4)
10 Dusk (8)
12 Angora wool (6)
14 Uneven, tattered (6)
16 Impermeable (8)
17 Agile (4)
20 Sweet topping (5)
21 Film extract (7)
23 Designed to fit (4, 2, 7)

DOWN

1 Hoard selfishly (3)
2 Depart (5)
3 Circular toy (4)
4 Turn up (6)
5 Moving to music (7)
6 Twenty-four hours ago (9)
8 Airstrip (6)
9 Exercise hall (9)
11 Scandinavian pirate (6)
13 Rushed (7)
15 Musical beat (6)
18 Indian dish of rice and meat (5)
19 Long, detailed story (4)
22 Small deer (3)

The Biggest Crossword Book In The World

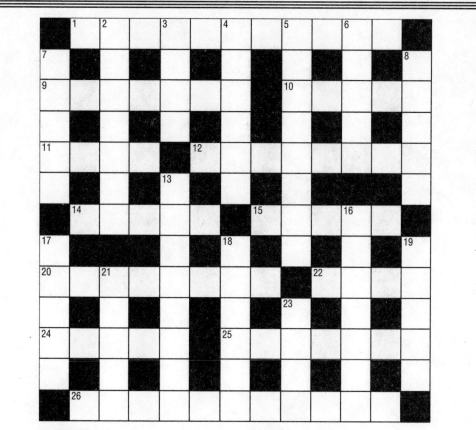

ACROSS
1 Thick beef steak (11)
9 Eccentric (7)
10 Demonstrate (5)
11 Cut in small strokes (4)
12 Woman with dark hair (8)
14 Full of interest (5)
15 Light meal (5)
20 Empty (8)
22 Funny story (4)
24 Departing (5)
25 Devon's main holiday resort (7)
26 Imitate (11)

DOWN
2 Soccer rule (7)
3 Excessively sentimental (4)
4 Come back (6)
5 Rival (8)
6 Brief (5)
7 Deafening (5)
8 Slope (5)
13 Fight (8)
16 Lawn game (7)
17 Grasslike plant (5)
18 Prestige (6)
19 Commonwealth country (5)
21 Adage (5)
23 Small songbird (4)

ACROSS

1 Personal quality (8)
5 By author unknown (4)
9 Do without (5)
10 Elizabethan sailor (5)
12 Arc (5)
13 Performing animal (4)
15 Against (6)
18 Saucepan stand (6)
20 Rhythm and Blues (4)
23 Skiing slope (5)
24 Flying insects (5)
27 Smooth and
 sophisticated (5)
28 Baby's biscuit (4)
29 Track competitors (8)

DOWN

1 Thin rope (4)
2 Solo operatic song (4)
3 Deduce (5)
4 Of the sea (6)
6 American state (8)
7 Degrees in a
 right angle (6)
8 Large grasshopper (6)
11 Cereal (3)
14 Singers and dancers (8)
16 Best (6)
17 Soft, gentle breeze (6)
19 Bad behaviour (6)
21 American postal code (3)
22 Expand (5)
25 Mud from a river (4)
26 Soap bubbles (4)

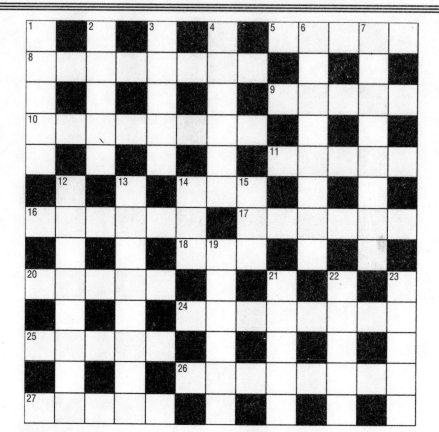

ACROSS

5 Type of tree (5)
8 Eastern man-drawn carriage (8)
9 Melody (5)
10 Small cruiser (8)
11 Entangle (5)
14 Asian country, - - - Lanka (3)
16 Tennis player, - - - Edberg (6)
17 Evil intent (6)
18 Vim, vigour (3)
20 Wobbly dessert (5)
24 Think deeply (8)
25 Hinder, put off (5)
26 Spiny mammal (8)
27 This planet (5)

DOWN

1 Tiny amount (5)
2 Despise (5)
3 Daisy-like flower (5)
4 Minister in charge of a church (6)
6 Commendable (8)
7 Sign, indication (8)
12 And similar things (2, 6)
13 Rich, wealthy (8)
14 The Scottish Nationalist Party (1, 1, 1)
15 Little devil (3)
19 Lace hole (6)
21 Scorch (5)
22 Swim (5)
23 Border (5)

The Biggest Crossword Book In The World

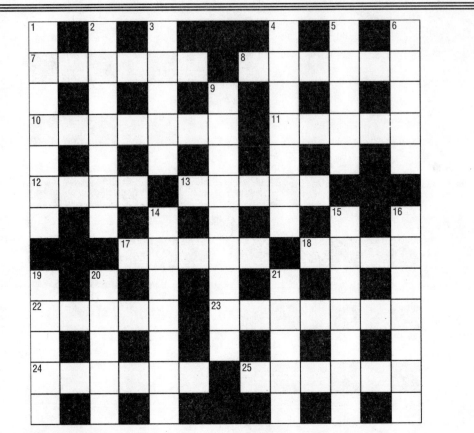

ACROSS

7 The best (6)
8 Slight pecularity (6)
10 Jim Carrey film (3, 4)
11 Pottery city on
the river Trent (5)
12 Tune (4)
13 Take (5)
17 Fireplace (5)
18 Midday (4)
22 Card game (5)
23 Frightened (7)
24 Deep gorge (6)
25 Small pastry (6)

DOWN

1 Intense delight (7)
2 Unspecified person (7)
3 Skinny animal (5)
4 Frightening creature (7)
5 Peter - - -, snooker
player (5)
6 Chromosomes (5)
9 Miser, niggard (9)
14 Prepared quickly (7)
15 Jason - - -, singer
and actor (7)
16 Liquorice-like
flavouring (7)
19 Spin (5)
20 Kitchen utensil (5)
21 Massive (5)

The Biggest Crossword Book In The World

ACROSS

1 Nobleman (5)
4 Former American President (7)
8 Bird of prey (7)
9 Wind (5)
10 Roman Emperor (4)
11 Bullfighter's shout (3)
12 Suburban house (4)
15 Singer and songwriter, - - - Wonder (6)
16 Scottish outlaw (3, 3)
19 Target (4)
21 Insane (3)
22 Tartan skirt (4)
26 Expel from one's country (5)
27 Fence (7)
28 Notion (7)
29 Finger or toe (5)

DOWN

1 Started (5)
2 Book (7)
3 Beside (4)
4 Mr Hyde's doctor? (6)
5 Detest (4)
6 Microscope glass (5)
7 Cancel (7)
13 Dignitary (inits) (3)
14 Separate compartment in a theatre (3)
15 Part of a circle (7)
17 Iron barrier (7)
18 Small burrowing mammal (6)
20 Friend (5)
23 Fortune-teller's cards (5)
24 Mass of floating ice (4)
25 Dried up (4)

ACROSS

1 **Ginger haired** radio and TV presenter (5, 5)
7 Feign illness (8)
8 Swindle (4)
9 Make with wool (4)
10 Haiti dictator (4, 3)
12 Relative distance (11)
14 Hotel porter (7)
16 Hit repeatedly (4)
19 Open-air pool (4)
20 Disturbed (8)
21 The NE part of the US (3, 7)

DOWN

1 White limestone (5)
2 Monaco's prince (7)
3 Breathe (4)
4 Discrepancy (8)
5 Unpleasant (5)
6 Prisoner's early release (6)
11 Topical (2-2-4)
12 Andre - - -, conductor (6)
13 The art of Japanese flower arrangement (7)
15 Sierra - - -, African country (5)
17 Scottish cloth (5)
18 Lively quality (4)

The Biggest Crossword Book In The World

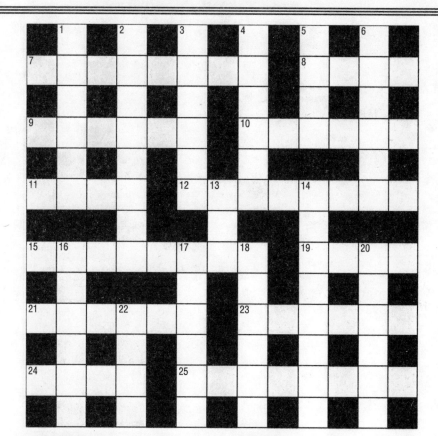

ACROSS
7 Enormous (8)
8 Dry by rubbing (4)
9 Give permission (6)
10 Dr Who's time
machine (6)
11 French city (4)
12 A Devon speciality (5, 3)
15 Sherlock Holmes'
sidekick (2, 6)
19 Greg Norman's sport (4)
21 Whole-hearted (3-3)
23 Means of approach (6)
24 Heal (4)
25 Hugs warmly (8)

DOWN
1 Great unhappiness (6)
2 Island state
of Australia (8)
3 Motionless (6)
4 Damage (6)
5 Water jug (4)
6 Water nymph, elf (6)
13 Brazilian city (3)
14 Paul Daniels, eg (8)
16 Handmade
cigarette (4-2)
17 Sofa (6)
18 Close to hand (6)
20 Jockey, - - - Piggott (6)
22 Prophetic sign (4)

The Biggest Crossword Book In The World

ACROSS

3 Pulse regulator (9)
8 Ire (4)
9 Most charming (8)
10 Bring about by force (6)
13 Metric unit of capacity (5)
14 Medicated tablet that soothes sore throats (7)
15 Rubbish receptacle (3)
16 Arrogant person (7)
17 Large crowd (5)
21 Again, anew (6)
22 Usually (8)
23 Beast with a mane (4)
24 Pressure measure (9)

DOWN

1 Slightly ill (3, 6)
2 Writer of plays (9)
4 Theatre gangway (5)
5 Premier division soccer club (7)
6 Opposed to (4)
7 Gaelic (4)
11 Lively (9)
12 Communication tool (9)
14 Set fire to (3)
15 Reading method for blind people (7)
18 Possibly (5)
19 Bob Hoskins film, - - - *Lisa* (4)
20 Bullets, etc. (4)

The Biggest Crossword Book In The World

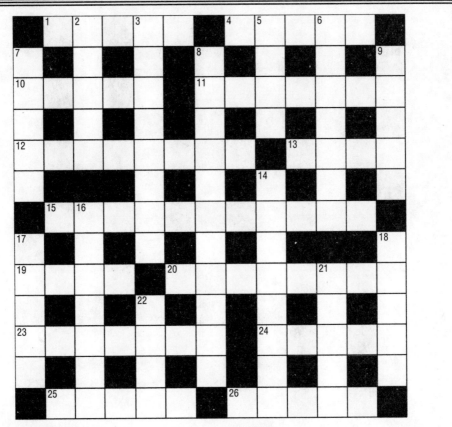

ACROSS

1 End of the war
   in Europe (1, 1, 3)
4 Quay (5)
10 Sweeping blow (5)
11 Sooner (7)
12 Height (8)
13 Percolate (4)
15 The PM's wife (6, 5)
19 Horse-drawn vehicle (4)
20 Assertive (8)
23 Diver (7)
24 Memorable American
   battle (5)
25 Frog sound (5)
26 Not sharp (5)

DOWN

2 Live (5)
3 Opening (8)
5 Previous name for
   Republic of Ireland (4)
6 Capital of Libya (7)
7 Common (5)
8 Style of embroidery (11)
9 Crawl, tread (5)
14 Altogether (3, 2, 3)
16 Shelter (7)
17 Express derision (5)
18 Bend forward and
   downward (5)
21 Grand Prix driver,
   - - - Prost (5)
22 Oscar-winning actress,
   - - - Thompson (4)

The Biggest Crossword Book In The World

ACROSS

1 Ardent (9)
8 Not succeed (4)
9 Lamb curry (5, 4)
10 Note sent through
   the post (6)
13 Former kingdom in
   central England (6)
15 Outcast (5)
16 Italian composer (5)
17 German river (5)
18 County town
   of Cornwall (5)
21 Artificial hairpiece (6)
22 Area around the
   North Pole (6)
25 Russian Communist (9)
26 Newscaster, - - - Ford (4)
27 Cricketing county (9)

DOWN

2 Love intensely (5)
3 Separately (5)
4 Hurt physically (6)
5 Take for granted,
   suppose (6)
6 Pain giver (9)
7 Atmosphere (7)
11 Agitated (9)
12 The best (5)
14 Mistake (5)
16 Pope's residence (7)
19 Kick back (6)
20 Money paid for release
   of a prisoner (6)
23 Cry of
   encouragement (5)
24 Spanish island (5)

The Biggest Crossword Book In The World

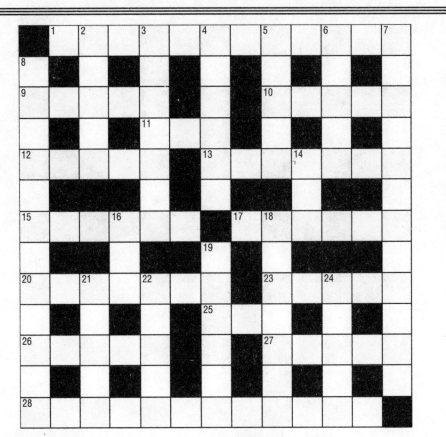

ACROSS
1 Worm, eg (12)
9 Portray in oils (5)
10 Firm embrace (5)
11 Sewer rodent (3)
12 Wrinkly material (5)
13 Chinese lamp? (7)
15 Ornamental leg chain (6)
17 Lucky escape (3-3)
20 Haughty, cold (7)
23 Giver (5)
25 Under the weather (3)
26 Former Argentinian President (5)
27 Projecting edge of the roof (5)
28 British racing driver (5, 7)

DOWN
2 Racket (5)
3 Farthest from the centre (7)
4 Marine reptile (6)
5 Breakfast rasher (5)
6 Type of quartz (5)
7 Old royal hunting ground (6, 6)
8 Extremely neat and clean (5-3-4)
14 Infant (3)
16 The whole (3)
18 Infinite (7)
19 Aspersion (6)
21 Small branch (5)
22 Cancel (5)
24 Work of fiction (5)

The Biggest Crossword Book In The World

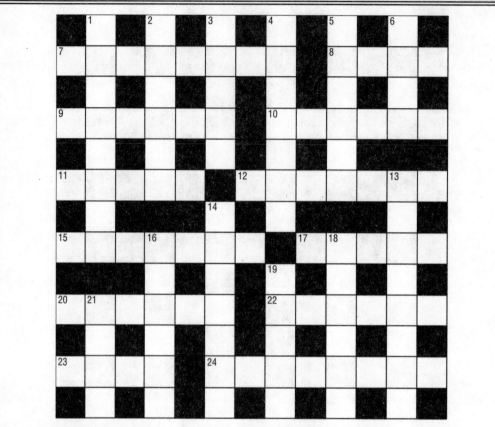

ACROSS
7 Maximum volume (8)
8 Detonator (4)
9 Increase suddenly (6)
10 Large bird cage (6)
11 Child (5)
12 Extend (7)
15 Small French coin (7)
17 Two pints (5)
20 Enthusiast (6)
22 Evening party (6)
23 Enrol (4)
24 Assess (8)

DOWN
1 Legitimate target (4, 4)
2 Spotted cat (6)
3 The same (5)
4 Sequence of hereditary rulers (7)
5 Bureau (6)
6 Former Soviet Union (1,1,1,1)
13 Sets right (8)
14 Not included (7)
16 Natural aptitude (6)
18 One of a kind (6)
19 Nile dam (5)
21 Famous public school (4)

ACROSS

1 Peppermint flavour liqueur (5, 2, 6)
7 Zest (5)
8 Mislead (7)
9 African capital (7)
10 Playground attraction (5)
11 Meg Ryan film, *- - - to a Kiss* (7)
17 Protect from the sun (5)
18 Boring (7)
20 Confiscate (7)
21 Worth (5)
22 Long-running TV series (3, 3, 2, 5)

DOWN

1 Fine brandy (6)
2 Naval flag (6)
3 Run away to wed (5)
4 Fenced (7)
5 Petty details (6)
6 Come out on inquiry (6)
8 Uninhabited (9)
12 Small male deer (7)
13 Give help or support (6)
14 Representative of a whole (6)
15 Sharp corner (3-3)
16 Agreement (6)
19 English county (5)

The Biggest Crossword Book In The World

ACROSS

1 Not any (4)
4 Glaring mistake (6)
8 Collarbone (8)
9 Rigid support (4)
10 Death bell (5)
11 American state and city (3, 4)
13 Cambodian Communist leader (3, 3)
15 Badge (6)
17 Liverpool racecourse (7)
19 Relieve (pain) (5)
22 Well ventilated (4)
23 Cake covering (8)
24 Substantial (6)
25 John - - -, British architect (4)

DOWN

2 Manmade fibre (5)
3 Cover completely (7)
4 Chop violently (4)
5 At whatever time (8)
6 Vacant (5)
7 Rough voice (6)
12 Paper decoration (8)
14 Source (6)
16 Gold or silver (7)
18 Herb used in cooking (5)
20 Hoard, collect (5)
21 Squirrel's nest (4)

The Biggest Crossword Book In The World

ACROSS

1 Object of humiliation (8, 5)
7 Clown (7)
8 Adjust, change (5)
9 Manufactured (4)
10 Brown sugar (8)
12 Long loose robe (6)
14 Road accident (4, 2)
16 Station at the end of a route (8)
17 Hospital room (4)
20 Cooker (5)
21 Not ordinary (7)
23 *Men Behaving Badly* star (4, 9)

DOWN

1 Racetrack circuit (3)
2 Overturn (2-3)
3 Group of animals (4)
4 Aromatic spice (6)
5 Function (7)
6 Abducted (9)
8 American aviator, - - - Earhart (6)
9 Heavyweight boxer (4, 5)
11 Curly-leaved salad plant (6)
13 Italian inventor (7)
15 Treasurer (6)
18 Sign of the zodiac (5)
19 Peaked cap (4)
22 Put in the required position (3)

The Biggest Crossword Book In The World

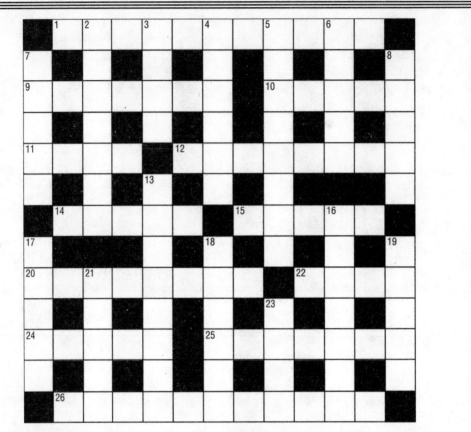

ACROSS
1 Charges (11)
9 Sense of slight (7)
10 Recurring series (5)
11 Cat noise (4)
12 Rigorous exam (4, 4)
14 Unaccompanied (5)
15 Growl angrily (5)
20 Sentimental in love (8)
22 Give out vapour (4)
24 Italian city (5)
25 Group of organisms (7)
26 Incessant (5-6)

DOWN
2 Generous (7)
3 Actor, - - - McGregor (4)
4 Organisation providing
  a service (6)
5 Event, occurrence (8)
6 Mother-of-pearl (5)
7 Rough, uneven (5)
8 Greek letter (5)
13 Flood (8)
16 Old pal's get-together (7)
17 Remains (5)
18 Paper handkerchief (6)
19 Untidy (5)
21 Chop small (5)
23 Look after (4)

The Biggest Crossword Book In The World

ACROSS

1 Get to know (8)
5 Sudden jerk (4)
9 Velvety cloth (5)
10 Roadside accommodation (5)
12 Of the countryside (5)
13 Narrow part of a bottle (4)
15 German POW camp (6)
18 Agatha Christie character (6)
20 Horizontal mine entrance (4)
23 Malice (5)
24 Not asleep (5)
27 Labourer (5)
28 Peak, summit (4)
29 Man-made object (8)

DOWN

1 Particle of matter (4)
2 Give up (4)
3 Make a formal request (5)
4 Zero (6)
6 Shocked (8)
7 Bank employee (6)
8 Excite (6)
11 Civil award (1, 1, 1)
14 Green or red pepper (8)
16 Soundless (6)
17 Dashboard (6)
19 *Castaway* star, - - - Reed (6)
21 Writing fluid (3)
22 Dancer, - - - Sleep (5)
25 Length times breadth (4)
26 Depart (4)

The Biggest Crossword Book In The World

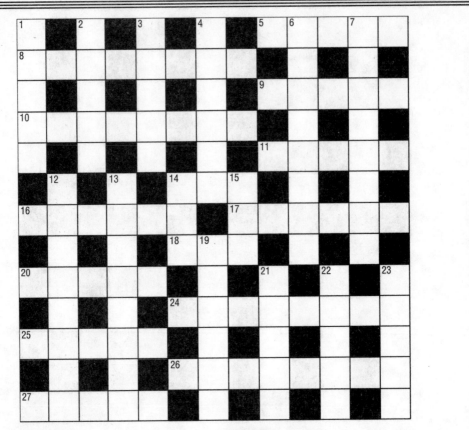

ACROSS

5 Circumference (5)
8 Day of the week (8)
9 Former American President (5)
10 Biting insect (8)
11 Deadly snake (5)
14 Hot beverage (3)
16 Go to bed (6)
17 Probe, antenna (6)
18 Dine (3)
20 Hidden store (5)
24 Gambling game (8)
25 Germaine - - -, feminist (5)
26 Horse-drawn vehicle (8)
27 Spirit of the lamp (5)

DOWN

1 Tread heavily (5)
2 Particular (5)
3 Distribute (5)
4 Baby's toy (6)
6 Copied (8)
7 Bothered (8)
12 Available supply (8)
13 Former British Prime Minister (8)
14 Golf peg (3)
15 To the rear of a ship (3)
19 Hooded jacket (6)
21 Promotional description (5)
22 Pilfer (5)
23 Nightclub owner, - - - Stringfellow (5)

The Biggest Crossword Book In The World

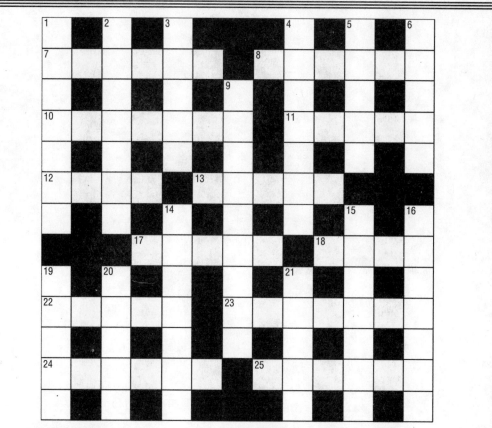

ACROSS

7 Stinging weed (6)
8 Hurried (6)
10 General pardon (7)
11 Pry into (5)
12 Entreaty (4)
13 Put up with (5)
17 Large feather (5)
18 Actress,
   - - - Beckinsale (4)
22 Fundamental (5)
23 Arctic whale (7)
24 Precious metal (6)
25 Jockey, - - - Swinburn (6)

DOWN

1 Sad (7)
2 Falkland Islands town (7)
3 Sudden burst of light (5)
4 Exterior (7)
5 Confusion (5)
6 Skilful, proficient (5)
9 Shakespeare play (9)
14 Meat seller (7)
15 Jungle knife (7)
16 Announce,
   make known (7)
19 Embarrass (5)
20 Sacred song (5)
21 Old coin (5)

The Biggest Crossword Book In The World

ACROSS

1 Single-masted vessel (5)
4 Strange event (7)
8 Point of view (7)
9 Visual riddle (5)
10 Dressmaking fold (4)
11 Small piece of coal (3)
12 Move in water (4)
15 Tom Hanks film (6)
16 Seize control
   (of a vehicle) (6)
19 Side tooth of
   an elephant (4)
21 Nervous twitch (3)
22 Forbid (4)
26 Celebrate (5)
27 Rule over (7)
28 Express disapproval (7)
29 Location (5)

DOWN

1 Fire from a gun (5)
2 Of the eyes (7)
3 Needy (4)
4 Cosmetics (4-2)
5 Hindu woman's
   garment (4)
6 Arm joint (5)
7 Muslim veil (7)
13 Fire remains (3)
14 Tear (3)
15 Cutting (humour) (7)
17 'Land of the Free' (7)
18 Variety of apple (6)
20 Number of
   Snow White's Dwarfs (5)
23 Very fat (5)
24 Sticky substance (4)
25 Gather in crops (4)

The Biggest Crossword Book In The World

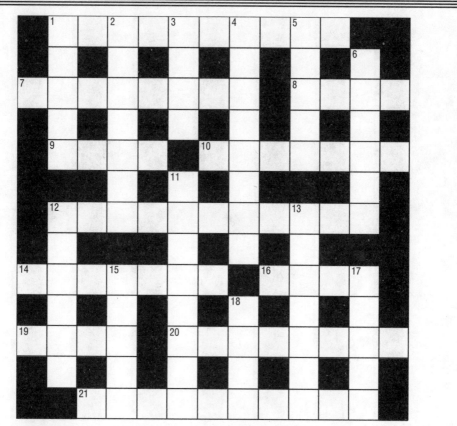

ACROSS

1 Bette Midler film (5, 5)
7 Remove from established position (8)
8 June 4th 1944 (1-3)
9 Cutting, sharp (4)
10 Somewhat old (7)
12 Man with magical powers? (5, 6)
14 Without purpose (7)
16 Ahead of true time (4)
19 Lemon peel (4)
20 Ballot, vote (8)
21 Middle Eastern carpet (7, 3)

DOWN

1 Lift up (5)
2 Guilty person (7)
3 Sporting team (4)
4 Disregard (8)
5 Excessive (5)
6 Seaman (6)
11 Cat's facial hair (8)
12 Restaurant worker (6)
13 Betrayer (7)
15 Flexible (5)
17 Lash of a whip (5)
18 Greek ewe's-milk cheese (4)

The Biggest Crossword Book In The World

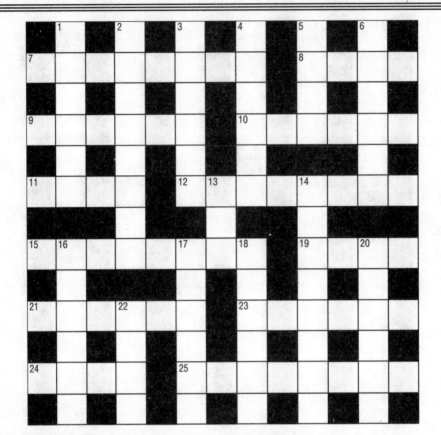

ACROSS

7 Long-distance race (8)
8 Large hole in the cliff (4)
9 Soothsayer (6)
10 Planet in the solar system (6)
11 *Bridge Over the River - - -*, action film (4)
12 Greyish-white metal (8)
15 Female child (8)
19 Extravagant promotion (4)
21 Sprinkler head (6)
23 Pick out (6)
24 Ancient Peruvian (4)
25 Capital of Australia (8)

DOWN

1 Piece of farm equipment (6)
2 Contagious (8)
3 Declaration of intent to harm (6)
4 Agreement (6)
5 Improvised jazz singing (4)
6 Disinclined (6)
13 Put into service (3)
14 Sailing vessel (8)
16 Quantity (6)
17 Deep furrow (6)
18 Modern (6)
20 Pie casing (6)
22 Great eagerness (4)

The Biggest Crossword Book In The World

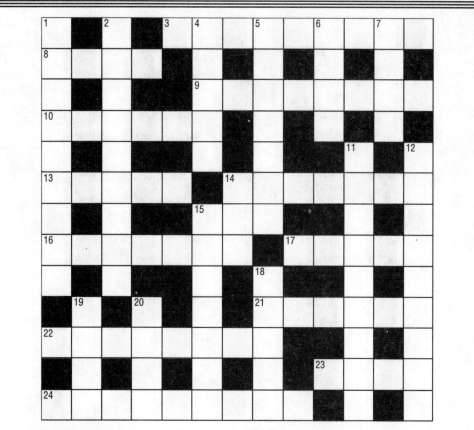

ACROSS

3 Short-legged dog (9)
8 Milk producing animal (4)
9 Member of a criminal group (8)
10 Cancel (a law) (6)
13 Very serious (5)
14 For a short while (7)
15 Pronounce (3)
16 Desire to drink (7)
17 Fly without the use of engines (5)
21 Wrinkle (6)
22 Intentional damage (8)
23 Medium sized (4)
24 Skydiving accessory (9)

DOWN

1 Combined totals (9)
2 The US President's official retreat (4, 5)
4 Fish with rod and line (5)
5 European country (7)
6 Landlord (4)
7 Require (4)
11 Written statement on oath (9)
12 Dorset resort (4, 5)
14 Coastal inlet (3)
15 Digestive organ (7)
18 Aroma (5)
19 Bye-bye! (2-2)
20 Francisco de - - -, artist (4)

The Biggest Crossword Book In The World

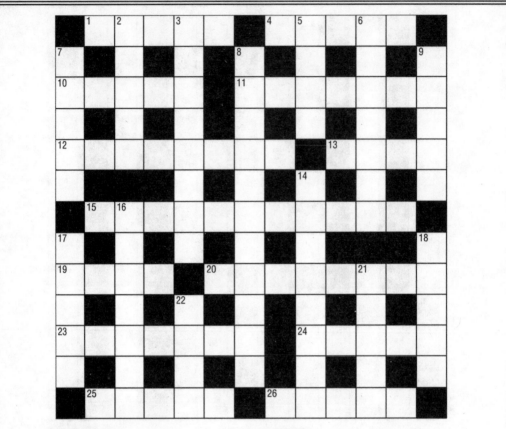

ACROSS

1 Parasitic insect (5)
4 Dark period (5)
10 Brownish uniform fabric (5)
11 Ancient (7)
12 Originates (8)
13 I beg your pardon! (4)
15 Underhand dealing (11)
19 Golfer, - - - Norman (4)
20 Earn vast amounts of money! (4, 2, 2)
23 American state (7)
24 Angry (5)
25 Allow in (5)
26 Wading bird (5)

DOWN

2 Oldest Japanese city (5)
3 Fitting, proper (8)
5 Small measurement (4)
6 Moorland plant (7)
7 Winter sportsman (5)
8 King Kong actress (4, 7)
9 Paul - - -, *The Raj Quartet* author (5)
14 Concurring (8)
16 Worked (dough) (7)
17 Once more (5)
18 Beneath (5)
21 Occupation (5)
22 Long coat (4)

The Biggest Crossword Book In The World

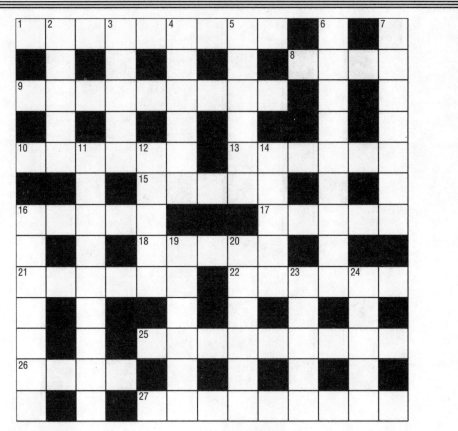

ACROSS

1 Toe spin (9)
8 Bucket (4)
9 Quentin - - -,
  film director (9)
10 Rule with authority (6)
13 Accompany (6)
15 Fully grown (5)
16 Obscure, darken (5)
17 Kofi - - -, UN chief (5)
18 Loathe, detest (5)
21 Dull (6)
22 Attribute (6)
25 Brought together (9)
26 Sea-girt land (4)
27 Air (9)

DOWN

2 US state (5)
3 Make a formal
  speech (5)
4 Have a certain range (6)
5 Underground
  passage (6)
6 Place to sleep! (4, 2, 3)
7 Greedy person (7)
11 With force (9)
12 Scanning device (5)
14 Freddie - - -,
  comedian (5)
16 Appendix (7)
19 Past, former (6)
20 American leopard (6)
23 Be outstandingly
  good (5)
24 Static (5)

The Biggest Crossword Book In The World

ACROSS
1 Fall to pieces (12)
9 Hire (5)
10 Extent (5)
11 Perish (3)
12 Underground room (5)
13 Tool for gripping nuts (7)
15 Confusion (6)
17 Leg bone (6)
20 Please, content (7)
23 Harbour (5)
25 Tiny vegetable (3)
26 Perform (5)
27 British poet (5)
28 Magical belief (12)

DOWN
2 Garibaldi's country (5)
3 Refreshing drink (4, 3)
4 Beat grain (6)
5 Israeli Prime Minister,
- - - Meir (5)
6 Paperwork (5)
7 Amusing (12)
8 Hugely successful
films (12)
14 Pen's tip (3)
16 Garland of flowers (3)
18 Live, dwell (7)
19 Office worker (6)
21 Gentleman of
the road (5)
22 Stringed instrument (5)
24 Sign of the zodiac (5)

The Biggest Crossword Book In The World

ACROSS

7 Frightening (8)
8 Firm, rigid (4)
9 Comfortable surroundings (6)
10 Yorkshire town (6)
11 Correct (5)
12 Dictated (7)
15 Deceived (7)
17 The - - -, seat of the Dutch government (5)
20 Mineral used as a gemstone (6)
22 Cornflakes, eg (6)
23 Actor, - - - Ackland (4)
24 Obscured (8)

DOWN

1 Thrive, prosper (8)
2 Hollow between two waves (6)
3 Type of plastic (5)
4 Caught fire (7)
5 Necklace (6)
6 Costing nothing (4)
13 Equals (8)
14 Wander, like a river (7)
16 Charge with wrongdoing (6)
18 Sudden (6)
19 Small oar (5)
21 Image (4)

The Biggest Crossword Book In The World

ACROSS

1 Landing gear (13)
7 British film and
TV award (5)
8 Confuse, bewilder (7)
9 Father of all Jews (7)
10 Talent (5)
11 Coarse gravel found
on beaches (7)
17 Monica - - -,
tennis player (5)
18 Florida city (7)
20 Gestures (7)
21 Military shop (5)
22 *Casualty* actor (5, 8)

DOWN

1 Hopeful (6)
2 Disfigure (6)
3 Contact (5)
4 Placid (7)
5 Living creature (6)
6 AA Milne's donkey (6)
8 Very important (9)
12 Kneeling cushion (7)
13 Lee Harvey - - -,
alleged assassin (6)
14 Double-breasted
overcoat (6)
15 Relatives by
marriage (2-4)
16 Idea (6)
19 Desmond - - -,
TV presenter (5)

The Biggest Crossword Book In The World

ACROSS

1 Golf stroke (4)
4 Greek island (6)
8 Repayment on
a house loan (8)
9 Politician, - - - Major (4)
10 Stench (5)
11 W Indian song in
African rhythm (7)
13 Search for food (6)
15 Belgian ferry port (6)
17 Mechanical piano (7)
19 Meat and vegetable dish
cooked on a skewer (5)
22 Sudden spell of
cold weather (4)
23 Deficiency (8)
24 Aircraft without an
engine (6)
25 Peer (4)

DOWN

2 German submarine (1-4)
3 Queen of the fairies (7)
4 Bring up (4)
5 Telephone
exchange worker (8)
6 Take pleasure in (5)
7 Selected (6)
12 Achieved (8)
14 The East (6)
16 Support for a
temporary table (7)
18 Mountainous country (5)
20 Carpenter's tool (5)
21 Secure by anchor (4)

The Biggest Crossword Book In The World

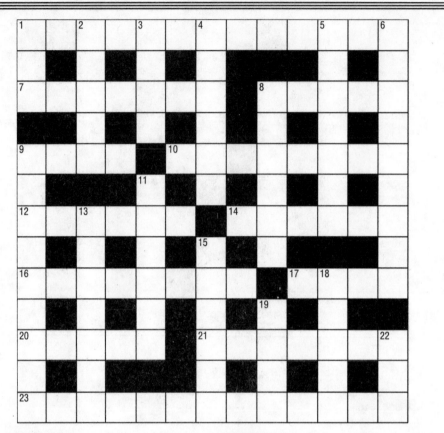

ACROSS

1 Proverb, - - - gathers no moss (1, 7, 5)
7 Cure-all (7)
8 Small fish (5)
9 Dropped (from the team) (4)
10 Oscar-winning film star (2, 6)
12 Entertained (6)
14 Mrs Thatcher? (6)
16 Frightful (8)
17 Caledonian (4)
20 Sweetener (5)
21 Self-admirer (7)
23 Memoirs (13)

DOWN

1 Snake (3)
2 Sixteenth of a pound (5)
3 Moisten with the tongue (4)
4 Almost (6)
5 Uncovering (7)
6 Outgoing person (9)
8 David, - - - England goalkeeper (6)
9 Russian Duchess (9)
11 Measure of quality for silk (6)
13 Vertical (7)
15 Popular 'whodunit' board game (6)
18 Potato wafer (5)
19 Acidic, sharp (4)
22 Have a go (3)

The Biggest Crossword Book In The World

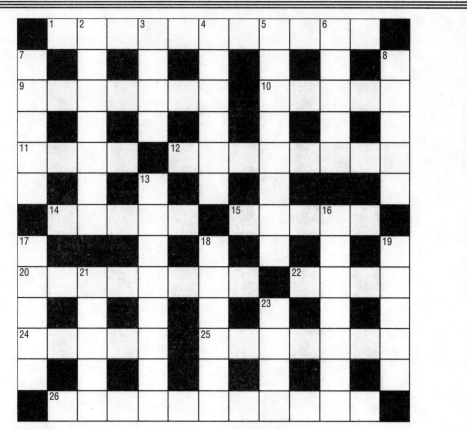

ACROSS

1 British actor (7,4)
9 French city (7)
10 Boxing film starring Sylvester Stallone (5)
11 Beer ingredient (4)
12 Sawdust filled box full of hidden presents (5, 3)
14 Irish county (5)
15 Dowdy woman (5)
20 Exact (2, 3, 3)
22 Jazz singer, - - - Fitzgerald (4)
24 Explode (5)
25 Army (7)
26 TV personality (4, 7)

DOWN

2 Flattened oval (7)
3 Small tide (4)
4 Save from danger (6)
5 Japanese ritual suicide (8)
6 Easily understood (5)
7 Dark coffee (5)
8 Imaginary being (5)
13 Eastern (8)
16 Wild duck (7)
17 Suspect (5)
18 Refuse to allow (6)
19 Frolic (5)
21 Body trunk (5)
23 Floor covering (4)

The Biggest Crossword Book In The World

ACROSS

1 Musical instrument (8)
5 Pierced ball (4)
9 State earnestly (5)
10 New Zealand native (5)
12 Hurl in the air (5)
13 Broad vegetable? (4)
15 Type of cloud (6)
18 Not substantial (6)
20 Lasting sweet (4)
23 Meat (5)
24 Religious belief (5)
27 Main artery (5)
28 State, aver (4)
29 Small circular fort (8)

DOWN

1 Soccer eleven (4)
2 Greek drink (4)
3 Land drained by river (5)
4 Part of a syringe (6)
6 Trespass (8)
7 Sliding box (6)
8 Legendary King
of the Britons (6)
11 Man's ancestor? (3)
14 In the open air (8)
16 Accident (6)
17 Basketwork fibre (6)
19 Commonwealth country,
- - - Leone (6)
21 Before (3)
22 Barely sufficient (5)
25 Wicked (4)
26 Rally (4)

The Biggest Crossword Book In The World

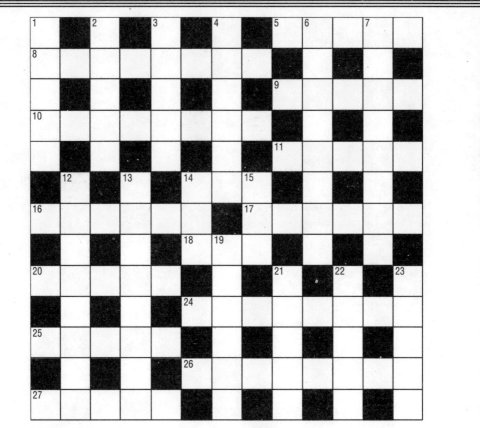

ACROSS

5 Card game (5)
8 Escalate (8)
9 Disease-producing agent (5)
10 Perplexed, bewildered (3, 2, 3)
11 Pool of money (5)
14 Layer of rock (3)
16 Chase (6)
17 Motive (6)
18 Effigy burnt on Bonfire Night (3)
20 Wanderer (5)
24 Scatter (8)
25 Of the pope (5)
26 Obtains (8)
27 Alphabetical list of contents (5)

DOWN

1 Indian tea (5)
2 Christmas plant (5)
3 Reduce in intensity (5)
4 Bring forward in argument (6)
6 First version (8)
7 Volcanic explosion (8)
12 German motorway (8)
13 Mischievous adventure (8)
14 Plead (3)
15 Free of moisture (3)
19 Referee (6)
21 Musical party (5)
22 Item of clothing (5)
23 Minimum (5)

The Biggest Crossword Book In The World

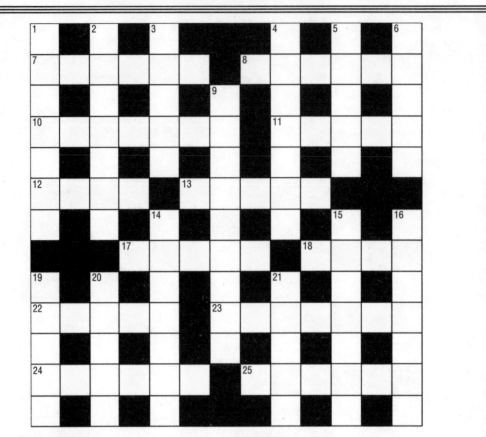

ACROSS

7 Disturbance, discontent (6)
8 Discard (6)
10 Violent wind (7)
11 Cringe (5)
12 Unsightly body fat (4)
13 Opening between two rooms (5)
17 Type of camera (5)
18 TV star, - - - Winton (4)
22 Fencing thrust (5)
23 Forbidden (7)
24 Go swiftly (6)
25 Become motionless (6)

DOWN

1 Vindicate (7)
2 Correct use of words (7)
3 Railway union (5)
4 Shetland Isles town (7)
5 Sham attack (5)
6 Early anaesthetic (5)
9 Tactical (9)
14 Drinking establishment (4, 3)
15 Arid, dry (7)
16 Not one or the other (7)
19 Unimpressed (5)
20 Poacher's trap (5)
21 Harsh sound (5)

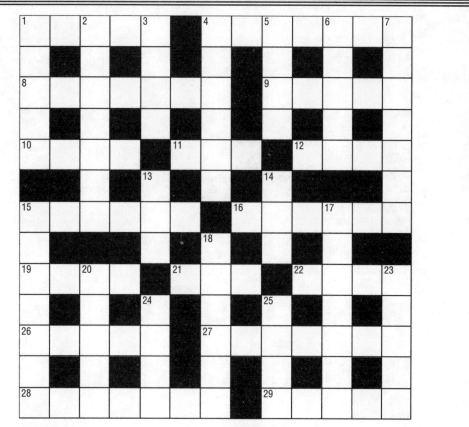

ACROSS

1 Brief raid (5)
4 Stomach (7)
8 *Winnie the Pooh* author (1, 1, 5)
9 Second planet (5)
10 Ten footed crustacean (4)
11 Epoch (3)
12 Headland (4)
15 Tie up (an animal) (6)
16 Hard-boiled sweet (6)
19 Confusion (4)
21 Pigeon sound (3)
22 Exhaled (4)
26 Money (slang) (5)
27 Operating room (7)
28 Ruth - - -, crime writer (7)
29 Florence Nightingale, eg (5)

DOWN

1 **Former** French currency (5)
2 Leftover cloth (7)
3 Shout out (4)
4 Take retaliation (6)
5 Plunge into water (4)
6 Association for brainy people (5)
7 Reserve fund (4, 3)
13 Small barrel (3)
14 Total (3)
15 Acrobat (7)
17 Long pillow (7)
18 Accommodation for walkers (6)
20 Beauty parlour (5)
23 In which place? (5)
24 Cattle shed (4)
25 Coax away from (4)

The Biggest Crossword Book In The World

ACROSS

1 Last book of the New Testament (10)
7 Harmful (8)
8 Continent (4)
9 Arab prince (4)
10 Scrap, do away with (7)
12 Cheer, comfort (11)
14 Bedding plant (7)
16 Smooth-tongued (4)
19 Spanish artist (4)
20 Former British prime minister (4, 4)
21 Dirty and wet (10)

DOWN

1 Humiliate, degrade (5)
2 Formal speech (7)
3 Extremely keen (4)
4 Cartoon grizzly! (4, 4)
5 Shoulder wrap (5)
6 Mel - - -, film star (6)
11 Command arrogantly (8)
12 Roman emperor (6)
13 Unlawful (7)
15 Think (5)
17 Mix (5)
18 Tailless amphibian (4)

The Biggest Crossword Book In The World

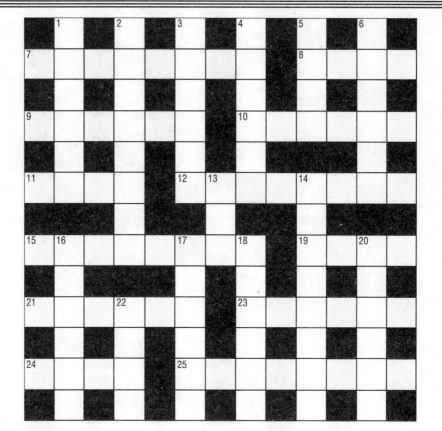

ACROSS
7 Infatuated (8)
8 Revolved rapidly (4)
9 Stir up (6)
10 Passionate (6)
11 Dab of colour (4)
12 Blocks (8)
15 Be quiet! (4, 4)
19 Rhyming verse (4)
21 Start again (6)
23 Patron saint
of England (6)
24 Loose hood (4)
25 Foolish, green (8)

DOWN
1 Centre of a nut (6)
2 Friendly, affable (8)
3 Meryl - - -, *Postcards
from the Edge* actress (6)
4 Stick (to) (6)
5 Capital of Norway (4)
6 Romeo's lover (6)
13 Chilly (3)
14 Ecstasy (8)
16 Coldest part of
a refrigerator (6)
17 Tense (2, 4)
18 Worry slightly (6)
20 Overwhelm (6)
22 Unsightly (4)

The Biggest Crossword Book In The World

ACROSS

3 End (9)
8 Set of cogs (4)
9 Hairdresser (8)
10 Italian resort (6)
13 Essential (5)
14 Provoked (7)
15 Dip in the middle (3)
16 Tormenting (7)
17 Over (5)
21 Scottish delicacy (6)
22 Cuddle lovingly (8)
23 Russian emperor (4)
24 Relevant to the
 matter in hand (9)

DOWN

1 Annoy (9)
2 Spotted dog (9)
4 Nickname of Rodrigo
 Diaz de Vivar (2, 3)
5 Postman's sack (7)
6 In poor taste (4)
7 Violent person (4)
11 Most powerful (9)
12 Opposing contestant (9)
14 Earmark (3)
15 Welsh mountain (7)
18 Bertie - - -, Irish PM (5)
19 Strong wind (4)
20 Electrical unit (4)

The Biggest Crossword Book In The World

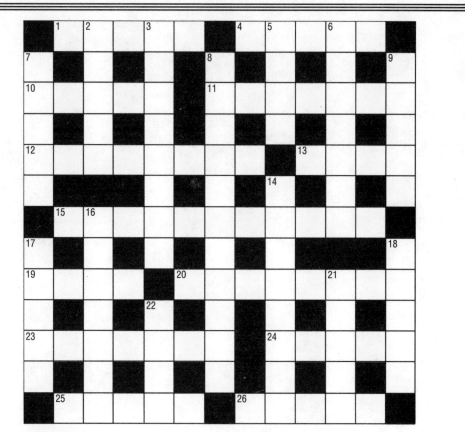

ACROSS

1 Of the same value (5)
4 Bungle (5)
10 Gust of wind (5)
11 Unit of land (7)
12 Reverse (8)
13 Arose (4)
15 Ginger Rogers dancing partner (4, 7)
19 Minus (4)
20 Armoured glove (8)
23 African river (7)
24 About (5)
25 Fool (5)
26 Meaning (5)

DOWN

2 Tremble (5)
3 Opinion (8)
5 *Castaway* author, - - - Irving (4)
6 Taste (7)
7 Head of an abbey (5)
8 Inspiring (11)
9 Islamic country (5)
14 Shellfish (8)
16 Started again (7)
17 Fire (5)
18 Thick slice of meat (5)
21 Peers, noblemen (5)
22 Nothing (4)

The Biggest Crossword Book In The World

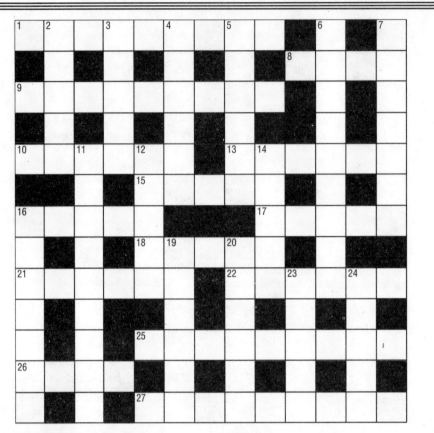

ACROSS

1 Unaware, forgetful (9)
8 Coke? (4)
9 Maryland port (9)
10 Capital of Iran (6)
13 Long for (6)
15 Kind, sort (5)
16 Animal with a
   fox-like face (5)
17 Stringed instrument (5)
18 Follow next (5)
21 Twenty-one shillings (6)
22 Entreaty (6)
25 Wretched (9)
26 Dumpling ingredient (4)
27 Magician's cry (3, 6)

DOWN

2 A pair of pheasants (5)
3 Lay to rest (5)
4 Exempt (6)
5 Bedlam (6)
6 Sleeping room (9)
7 Shiny silk (7)
11 Clumsy (3-6)
12 Correspond (5)
14 Detach (5)
16 Very drunk! (7)
19 Inborn (6)
20 Maintenance costs (6)
23 Astound (5)
24 Brilliant display (5)

The Biggest Crossword Book In The World

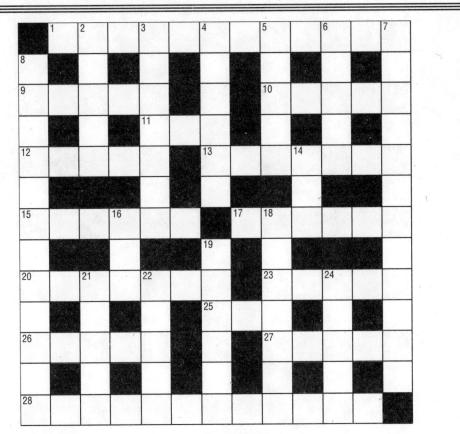

ACROSS

1 Favourable (12)
9 Simple fellow? (5)
10 Legally acceptable (5)
11 Flightless bird (3)
12 Local tax on property (5)
13 Frederick - - -,
  novelist (7)
15 Count (6)
17 Save from ransom (6)
20 Ornamental ropework (7)
23 Of the ears (5)
25 Evil deed (3)
26 Condiment container (5)
27 Australian wild dog (5)
28 Scientific workshops (12)

DOWN

2 Send money
  for goods (5)
3 Skilful management (7)
4 Cold-shoulder (6)
5 At no time (5)
6 Embed (5)
7 Nelson's wife (4, 8)
8 Enormously large (12)
14 Blue (3)
16 Drinking place (3)
18 Heavyweight boxer,
  - - - Holyfield (7)
19 Outcome (6)
21 Tiny particle (5)
22 Become different (5)
24 Wash lightly (5)

The Biggest Crossword Book In The World

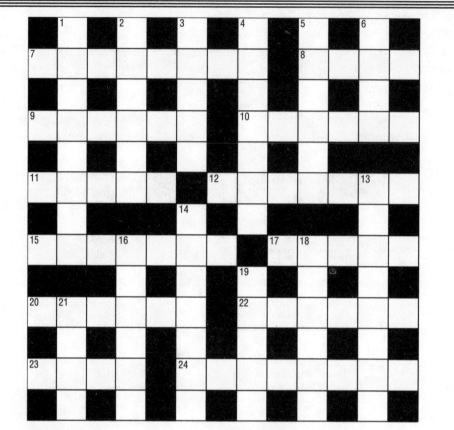

ACROSS

7 Climbing shrub (8)
8 Deceased (4)
9 Italian city (6)
10 US tap (6)
11 Broken ship (5)
12 Male relation (7)
15 Excess of liabilities (7)
17 Sack (5)
20 Opposite to nadir (6)
22 Pillar (6)
23 Wind in loops (4)
24 Increased in size (8)

DOWN

1 Differ (8)
2 Sloping (type) (6)
3 Faith (5)
4 Ceremonious sounding of trumpets (7)
5 Alter slightly (6)
6 Create (4)
13 Hinder (8)
14 Type of biscuit (4, 3)
16 Frozen spike (6)
18 Rectangular shape (6)
19 Range of activity (5)
21 Greek god of love (4)

The Biggest Crossword Book In The World

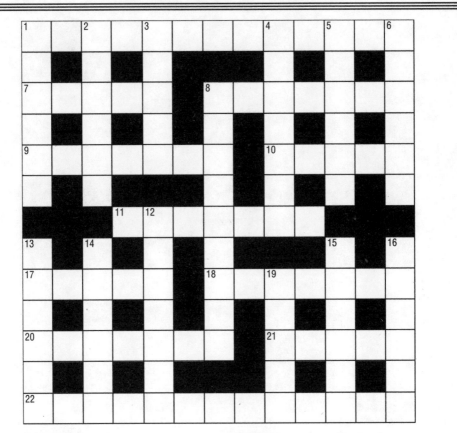

ACROSS

1 Give away
a secret (5,3,5)
7 Dark-coloured (5)
8 Keep an eye on (7)
9 Lattice frame (7)
10 Snow drop? (5)
11 Without making
a noise (7)
17 Move like a hunter (5)
18 Region of hell (7)
20 Absence of
government (7)
21 Traded (5)
22 Television and radio
presenter (5, 8)

DOWN

1 Calm and dignified (6)
2 Part of the foot (6)
3 Devoted (5)
4 Shy (7)
5 In a foreign country (6)
6 Kebab spike (6)
8 Profanity (9)
12 Unfortunate (7)
13 Muscular injury (6)
14 Picture made from small
pieces of glass/stone (6)
15 Courteous (6)
16 Born to die (6)
19 Bored (3, 2)

The Biggest Crossword Book In The World

ACROSS

1 Welsh emblem (4)
4 Season of the year (6)
8 Joined together again (8)
9 Curved structure (4)
10 Legendary maiden (5)
11 Violinist (7)
13 Barely sufficient (6)
15 Took notice of (6)
17 Aviation pioneer,
- - - Wright (7)
19 Bore a hole (5)
22 Short letter (4)
23 Dance hall (8)
24 Cupboard (6)
25 Converge (4)

DOWN

2 Foe (5)
3 Important person (7)
4 Location of a building (4)
5 Twelve o'clock (8)
6 South African
antelope (5)
7 Project (6)
12 Course subjects (8)
14 Chain of police (6)
16 Tympanic membrane (7)
18 Best possible (5)
20 Unrestrained (5)
21 Strip of wood (4)

The Biggest Crossword Book In The World

ACROSS

1 TV presenter (6, 7)
7 Persistent illness (7)
8 Braid of hair (5)
9 Tube (4)
10 Conclusive (8)
12 Clergyman (6)
14 Greek goddess of war (6)
16 Leonardo da Vinci painting (4, 4)
17 Gesture (4)
20 Togetherness (5)
21 Ian - - - James Bond author (7)
23 Ancient Egyptian writing (13)

DOWN

1 America (1, 1, 1)
2 Keepsake (5)
3 Capital of the Ukraine (4)
4 Fast social group? (3, 3)
5 Beach (7)
6 Paris cathedral (5, 4)
8 Base beneath a statue (6)
9 Devon holiday resort (9)
11 Miscellaneous (6)
13 Keep within limits (7)
15 Advantageous (6)
18 Plea of being elsewhere (5)
19 Military vehicle (4)
22 Heating fuel (3)

The Biggest Crossword Book In The World

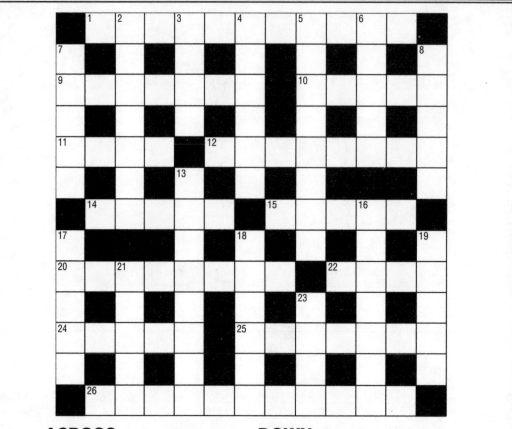

ACROSS

1 British comic (5, 6)
9 Unethical (7)
10 Out of order (5)
11 Elsewhere (4)
12 Kent ferry port (8)
14 Small stand for sale of goods (5)
15 Pleasant odour (5)
20 Old-fashioned (8)
22 Working cattle (4)
24 Frank - - -, British boxer (5)
25 Composer (7)
26 Girl who encourages sporting teams (11)

DOWN

2 Castle fortification (7)
3 Quality of a person (4)
4 Underground room (6)
5 Biblical ship (5, 3)
6 Heather plant (5)
7 Opponent (5)
8 Awry (5)
13 American gangster (2, 6)
16 Mish-mash (7)
17 Pastime (5)
18 Stoat-like mammal (6)
19 Grind (teeth) together (5)
21 Honesty (5)
23 Killer whale (4)

The Biggest Crossword Book In The World

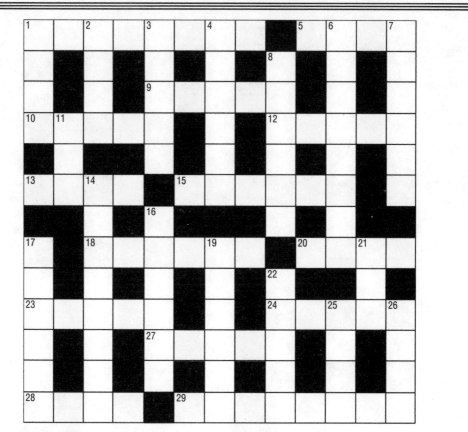

ACROSS

1 Soft drink (8)
5 Country, capital Havana (4)
9 Oyster's gem (5)
10 Spring flower (5)
12 Light brown (5)
13 Told fibs (4)
15 Heart disorder (6)
18 Small spot (6)
20 Act (4)
23 Two times (5)
24 Entrails (5)
27 Singer, - - - Ross (5)
28 North Atlantic Treaty Organisation (4)
29 Grow, increase (8)

DOWN

1 Missing (4)
2 Grinding machine (4)
3 Chilly (5)
4 Fire-breathing beast (6)
6 Absolute limit (8)
7 Major road (6)
8 Although (6)
11 Psychic, - - - Geller (3)
14 Clearly explained (8)
16 Obstruct (6)
17 Regular customer (6)
19 Motor racing competition (2, 4)
21 Age (3)
22 Marsupial (5)
25 Jumping insect (4)
26 Adore (4)

The Biggest Crossword Book In The World

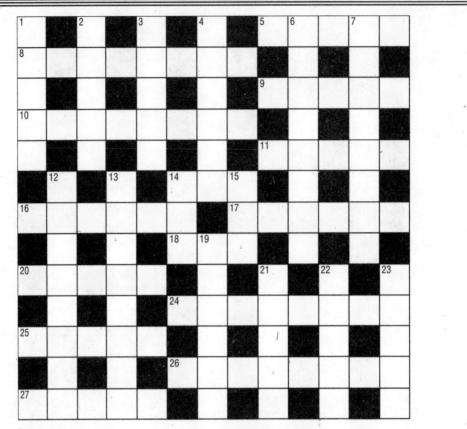

ACROSS

5 Dame Judi - - -, award-winning actress (5)
8 Altered course (8)
9 Construct (5)
10 Jersey's detective (8)
11 Part of a car's bodywork (5)
14 TV host, - - - O'Connor (3)
16 Turned into (6)
17 Kevin - - -, football manager (6)
18 Sarcastic (3)
20 Musical note (5)
24 Cruelty (8)
25 Comedian (5)
26 Apron (8)
27 Furious, cross (5)

DOWN

1 Sun-dried brick (5)
2 Yellowish-white colour (5)
3 Scott's companion to the South Pole (5)
4 Invalidate (6)
6 Teaches (8)
7 Street closed at one end (3-2-3)
12 Large narrow-necked bottle (8)
13 Wellknown (8)
14 Drizzle (3)
15 Heavens above! (3)
19 Dried grape (6)
21 Crow (5)
22 Diplomatic minister (5)
23 Administrative centre of East Sussex (5)

The Biggest Crossword Book In The World

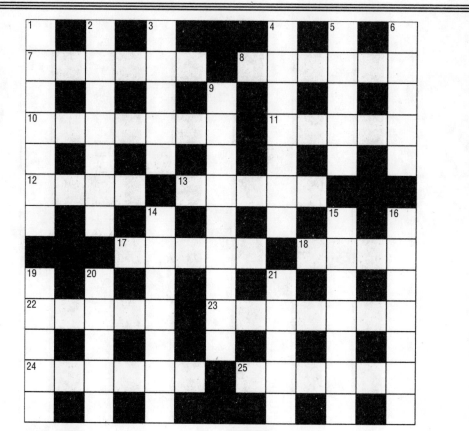

ACROSS

7 Purple (6)
8 Force, strength (6)
10 Ornamental staff (7)
11 Freedom from war (5)
12 Field of sight (4)
13 Low in price (5)
17 Bear? (5)
18 European volcano (4)
22 Scottish lord (5)
23 Small guitar (7)
24 Author, - - - Rushdie (6)
25 Picture-house (6)

DOWN

1 Elusive (7)
2 Crouched in fear (7)
3 Barbra Streisand film (5)
4 Exhibit (7)
5 Terry - - -, TV and radio presenter (5)
6 Wept, sobbed (5)
9 Method of performance (9)
14 Not abrupt (7)
15 Spoke (7)
16 Prehistoric person (7)
19 Narrow-necked bottle (5)
20 Outlaw, - - - the Kid (5)
21 Shockingly vivid (5)

ACROSS

1 Lowest point (5)
4 Mix up (playing cards) (7)
8 Vest (7)
9 Waltz, eg (5)
10 Lounge about (4)
11 Lout (slang) (3)
12 Tennis star, - - - Sampras (4)
15 Put up with (6)
16 Memorised (6)
19 Elude (4)
21 Gender (3)
22 Baby kangaroo (4)
26 Building remains (5)
27 Expelled from a property (7)
28 Outshine (7)
29 Jeopardy (5)

DOWN

1 Of the nose (5)
2 Suspended loosely (7)
3 Overturn (a car) (4)
4 Comedy programme (6)
5 Open, unfasten (4)
6 Barrier (5)
7 Component (7)
13 Meddle, snoop (3)
14 Complete collection (3)
15 Ratify (7)
17 Male fowl (7)
18 Erase (6)
20 Paper knuckle on a chop (5)
23 Mountain song (5)
24 Very special old pale (4)
25 Walk lamely (4)

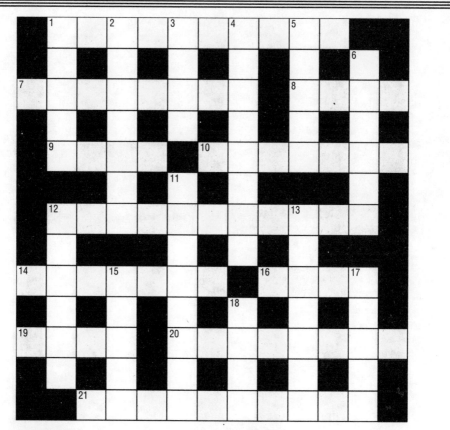

ACROSS

1 Cockney film star (3, 7)
7 Court order (8)
8 Sudden commercial activity (4)
9 Dribble (4)
10 Place apart (7)
12 Breathtaking (11)
14 Large tent (7)
16 Paul - - -, England footballer (4)
19 Tradesman's assistant (4)
20 Total sales (8)
21 Comic Relief fund-raising event (3, 4, 3)

DOWN

1 Tied (5)
2 Christen (7)
3 More than (4)
4 Hiker's bag (8)
5 Peace Prize founder (5)
6 Hotel worker (6)
11 Michael - - -, cricketer (8)
12 Sacred beetle (6)
13 Sprinter, - - - Christie (7)
15 Line of waiting people (5)
17 Lyrical poem (5)
18 Small dagger (4)

The Biggest Crossword Book In The World

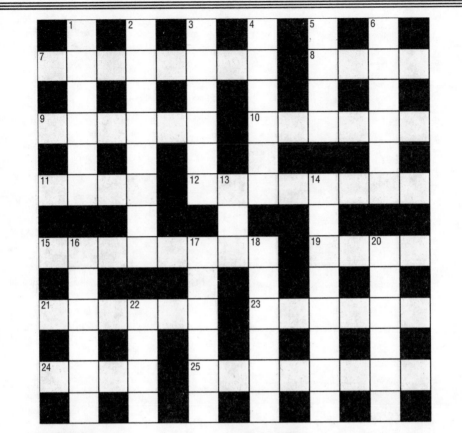

ACROSS
7 Tendon (8)
8 Young child (4)
9 Enjoy (6)
10 Beginning (6)
11 Talking bird (4)
12 Put up with (8)
15 Disney film,
 - - - *Beauty* (8)
19 Pull along (4)
21 French ball game (6)
23 Corrects (6)
24 Yell violently (4)
25 Thickness (8)

DOWN
1 Distinctive dress (6)
2 Japanese suicide
 pilot (8)
3 Very, very warm (3-3)
4 Leisurely walk (6)
5 Incite by
 encouragement (4)
6 Not present (6)
13 Possess (3)
14 Set free (8)
16 Type of sponge (6)
17 In prison (slang) (6)
18 Billy - - -, evangelist (6)
20 Muddled (6)
22 After time (4)

The Biggest Crossword Book In The World

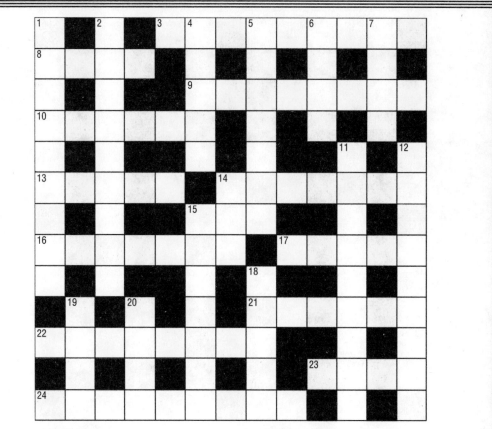

ACROSS

3 Inspired (9)
8 First male child (4)
9 Sir Alec - - -, British actor (8)
10 Farm implement (6)
13 Doctor's stand-in (5)
14 Largest of the Balearic islands (7)
15 Sicken (3)
16 Tornado (7)
17 Lady golfer, - - - Davies (5)
21 Leading oil-producing country (6)
22 Italian noblewoman (8)
23 Solid medicine (4)
24 Irish comedian (4, 5)

DOWN

1 Small sausage (9)
2 Walt Disney film (9)
4 Should (5)
5 First (7)
6 Skin complaint (4)
7 Uncomplicated (4)
11 Shocking (9)
12 Large, hairy spider (9)
14 Russian space station (3)
15 Spray can (7)
18 Glide on ice (5)
19 American state (4)
20 Soreness on eyelid (4)

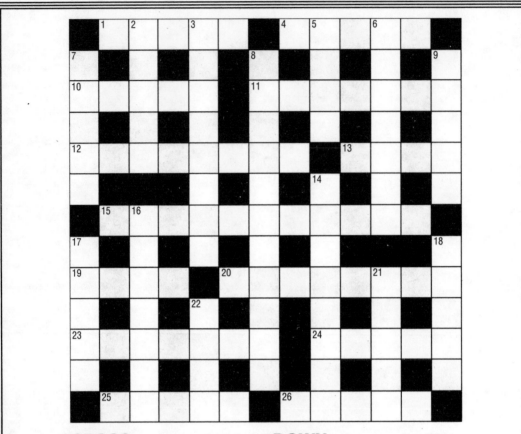

ACROSS

1 Clergyman (5)
4 Split (5)
10 Seat for one person (5)
11 Graceful (7)
12 Easily bent (8)
13 Impart (4)
15 Gangster movie
actor (5, 6)
19 Material damage (4)
20 Rude (8)
23 Factory restaurant (7)
24 Narrow street (5)
25 Blemish (5)
26 Declare (5)

DOWN

2 Foolish (5)
3 Passenger plane (8)
5 News article (4)
6 Look at closely (7)
7 Chafe (5)
8 Substitute (11)
9 Say something (5)
14 Lacking knowledge (8)
16 Opposed to (7)
17 Thin piece of wood (5)
18 English diary writer (5)
21 Small bay (5)
22 The abominable
snowman (4)

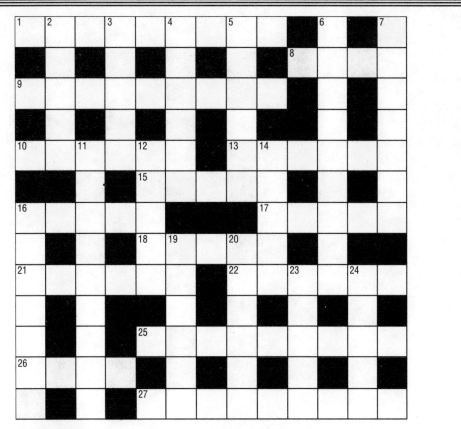

ACROSS
1 Company logo (9)
8 Prejudice (4)
9 Spontaneously (9)
10 Boiler attendant (6)
13 Poser (6)
15 Revolt (5)
16 Capital of Bangladesh (5)
17 Garish (5)
18 Mr Claus (5)
21 Attraction (6)
22 Trying experience (6)
25 Life story (9)
26 Nan (4)
27 Very poor (9)

DOWN
2 Respond (5)
3 Intoxicated (5)
4 Scanty (6)
5 Connect (6)
6 Very small (9)
7 Receptacle used by smoker (7)
11 Large ape (9)
12 Rub out (5)
14 Enigma Variations composer (5)
16 Spanish tenor (7)
19 Fine clothes (6)
20 Tom Cruise film (3, 3)
23 Speak slowly (5)
24 First of the Three Musketeers (5)

The Biggest Crossword Book In The World

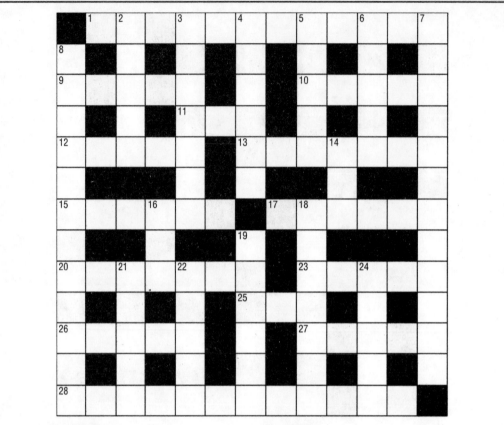

ACROSS

1 Stage musical (4, 3, 5)
9 Asian country (5)
10 Engine (5)
11 Vase (3)
12 Mass of salt water (5)
13 Offer sympathy (7)
15 Promise, pledge (6)
17 Mixture of sand and stones (6)
20 Pamper (7)
23 Dutch cheese (5)
25 Mongrel dog (3)
26 Lift with great effort (5)
27 Random arrangement (2, 3)
28 Bakery product (6, 6)

DOWN

2 Combine (5)
3 Trustworthy (supporter) (7)
4 Subtle difference in colour (6)
5 Evil spirit (5)
6 Housey-housey (5)
7 Secret observation (12)
8 Skilful (12)
14 Genetic fingerprints (1, 1, 1)
16 African antelope (3)
18 Kids TV programme (7)
19 Recover, regain (6)
21 Sketched (5)
22 Garden vegetables (5)
24 Wedding official (5)

The Biggest Crossword Book In The World

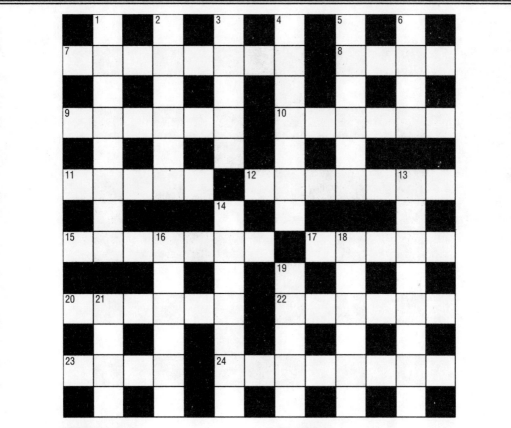

ACROSS

7 Racing vehicle (5, 3)
8 Mislay (4)
9 Get (6)
10 Tatty (6)
11 Footwear (5)
12 Regulate (7)
15 Extremely innocent (7)
17 Silly (5)
20 Timber decay (3-3)
22 Approach and speak to (6)
23 Make secure (4)
24 Uninhabited and bleak (8)

DOWN

1 Unyielding, obstinate (8)
2 Anti-aircraft fire (3-3)
3 Light doughy cake (5)
4 West county city (7)
5 Flexible (6)
6 Bird charity (1,1,1,1)
13 Adverse, contrary (8)
14 Undercurrent (3,4)
16 I have found it ! (6)
18 The supernatural (6)
19 Minister's house (5)
21 Tuber (4)

The Biggest Crossword Book In The World

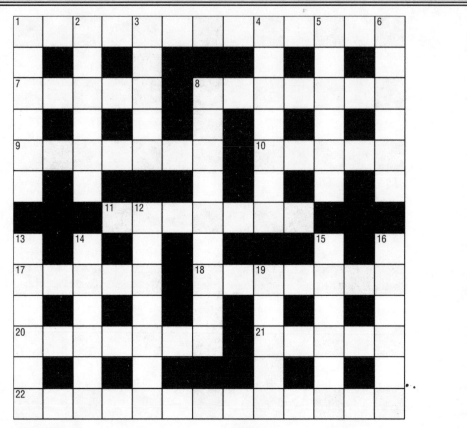

ACROSS

1 Frequent visitor to the doctors (13)
7 Subject (5)
8 *Oliver Twist* author (7)
9 Disgusting (7)
10 Kingly (5)
11 Take liberties (7)
17 John Logie - - -, television inventor (5)
18 Roaming (7)
20 Skeleton (7)
21 Structure (5)
22 *EastEnders*' actor (5, 8)

DOWN

1 Racing car (3, 3)
2 Give pleasure to (6)
3 Mediterranean island (5)
4 Seemly behaviour (7)
5 Glacial period (3, 3)
6 Chesspiece (6)
8 Bandages (9)
12 Excessive official formalities (3, 4)
13 Counting frame with beads (6)
14 Penetrate sharply (6)
15 Actor, - - - Woodward (6)
16 Shelter (6)
19 Italian gangsters (5)

The Biggest Crossword Book In The World

ACROSS

1 Reddish-gold pond fish (4)
4 TV personality, - - - Turner (6)
8 Sample (8)
9 Fly upwards (4)
10 First public appearance (5)
11 Aviation company (7)
13 Rowan Atkinson's TV character (2, 4)
15 Four-footed reptile (6)
17 First month (7)
19 Apologetic (5)
22 Fly like a sparrow (4)
23 Nocturnal mammal (8)
24 Mystery (6)
25 Pull hard (4)

DOWN

2 Currency of India (5)
3 Ban, bar (7)
4 Organised fighting force (4)
5 Concrete, real (8)
6 Artist's tripod (5)
7 German composer (6)
12 Trespasser (8)
14 Truly, honestly (6)
16 Scientific study of animals (7)
18 Release (5)
20 Natural glue (5)
21 Coarse sandstone (4)

The Biggest Crossword Book In The World

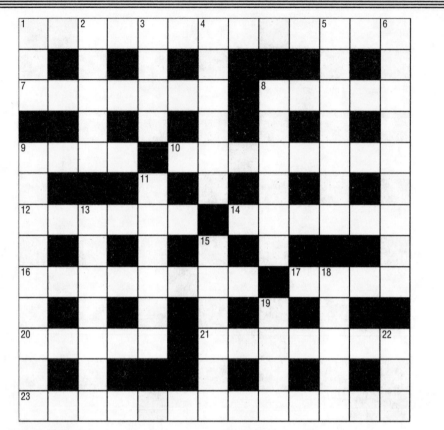

ACROSS

1 Not important (13)
7 Plain (7)
8 Seaside promenade (5)
9 Ancient (4)
10 Arm of the Atlantic (5, 3)
12 Sensitive (6)
14 Jeremy - - -,
TV prankster (6)
16 Surround (8)
17 Not common (4)
20 Long lock of hair (5)
21 Poisonous chemical
compound (7)
23 Fashionable London
thoroughfare (7, 6)

DOWN

1 Anger, wrath (3)
2 Excel (5)
3 Mirth (4)
4 Confine to camp (6)
5 Stimulated (7)
6 Head to head (4-1-4)
8 Rankle (6)
9 Real, proper (9)
11 Group of singers (6)
13 Ambigious (7)
15 Courageous, brave (6)
18 Burning (5)
19 Gasp for breath (4)
22 Newt (3)

The Biggest Crossword Book In The World

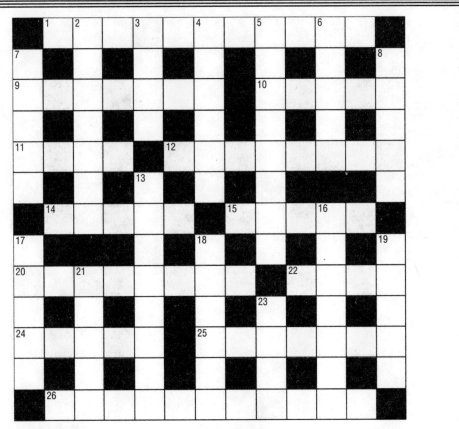

ACROSS

1 First thing in the morning (5, 2, 4)
9 Garden feature (7)
10 Great strength (5)
11 Beat with a whip (4)
12 Comfy chair (8)
14 Man-made fibre (5)
15 Breath through the nose (5)
20 Impractical (8)
22 Gown (4)
24 Binge (5)
25 Very strict (7)
26 Miscellaneous items (4, 3, 4)

DOWN

2 Clergyman's house (7)
3 Ship's company (4)
4 Gas forming part of the air (6)
5 Dough pudding (8)
6 Railway freight truck (5)
7 Wander aimlessly (5)
8 Tale, saga (5)
13 Futile (8)
16 Launched (7)
17 Elevate (5)
18 Former British Prime Minister (6)
19 Celebration (5)
21 Pungent (5)
23 Container (4)

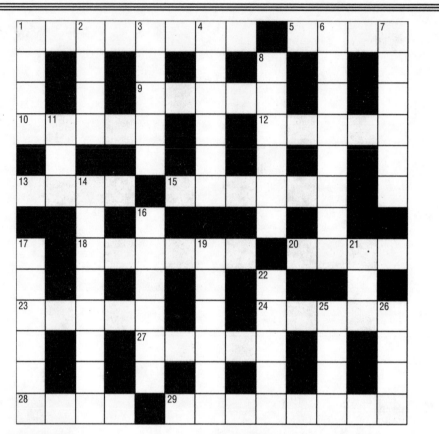

ACROSS

1 Deceive (8)
5 Curly cabbage (4)
9 Repent (5)
10 Aggregate (5)
12 Rabbit's cage (5)
13 Ballpoint pen (4)
15 Miscellaneous mixture (6)
18 Extinguished (6)
20 Leading performer (4)
23 Mischievous child (5)
24 Equal (5)
27 Gatekeeper's house (5)
28 Put underground (4)
29 Line on a map (8)

DOWN

1 Owl's cry (4)
2 Leave out, skip (4)
3 Large sea mammal (5)
4 Type of pasta (6)
6 Purple precious stone (8)
7 Four score (6)
8 Watch, see (6)
11 French word for 'yes' (3)
14 Room heater (8)
16 Provide (6)
17 Take in (6)
19 Mass departure of people (6)
21 Dined (3)
22 Wide-awake (5)
25 Container for cut flowers (4)
26 Oasis band member, - - - Gallagher (4)

The Biggest Crossword Book In The World

ACROSS

5 Football coach,
- - - Venebles (5)
8 Described (8)
9 Fertile desert spot (5)
10 Shirk (8)
11 Two-masted sailing
vessel (5)
14 Chair, seat (3)
16 Winged insect (6)
17 Tower of London
warder (6)
18 Formerly (3)
20 British airport (5)
24 Newspaper articles (8)
25 Old Roman tongue (5)
26 Weakened (8)
27 Take possession
forcibly (5)

DOWN

1 Ordain (5)
2 Home, dwelling (5)
3 Poker hand (5)
4 Venerate (6)
6 Evita? (3, 5)
7 Waterproof garment (8)
12 Control (8)
13 Swiss ski resort (2, 6)
14 Cage (3)
15 River flowing between
England and Wales (3)
19 County town
of Devon (6)
21 Nevertheless (5)
22 Chatter (5)
23 Stage whisper (5)

The Biggest Crossword Book In The World

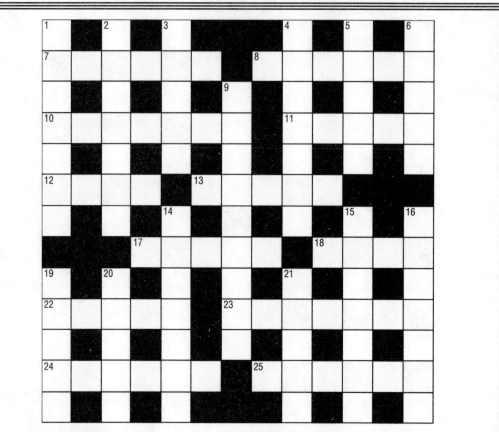

ACROSS
7 Irish gypsy (6)
8 Trinket of little value (6)
10 Walk heavily (7)
11 Crystallised sugar (5)
12 Mexican dish in a folded tortilla (4)
13 Juliet's lover (5)
17 Distinctive pattern (5)
18 Flexible pipe (4)
22 Fury (5)
23 Evasive (7)
24 Advertising catchword (6)
25 Amend, anew (6)

DOWN
1 Written law (7)
2 Improve (7)
3 Jumped (5)
4 Short axe (7)
5 Black wood (5)
6 Actress, - - - Streep (5)
9 Put into safekeeping (9)
14 Impetuous person (7)
15 Landlocked South American country (7)
16 Shameless woman (7)
19 Bend, curve (5)
20 Paddle-boat (5)
21 Excellent (5)

ACROSS

1 Honour (5)
4 European language (7)
8 Old-fashioned living room (7)
9 Well turned-out (5)
10 Small waterfowl (4)
11 Pretend (3)
12 Coral formation (4)
15 Flask (6)
16 All over the world (6)
19 One of a pair (4)
21 US spy group (inits)
22 Bother (4)
26 Underwater detection system (5)
27 Obtain (7)
28 Serious (7)
29 Large guest house (5)

DOWN

1 Ruined, broken (5)
2 Sleeping (7)
3 Narrow opening (4)
4 Enhance (6)
5 Main point (4)
6 Visual representation (5)
7 Detestable (7)
13 Brand (3)
14 Imp (3)
15 Fine cotton (7)
17 Bunch of flowers (7)
18 Clinging marine creature (6)
20 Target area nearest the bull (5)
23 Metal (5)
24 Exhort (4)
25 Scottish lake (4)

The Biggest Crossword Book In The World

ACROSS

1 Mild, white cheese (10)
7 Vapour (8)
8 Ram down (concrete) (4)
9 Exclamation
of relief (4)
10 Welsh town (7)
12 Keep busy (6, 5)
14 John - - -, author (2, 5)
16 Minor exam (4)
19 Fog (4)
20 Equestrian sport (8)
21 *Terms of - - -,*
Oscar-winning film (10)

DOWN

1 Chew noisily (5)
2 Simplest (7)
3 In addition (4)
4 Cold dessert (3-5)
5 Rubber ingredient (5)
6 Force of collision (6)
11 Resent (8)
12 Abstract, summary (6)
13 Supervise (7)
15 Football club,
- - - Villa (5)
17 Taut, tense (5)
18 Stock market
speculator (4)

The Biggest Crossword Book In The World

ACROSS

7 Furious (8)
8 Spirit mixed
  with water (4)
9 Queen's title (6)
10 Religious speech (6)
11 British comedian,
   - - - Sykes (4)
12 False teeth (8)
15 Sudden disturbance (8)
19 Unchanged (4)
21 Eastern garment (6)
23 Drinking toast (6)
24 Wait patiently (4)
25 Plentiful (8)

DOWN

1 Make oneself popular (6)
2 Second-rate (8)
3 Area encircled
  by water (6)
4 Thomas - - -, inventor (6)
5 Type of gelatine (4)
6 Surly, grumpy (6)
13 Wonderbra model,
   - - - Herzigova (3)
14 Shaky, infirm (8)
16 Calm (6)
17 Property wrecker (6)
18 London theatre (6)
20 Harbour for yachts (6)
22 Dinosaur (1-3)

The Biggest Crossword Book In The World

ACROSS

3 Domineering woman (9)
8 Bee's home (4)
9 Hard to understand (8)
10 Unlawful killing (6)
13 Move forward strongly (5)
14 Pathetic (7)
15 Close-fitting head covering (3)
16 Violent person (7)
17 Secret spy (5)
21 Artillery gun (6)
22 Attractive (8)
23 Food with a soft cheese like consistency (4)
24 Devious (9)

DOWN

1 Branch of science (9)
2 Bank's borrowing facility (9)
4 Sudden fear (5)
5 Berry-like fruit (7)
6 Land measure (4)
7 Male bird (4)
11 Period following midday (9)
12 Radioactive metal (9)
14 Criticise harshly (3)
15 Sarcastic, cutting (7)
18 Happen (5)
19 Acquire, obtain (4)
20 Sea-rescue group (1, 1, 1, 1)

ACROSS

1 Investigate (5)
4 Official documents (5)
10 Pleated frilling (5)
11 Curly lock of hair (7)
12 South American headland (4, 4)
13 Silent, speechless (4)
15 *Rockford Files* actor (5, 6)
19 Special effort (4)
20 Bestial deed (8)
23 Rudolf - - -, ballet dancer (7)
24 More than enough (5)
25 Scoff (5)
26 Musty (5)

DOWN

2 Go over the main points (5)
3 Former Soviet leader (8)
5 Arm bone (4)
6 Corrupt (7)
7 Vincent - - -, horror actor (5)
8 Privilege, right (11)
9 Scatter (5)
14 Conceited (8)
16 Loser (4-3)
17 Pay out (money) (5)
18 Welsh county (5)
21 Drive forward (5)
22 Sort, kind (4)

The Biggest Crossword Book In The World

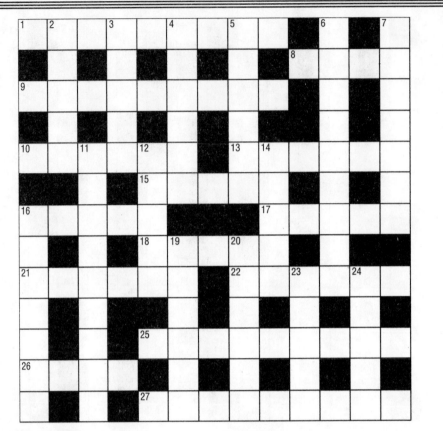

ACROSS

1 Entertainment (9)
8 Mountain stream (4)
9 *North by - - -*,
Hitchcock film (9)
10 Dog's home (6)
13 Appearance, look (6)
15 Confused situation (3-2)
16 Funeral song (5)
17 Very old saying (5)
18 Shaving implement (5)
21 Cheerio! (3-3)
22 Go back on
(a promise) (6)
25 Full of high spirits (9)
26 Fertile soil (4)
27 Largest living
mammal (4, 5)

DOWN

2 North American deer (5)
3 Smooth, glossy fabric (5)
4 *Jungle Book*
character (6)
5 Capital of
the Bahamas (6)
6 Frantic (9)
7 Ninepin (7)
11 Inhabitant of Oslo? (9)
12 Nail board (5)
14 Surplus (5)
16 Fiasco (7)
19 Signal receiver (6)
20 Highly decorated (6)
23 Cry of a horse (5)
24 Thin porridge (5)

The Biggest Crossword Book In The World

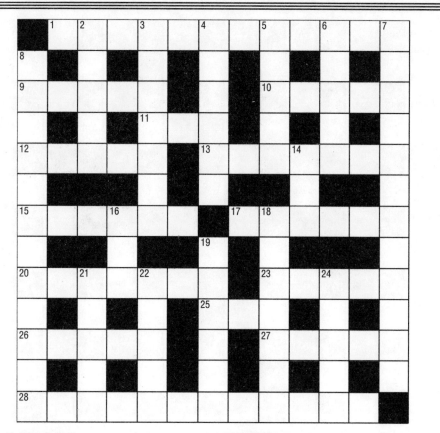

ACROSS

1 Work in harmony (4, 8)
9 Addictive drug (5)
10 Alexandre - - -, French novelist (5)
11 Honey-producing insect (3)
12 Police patrol car (5)
13 Person in charge of an inquest (7)
15 Ancient Greek city (6)
17 Water parted by Moses (3, 3)
20 Originate (7)
23 Island in the Bay of Naples (5)
25 Buck's mate (3)
26 Lag behind (5)
27 Reach maturity (5)
28 Acceptable (12)

DOWN

2 Marriage (5)
3 Beat, thrash (7)
4 Material thing (6)
5 Fluffy duck (5)
6 Merciful (5)
7 Doubts (12)
8 Sane (6, 6)
14 Peculiar (3)
16 Sprinted (3)
18 Quotation (7)
19 Soft felt hat (6)
21 Anticipate (5)
22 Book of maps (5)
24 Scottish musician (5)

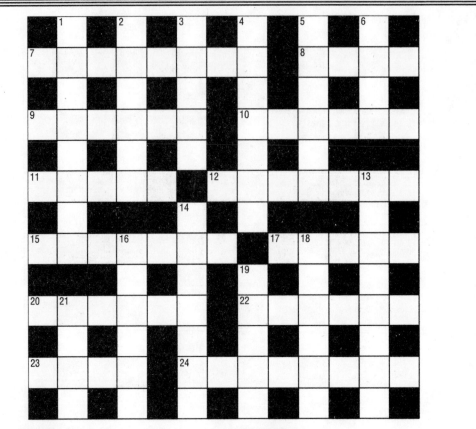

ACROSS

7 Yet (5, 3)
8 Leer (4)
9 Live-in home help (2, 4)
10 Food cupboard (6)
11 Reversal of political policy (1-4)
12 Proper (7)
15 Clive Dunn's No 1 hit (7)
17 Foster permanently (5)
20 Abhor (6)
22 Rush of questions (6)
23 Large inlet (4)
24 Galaxy (8)

DOWN

1 In an excited state (8)
2 Mend (6)
3 Milk farm (5)
4 Item of footwear (7)
5 Car engine cover (6)
6 Smear (4)
13 Frothy coffee (8)
14 Make an emergency parachute jump (4, 3)
16 Inform (6)
18 Soothing (sound) (6)
19 Dodge (5)
21 Burden (4)

The Biggest Crossword Book In The World

ACROSS
1 Fairground switchback (6, 7)
7 Difficult question (5)
8 Protect (7)
9 Excess (7)
10 Yellow-brown pigment (5)
11 Danny De Vito film (7)
17 Shock, dismay (5)
18 Sale (7)
20 Person under tuition (7)
21 Long seat (5)
22 Condiment duo (4, 3, 6)

DOWN
1 Peace (6)
2 Sheen (6)
3 Register, sign on (5)
4 Decamp (7)
5 Chinese exercise (3, 3)
6 Washed lightly (6)
8 Punish (9)
12 Olympic Games venue (7)
13 Australian airline (6)
14 Lie ungainly (6)
15 Abduct (6)
16 Ship's 'brake' (6)
19 Thick wire (5)

The Biggest Crossword Book In The World

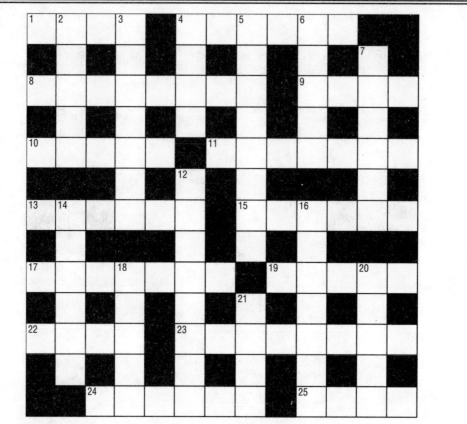

ACROSS

1 German composer (4)
4 Scold (6)
8 Confiding (8)
9 Attack (4)
10 Move furtively (5)
11 Vast (7)
13 Vibrate noisily (6)
15 Not wide (6)
17 Ant-like insect (7)
19 Wind instrument (5)
22 Ground grain (4)
23 Personal property (8)
24 Song that tells a story (6)
25 Manure (4)

DOWN

2 Protective garment (5)
3 Male spouse (7)
4 Upper edge
of a vessel (4)
5 Group of soldiers (8)
6 Number (5)
7 Complete failure (6)
12 Urgently needed (8)
14 Fluctuating (6)
16 Connected (7)
18 Mediterranean island (5)
20 Claw (5)
21 Cooking fat (4)

The Biggest Crossword Book In The World

ACROSS

1 Coloured inner shell (6-2-5)
7 Own up (7)
8 Holy person (5)
9 Bridge support (4)
10 Trustworthy (8)
12 Shorthand inventor (6)
14 Excellent (6)
16 Tactful person (8)
17 Clown (4)
20 Crowd scene actor (5)
21 West Country town (7)
23 Norma Jean Baker (7, 6)

DOWN

1 Raincoat (3)
2 Trace (5)
3 Where Adam met Eve (4)
4 Gourmet's shellfish (6)
5 Pleasant-natured (7)
6 Rubbish container (6, 3)
8 Blunder (4, 2)
9 Fanciful plan (4, 5)
11 Indian pasty (6)
13 Result forecaster (7)
15 Secure (6)
18 River mammal (5)
19 Popular board game (4)
22 Nickname for Labour MP Aneurin Bevin (3)

The Biggest Crossword Book In The World

ACROSS

1 British actress (4, 7)
9 Parachute string (3-4)
10 Steam bath (5)
11 Boutique (4)
12 Radio (8)
14 Shade tree (5)
15 Crest (5)
20 Village featured in The Archers (8)
22 Small amount (4)
24 Talent (5)
25 Forsake (7)
26 Discovered (11)

DOWN

2 Get better (7)
3 Eager (4)
4 Appoint (6)
5 Word blindness (8)
6 Stir, waken (5)
7 Try to sieze (5)
8 Flower with velvety petals (5)
13 Novelist, - - - Steel (8)
16 Native of Newcastle? (7)
17 Pause in concentration (5)
18 Overcome with horror (6)
19 US state, capital Augusta (5)
21 Perfect happiness (5)
23 Cab (4)

The Biggest Crossword Book In The World

ACROSS

1 Conforming to established views (8)
5 Colour (4)
9 Retrieve (5)
10 Nephew's sister (5)
12 Love (5)
13 Town crier's shout (4)
15 Decorative badge (6)
18 Obtained as profit (6)
20 Pack tidily away (4)
23 Pigs (5)
24 Underground root (5)
27 Lamp (5)
28 Karl - - -, communist (4)
29 One of Arthur's knights (8)

DOWN

1 Frank, overt (4)
2 Ripped (4)
3 Proposal (5)
4 Stableman (6)
6 Rebound (8)
7 Annually (6)
8 Follow closely (6)
11 Bitterly cold (3)
14 Kitchen gadget (3-5)
16 Brisk (6)
17 Knowledge (6)
19 A problem (6)
21 Be in debt (3)
22 Room at the top of a house (5)
25 Bird's beak (4)
26 Defeat (4)

The Biggest Crossword Book In The World

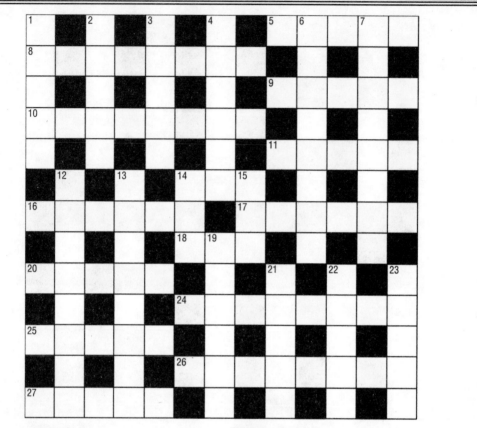

ACROSS

5 Sacred water lily (5)
8 Car repairer (8)
9 Famous Dutch porcelain (5)
10 Ocean (8)
11 Initial (5)
14 Open grassland (3)
16 Solid content (6)
17 Gambler (6)
18 Choose (3)
20 Apples, eg (5)
24 Drink (8)
25 Crescent-shaped (5)
26 Cutting instrument with two blades (8)
27 County between London and the North Sea (5)

DOWN

1 Smudge (5)
2 Castigate (5)
3 Lose consciousness temporarily (5)
4 Robust (6)
6 Compliant (8)
7 Detach (8)
12 Sullen person (8)
13 Maim (8)
14 Author, - - - Tolstoy (3)
15 Fitting (3)
19 Talk on a religious theme (6)
21 Robbery (5)
22 Council chief (5)
23 Separate the fibres (5)

The Biggest Crossword Book In The World

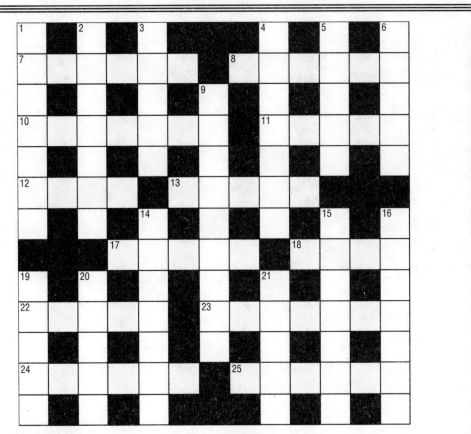

ACROSS

7 Load (6)
8 Break, opening (6)
10 Navigation aid (7)
11 Mysterious (5)
12 Horse's constraint (4)
13 Sculptor, - - - Epstein (5)
17 Native of Havana (5)
18 Area of London renowned for its restaurants (4)
22 David - - -, cricketer (5)
23 Hole (7)
24 Punctual (6)
25 Italian fashion designer (6)

DOWN

1 Hide, cloud (7)
2 Home of the Russian government (7)
3 Allowed by law (5)
4 King's deputy (7)
5 Attack suddenly (5)
6 Advantage (5)
9 Moving staircase (9)
14 String used to secure a tent (7)
15 Up-to-date (7)
16 Flowering garden plant (7)
19 Openmouthed (5)
20 Dive (5)
21 Right-angled joint (5)

The Biggest Crossword Book In The World

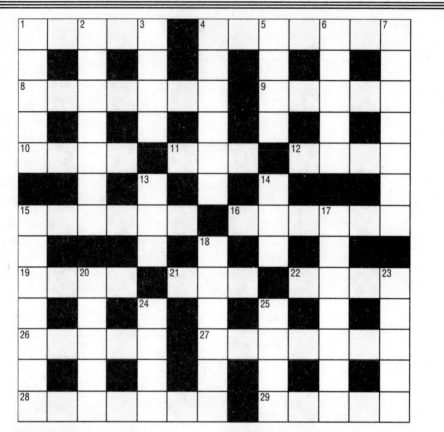

ACROSS

1 Wild (5)
4 Prehistoric elephant (7)
8 Milk pudding (7)
9 Precocious girl (5)
10 Among (4)
11 Run slowly (3)
12 Spoken, by mouth (4)
15 Grab (6)
16 Flat-bottomed
Oriental boat (6)
19 Knuckle of pork (4)
21 Quilt warmth (3)
22 Price paid (4)
26 Financial profit (5)
27 Muslim leader (3, 4)
28 Unfasten (7)
29 Sacred table (5)

DOWN

1 Islamic religious
ruling (5)
2 Exact copy (7)
3 Continuous
strip of film (4)
4 Area of grazing land (6)
5 Silent acting (4)
6 Sequence (5)
7 Pied Piper's town (7)
13 Cooling cube (3)
14 Posed (3)
15 One quick to learn (7)
17 Seer (7)
18 Consolation (6)
20 Politician,
- - - Parkinson (5)
23 Singer (5)
24 Greek B (4)
25 US space centre (4)

The Biggest Crossword Book In The World

ACROSS
1 Capsize (4, 6)
7 Cheers (8)
8 Summit (4)
9 Extra bonus (4)
10 Object of little value (7)
12 Get in touch (11)
14 Species of ox (7)
16 Feed to excess (4)
19 Clamping tool (4)
20 Having great worth (8)
21 Fast dance (10)

DOWN
1 Group of soldiers (5)
2 Platform (7)
3 Charge for using a road or bridge (4)
4 Keep in check (8)
5 Acquire an ability (5)
6 Tranquil (6)
11 Sweater (8)
12 Uncle's child (6)
13 Side by side (7)
15 Newly made (5)
17 Italian city (5)
18 Otherwise (4)

The Biggest Crossword Book In The World

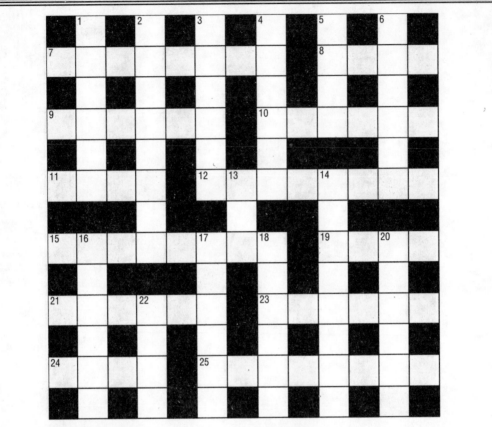

ACROSS

7 Advertising material sent by post (8)
8 Singer, - - - Armatrading (4)
9 Apprehended (6)
10 Food store (6)
11 New Zealand fruit? (4)
12 Meat and plant eating animal (8)
15 Towelling garment (8)
19 Heavy blunt weapon (4)
21 Be on one's guard (6)
23 One or the other (6)
24 Govern (4)
25 Pioneer (8)

DOWN

1 African country (6)
2 Lethargic (8)
3 Ethnic area (6)
4 Former Soviet leader (6)
5 Slightly open (4)
6 Swerve about wildly (6)
13 Disorderly crowd (3)
14 Holiday (8)
16 Tree-lined way (6)
17 Team's first batsman (6)
18 Free from liability (6)
20 Twin-speaker sound (6)
22 Red Sea port (4)

The Biggest Crossword Book In The World

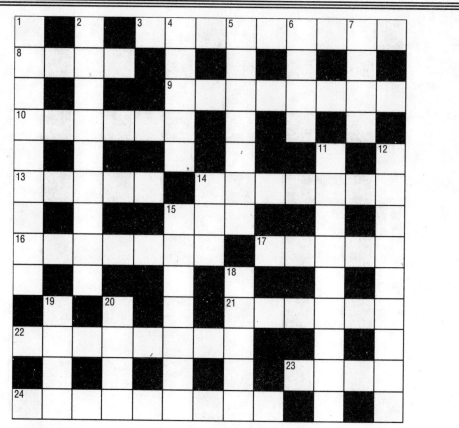

ACROSS

3 Small yellow flower (9)
8 Give over (4)
9 Sailing vessel with high mast (4, 4)
10 Capital of Taiwan (6)
13 Ted - - -, British politician (5)
14 Lawless youth (7)
15 Shy and modest (3)
16 Son of Lancelot (7)
17 Comedy actress, - - - Walters (5)
21 Large prawns (6)
22 Paper ingredient (4, 4)
23 Slimming programme (4)
24 Benefit, good (9)

DOWN

1 Salad item (6, 3)
2 Excellent (9)
4 To such time as (5)
5 *War and Peace* author (7)
6 Upward slope (4)
7 Kitchen cupboard (4)
11 Second World War battle (2, 7)
12 Instantaneous (9)
14 Brick-carrier (3)
15 Take prisoner (7)
18 The trembling poplar (5)
19 Mouse-like mammal (4)
20 Holy statue (4)

ACROSS

1 Blockade (5)
4 Tree (5)
10 Hollywood statuette (5)
11 Tombstone reading (7)
12 Addictive drug (8)
13 Small restaurant (4)
15 Houses of
   Parliament (11)
19 Harbour (4)
20 Worshiped (8)
23 Enduring energy (7)
24 Abrupt (5)
25 Wooden spike (5)
26 Goodbye (5)

DOWN

2 Become subject to (5)
3 Strangle (8)
5 Bitter to taste (4)
6 Absurd pretence (7)
7 Nobleman (5)
8 *EastEnders* actress (7, 4)
9 Robber (5)
14 Placed apart (8)
16 Amelia - - -, first woman
   to fly solo across
   the Atlantic (7)
17 Involuntary muscle
   contraction (5)
18 Common viper (5)
21 Opening tennis shot (5)
22 Mark shown for
   a correct answer (4)

The Biggest Crossword Book In The World

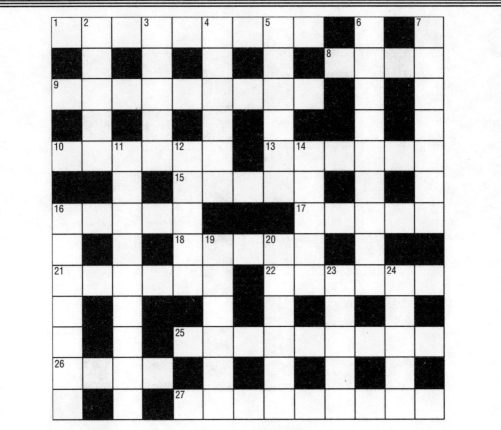

ACROSS

1 Connect, attach (9)
8 Undying spirit (4)
9 Butter substitute (9)
10 Middle (6)
13 Abscond (6)
15 Decline suddenly
   in value (5)
16 Football
   competition (1, 1, 3)
17 Group of eight
   musicians (5)
18 Make sure (5)
21 Ice cream dish (6)
22 Military policeman (6)
25 Step by step (9)
26 Cereal fed to horses (4)
27 Artificial language (9)

DOWN

2 Distress signal (5)
3 Oblong block
   of metal (5)
4 Middle Eastern
   country (6)
5 Bicycle for two (6)
6 Flamboyant (9)
7 Mild (weather) (7)
11 Prince of Tides
   film star (4, 5)
12 Animal charity (inits)
14 Wheel part (5)
16 Decorate (7)
19 Red card suit (6)
20 Crib (6)
23 Theatre play (5)
24 Give out (5)

The Biggest Crossword Book In The World

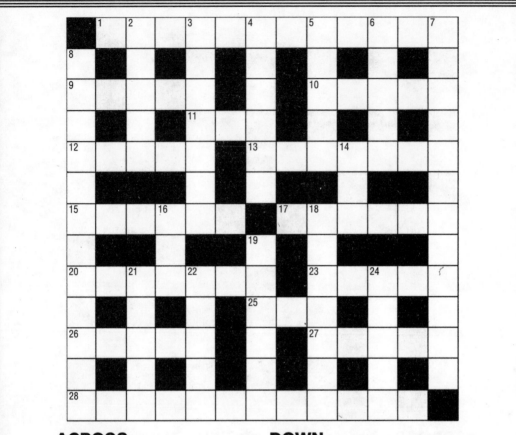

ACROSS

1 Discovery (12)
9 Bring together (5)
10 Dreadful (5)
11 Pose for a
photographer (3)
12 Catastrophic situation (5)
13 Qualify for (7)
15 Music industry award (6)
17 Official count
of population (6)
20 Eyeglass (7)
23 Masculine? (5)
25 In addition (3)
26 Girl's name (5)
27 Norwegian (5)
28 Meat and
mash dish (9, 3)

DOWN

2 Team race (5)
3 Garden plant (7)
4 Chuckle (6)
5 Sunday joint (5)
6 Out of condition (5)
7 Returning heavenly
body (7, 5)
8 Musical pieces (12)
14 Hostelry (3)
16 Cattle cry (3)
18 Noel - - -,
TV personality (7)
19 Shooting star (6)
21 Guts, bravery (5)
22 Train (5)
24 Royal dog (5)

The Biggest Crossword Book In The World

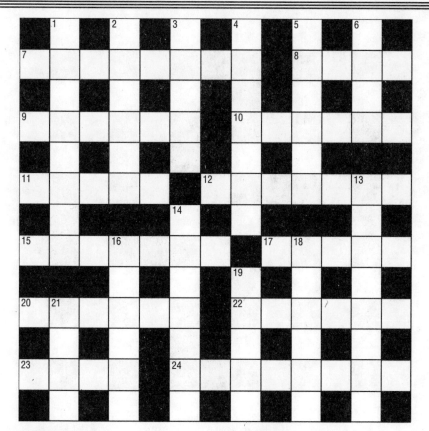

ACROSS

7 Unsolicited letters (4, 4)
8 Good Queen (4)
9 Indian PM,
   - - - Gandhi (6)
10 Difficult time (6)
11 Splutter! (5)
12 First book of the Old
   Testament (7)
15 Morally right (7)
17 Wedge placed
   under a wheel (5)
20 Censure severely (6)
22 Chinese fruit (6)
23 Old lighting gas (4)
24 Impractical person (8)

DOWN

1 Deserter (8)
2 Winter sport (6)
3 Unit of weight
   used for gems (5)
4 Defame (7)
5 Do a favour for (6)
6 Wine, - - - spumante (4)
13 Rise in number (8)
14 Tiny nation in the
   Arabian Gulf (7)
16 Propose (6)
18 Jeer (6)
19 Foreigner (5)
21 In a different way (4)

The Biggest Crossword Book In The World

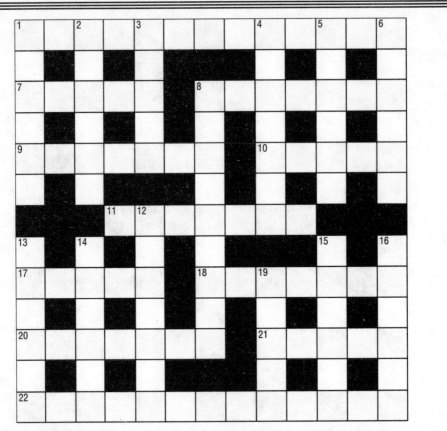

ACROSS

1 Bitterly (13)
7 Martial art (5)
8 Rascal, rogue (7)
9 Selfish driver (4-3)
10 Shred (cheese) (5)
11 Conspire (7)
17 Call off (5)
18 Figure (7)
20 Free time (7)
21 Lofty building (5)
22 Sweets and cakes (13)

DOWN

1 Turkish capital (6)
2 Hire payment (6)
3 Lurk, skulk (5)
4 Compelled (7)
5 Steven - - -, film star (6)
6 Over there (6)
8 Self-appointed crime-fighter (9)
12 Thrust forward (7)
13 Traditional Scottish language (6)
14 Medicine (6)
15 Look in a casual manner (6)
16 Thick, slushy mixture (6)
19 Saying (5)

The Biggest Crossword Book In The World

ACROSS

1 Asian desert (4)
4 Mediterranean country (6)
8 New alcoholic drinks (8)
9 Large mountain goat (4)
10 Spread out (5)
11 Pedalled transport (7)
13 Suspension of business (6)
15 Airport waiting room (6)
17 Sea creature with large claws (7)
19 Bar for imparting pressure (5)
22 Animal's father (4)
23 New York borough (3, 5)
24 Playground apparatus (6)
25 Take notice of (4)

DOWN

2 Lowest deck of a ship (5)
3 Third stage of man (4, 3)
4 Shoe with thick wooden sole (4)
5 Medicated lozenge (8)
6 Blend (5)
7 Post-flight ailment (3, 3)
12 Fibrous fire-proof mineral (8)
14 Bizarre (6)
16 Discover (7)
18 Soft leather (5)
20 Premium Bond prize picker (5)
21 Cry of a cat (4)

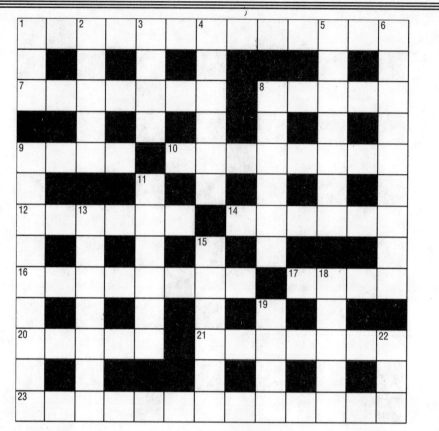

ACROSS

1 *Babes in the Wood* actress (8, 5)
7 Interest (7)
8 Pale purple (5)
9 Next (4)
10 Hardened criminal (8)
12 Instrument for lifting and moving coal (6)
14 Breathing disorder (6)
16 Rubber-soled shoe (4-4)
17 Not hard (4)
20 Prepared (5)
21 Useful facility (7)
23 *Coronation Street* actress (9, 4)

DOWN

1 Dry wine (3)
2 Gambling resort, - - - Carlo (5)
3 Oasis singer, - - - Gallagher (4)
4 Building where aircraft are stored (6)
5 Feed (7)
6 Firm (9)
8 Pester in a hostile way (6)
9 Working party (4, 5)
11 Bell-tower (6)
13 Art of paper-folding (7)
15 Degree of hope (6)
18 Seance board (5)
19 Net (4)
22 Japanese money (3)

The Biggest Crossword Book In The World

ACROSS

1 Liable to catch fire (11)
9 Customary (7)
10 Spirit (5)
11 Exchange (4)
12 Free oneself (3-5)
14 Improvised performance (2, 3)
15 Nude (5)
20 Cosmetic (8)
22 Portuguese holiday resort (4)
24 Form (5)
25 Area made wet to test driver's skills (7)
26 American actress (5, 6)

DOWN

2 Miser (7)
3 Flowering plant (4)
4 Place for buying and selling (6)
5 Liqueur made from raw eggs (8)
6 Big (5)
7 Crop up (5)
8 German soldier? (5)
13 Careful and steady (8)
16 Specimen (7)
17 Tightly packed (5)
18 Discarded material washed ashore (6)
19 Noise (5)
21 Avoid, dodge (5)
23 Tend (4)

The Biggest Crossword Book In The World

ACROSS

1 Constricting snake (8)
5 Sound rebound (4)
9 Fourteen pounds (5)
10 Musical pace (5)
12 Penniless (5)
13 Hunt (4)
15 Swiss city (6)
18 Small parcel (6)
20 Hindu meditation and exercise (4)
23 Search blindly (5)
24 Ring-shaped coral island (5)
27 In the lead (5)
28 As well (4)
29 Legendary dragon slayer (2, 6)

DOWN

1 Border against (4)
2 Eve's partner (4)
3 Actor and director, - - - Welles (5)
4 Scribble (6)
6 American state (8)
7 George - - -, author (6)
8 Ancient language (6)
11 Farm animal (3)
14 Investigates (8)
16 Yell (6)
17 Eastern temple (6)
19 Former king of Wessex (6)
21 Hair-styling substance (3)
22 Sponge money off (5)
25 Actor, - - - Sharif (4)
26 Crippled (4)

The Biggest Crossword Book In The World

ACROSS

5 Blood sucker (5)
8 Brought forward (8)
9 Distant, reserved (5)
10 Aromatic herb (8)
11 Assignation (5)
14 Domestic animal (3)
16 French art gallery (6)
17 Followed orders (6)
18 Slight blow (3)
20 Musical instrument (5)
24 Thrashing (8)
25 Indiscreet act (5)
26 Fallacy (8)
27 Greeting (5)

DOWN

1 Italian foodstuff (5)
2 Frank, indiscreet (5)
3 Soldier from down under (5)
4 *Soldier, Soldier* star, - - - Flynn (6)
6 Makes bigger (8)
7 Chinese dish (4, 4)
12 Appoint to a position (8)
13 Momentous (8)
14 Balloonist, - - - Lindstrand (3)
15 Peak (3)
19 Concurred (6)
21 Circa (5)
22 Stiff (5)
23 Type of aunt to share troubles with (5)

The Biggest Crossword Book In The World

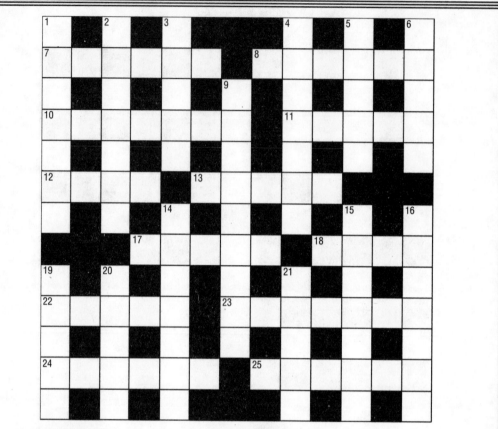

ACROSS

7 Capital of New
South Wales (6)
8 Orson - - -,
film legend (6)
10 Daunting (7)
11 Award (5)
12 One of the
deadly sins (4)
13 Salty (5)
17 Dress (5)
18 Following (4)
22 Lacking skill (5)
23 Hard-shelled creature (7)
24 Angel (6)
25 Cooking formula (6)

DOWN

1 Attack (7)
2 Hostile (7)
3 Storehouse (5)
4 Reply (7)
5 Calvin - - -, fashion
designer (5)
6 Pale-faced (5)
9 American singer (5, 4)
14 Visibly anxious (7)
15 Bedding plant (7)
16 Adhesive label (7)
19 Small songbird (5)
20 Stationery (5)
21 Rain with snow (5)

The Biggest Crossword Book In The World

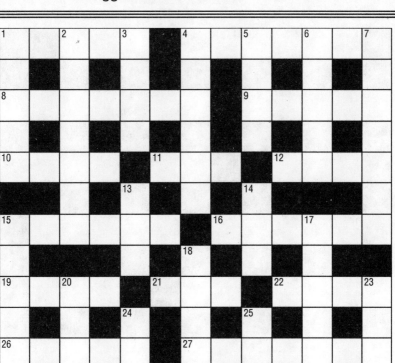

ACROSS

1 Large aircraft (5)
4 Eccentric person (7)
8 Ribbon (7)
9 Clothing (5)
10 Destroy (4)
11 Solemn promise (3)
12 Assassinate (4)
15 Sign of the zodiac (6)
16 Item of crockery (6)
19 Medium-sized cat (4)
21 Japanese form of Buddhism (3)
22 Small island off the coast of Italy (4)
26 Blacksmith's block (5)
27 Missing Derby winner (7)
28 Oriental (7)
29 Egg covering (5)

DOWN

1 Court decision maker? (5)
2 Specific task (7)
3 Sworn statement (4)
4 US state (6)
5 Wooden rail (4)
6 Jean - - -, racing driver (5)
7 Final part of a race (4, 3)
13 Wooden pin (3)
14 Half a score (3)
15 Mosaic-type picture (7)
17 Perfumed toilet water (7)
18 Liam - - -, *Schindler's List* actor (6)
20 Ben - - -, mountain (5)
23 Girl's name (5)
24 Blue-black sour fruit (4)
25 Supreme Greek god (4)

The Biggest Crossword Book In The World

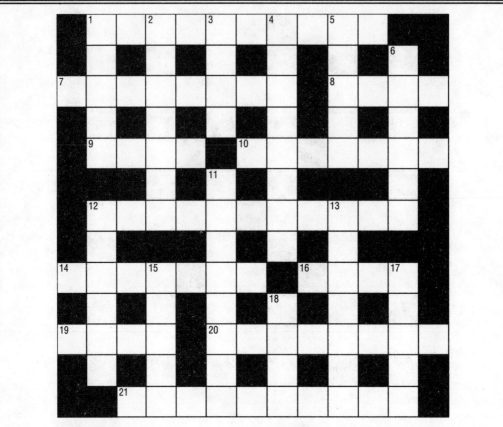

ACROSS

1 Owner (10)
7 Situation (8)
8 Work hard (4)
9 Light in colour (4)
10 Bodily height (7)
12 Resolved, settled (11)
14 Sleeping quarters (7)
16 Tall, lofty (4)
19 Sure thing (4)
20 Rowdy young person (8)
21 Had power over (10)

DOWN

1 Conclusive evidence (5)
2 Point of view (7)
3 Mike - - -, actor
   and comedian (4)
4 Founder of the theory
   of relativity (8)
5 Attack (5)
6 Fiery, passionate (6)
11 Augusto - - -,
    Chilean dictator (8)
12 Bright, intelligent (6)
13 Of little importance (7)
15 Proportion (5)
17 Listened to (5)
18 Emblem (4)

The Biggest Crossword Book In The World

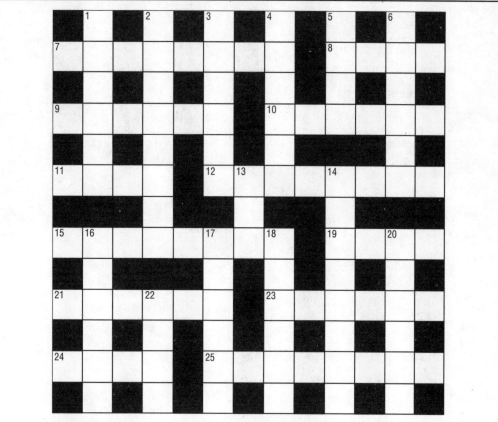

ACROSS

7 Deserts (8)
8 Ship's floor (4)
9 Covered passageway (6)
10 Rabbit hole (6)
11 Biting insect (4)
12 Corn chip (8)
15 Feminine (8)
19 Member of the Conservative party (4)
21 Altitude (6)
23 Equality (6)
24 Betting chances (4)
25 Trapped (8)

DOWN

1 Titania's husband (6)
2 Foot soldiers (8)
3 Humble (6)
4 Line on a weather map (6)
5 Sussex river (4)
6 Place of learning (6)
13 Acorn tree (3)
14 Information superhighway? (8)
16 List of matters to be discussed (6)
17 Complete (6)
18 Realm, dominion (6)
20 Somewhat (6)
22 Sudden blast of wind (4)

The Biggest Crossword Book In The World

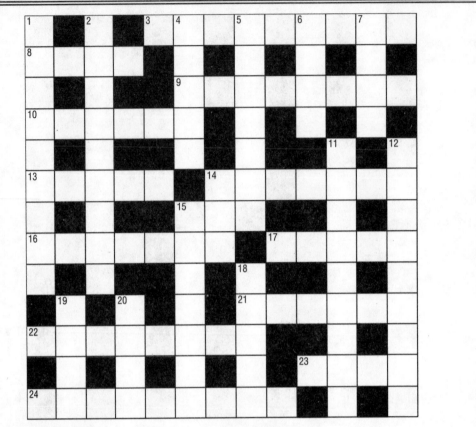

ACROSS

3 Poisonous fungus (9)
8 Ten cents piece (4)
9 Riding trousers (8)
10 Breakfast cereal (6)
13 Speedy (5)
14 Sweet made of nuts and caramilised sugar (7)
15 Bounder (3)
16 Reveal (7)
17 Council regulation (5)
21 Lasso (6)
22 Slaughter (8)
23 Bolt (4)
24 Sea walk (9)

DOWN

1 Misfit (3, 3, 3)
2 Defective (9)
4 Planet's path (5)
5 Reactionary (3-4)
6 Diplomacy (4)
7 Cooker (4)
11 Rustic person (9)
12 Scottish pop group (3, 3, 3)
14 Expected score (3)
15 Sure (7)
18 Ask with deep feeling (5)
19 Perceive by ear (4)
20 Former name of Thailand (4)

The Biggest Crossword Book In The World

ACROSS

1 Reject (5)
4 Small anchor (5)
10 Savoury Indian dish (5)
11 Study of past events (7)
12 Plan of procedure (8)
13 Greyish-yellow (4)
15 Numbing drug (11)
19 Choose, select (4)
20 Ecstatic (8)
23 Fire, sack (7)
24 Era (5)
25 Crazy (5)
26 Crime writer,
   - - - Wallace (5)

DOWN

2 Simmer in liquid (5)
3 Arctic sledge puller (8)
5 Direction (4)
6 Pasta dumplings (7)
7 Prolonged
   ill-treatment (5)
8 Stamp collector (11)
9 Treacle (5)
14 Mattress support (8)
16 Capital of Cyprus (7)
17 English porcelain (5)
18 Hawaiian greeting (5)
21 Plants (5)
22 Droop (4)

The Biggest Crossword Book In The World

ACROSS

1 Manual skill (9)
8 Guide (4)
9 Custom (9)
10 Court judgement (6)
13 Town of St Francis (6)
15 Give formally (5)
16 Literary composition (5)
17 Similar (5)
18 Squeeze (5)
21 Protective cover (6)
22 Dairy product (6)
25 Suppressed (9)
26 Depend upon (4)
27 Chit-chat (5, 4)

DOWN

2 Eagle's nest (5)
3 Style of architecture (5)
4 Reprehensible person (6)
5 Inhabitant of Troy? (6)
6 Essential (9)
7 Large building (7)
11 Meat dish simmered in gravy (9)
12 Land of the Pharaohs (5)
14 Hide (5)
16 Capture, trap (7)
19 Musical beat (6)
20 Write illegibly (6)
23 Even number (5)
24 Odour, stink (5)

ACROSS

1 Stadium (12)
9 Of birth (5)
10 Welsh county (5)
11 Permit (3)
12 Final Greek letter (5)
13 Originator (7)
15 Cartoon sailor (6)
17 Art of growing
dwarf trees (6)
20 Hiker (7)
23 Deliberate starting
of fires (5)
25 Busy insect (3)
26 Army blouse (5)
27 Bungling,
incompetent (5)
28 Make a mistake (4, 1, 7)

DOWN

2 Thirty-nine inches (5)
3 Sir Edmund - - -,
mountaineer (7)
4 Spasm (6)
5 Bird of prey (5)
6 Stealing (5)
7 Excessive (12)
8 Merged together (12)
14 Stiff bristle of grass (3)
16 Outgoing tide (3)
18 Applause (7)
19 Type of nut (6)
21 Fleshy fruit (5)
22 Stretchable fabric (5)
24 Garden vegetable (5)

The Biggest Crossword Book In The World

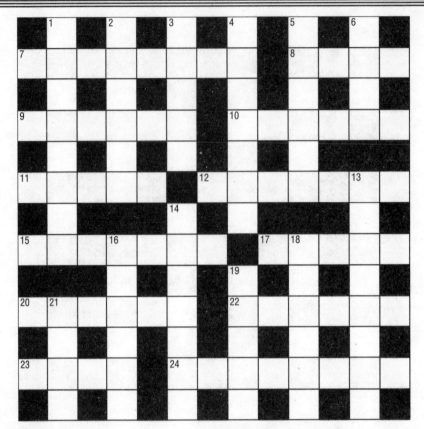

ACROSS
7 Enduring (8)
8 Pavement edge (4)
9 A group of acrobats (6)
10 Cricket dismissal (3, 3)
11 Weasel-like animal (5)
12 All-in-one outfit
   for a young child (7)
15 Tense, irritable (7)
17 Permit (5)
20 Flowering grass (6)
22 Astounded (6)
23 Scottish loch (4)
24 Viking boat (8)

DOWN
1 Thick slice of bread? (8)
2 Jellyfish (6)
3 Side of a cut gem (5)
4 Endless (7)
5 Thin (6)
6 Pakistani language (4)
13 Old name for
   Zimbabwe (8)
14 Shrill sound (7)
16 Inflict (6)
18 Co-ordinate (6)
19 Female goat (5)
21 Word said at the
   end of a prayer (4)

The Biggest Crossword Book In The World

ACROSS

1 Popular soccer programme (5, 2, 3, 3)
7 Articles for sale (5)
8 Top naval officer (7)
9 Direction on a letter (7)
10 Cowboy show (5)
11 Greeting (7)
17 Educate, train (5)
18 Clumsy (7)
20 Encroach (7)
21 Capital of Morocco (5)
22 Loud radio (6, 7)

DOWN

1 Mo - - -, politician (6)
2 Long critical outburst (6)
3 Hurry (5)
4 Commonplace (7)
5 Treat with contempt (6)
6 Lemon-coloured (6)
8 Link, connect (9)
12 Wear out (7)
13 Thin cord (6)
14 Gossip, chatter (6)
15 First move (6)
16 Newspaper boss (6)
19 Indian dish (5)

The Biggest Crossword Book In The World

ACROSS

1 Unit of Italian currency (4)
4 Danger (6)
8 Dry, golden-brown brandy (8)
9 African country (4)
10 Drive out (5)
11 Singer, - - - Bassey (7)
13 Tusked seal (6)
15 Agile (6)
17 Prince Charles' son (7)
19 Female monarch (5)
22 Jealousy (4)
23 Untarnished (8)
24 Hypnotic state (6)
25 Deadened, unfeeling (4)

DOWN

2 Home of Rangers Football club (5)
3 Non-professional (7)
4 Search (4)
5 A courgette (8)
6 Happen again (5)
7 Edith - - -, executed British nurse (6)
12 Hired killer (8)
14 Sigourney Weaver film (6)
16 Sentimental (7)
18 Coat (of paint) (5)
20 Derby racecourse (5)
21 Bob - - -, veteran comic (4)

ACROSS

1 Believing in luck (13)
7 Incomplete (7)
8 Grasslike plant (5)
9 Urchin (4)
10 British politician (4, 4)
12 Near-sighted (6)
14 Fight (6)
16 Essential framework (8)
17 Military status (4)
20 Precise (5)
21 Please greatly (7)
23 In a torpid manner (13)

DOWN

1 Small drink (3)
2 Hooded jacket (5)
3 Charity for the blind (1, 1, 1, 1)
4 Soap ingredient (6)
5 Remnant (7)
6 John - - -, American novelist (9)
8 US space station (6)
9 Unwelcome surprise (9)
11 Divide in two (6)
13 Ham it up! (7)
15 Leader? (3, 3)
18 Guardian spirit (5)
19 Knighted actor, - - - Guinness (4)
22 Object to play with (3)

The Biggest Crossword Book In The World

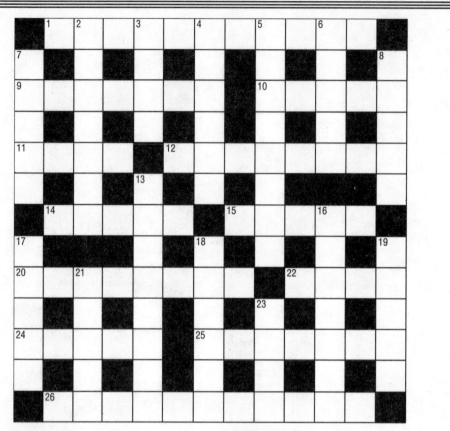

ACROSS

1 Bill in *2point4 children* (7, 4)
9 Stone-fruit (7)
10 Lid (5)
11 Breeding horse (4)
12 Native of Belgrade (8)
14 Weighty (5)
15 Meat jelly (5)
20 Ceremonial (8)
22 Darts throwing line (4)
24 Irish police force (5)
25 Deep red colour (7)
26 Gulf War operation name (6, 5)

DOWN

2 On the way (2, 5)
3 Skin irritation (4)
4 Change in planned journey (6)
5 Hockey-like game (8)
6 Belly button! (5)
7 Poorly-drained land (5)
8 Long for (5)
13 Abandon (8)
16 Cutting tooth (7)
17 Large pincers (5)
18 Lucky symbol (6)
19 Beatles' hit, - - - *Lane* (5)
21 Slapstick (5)
23 Raise up (4)

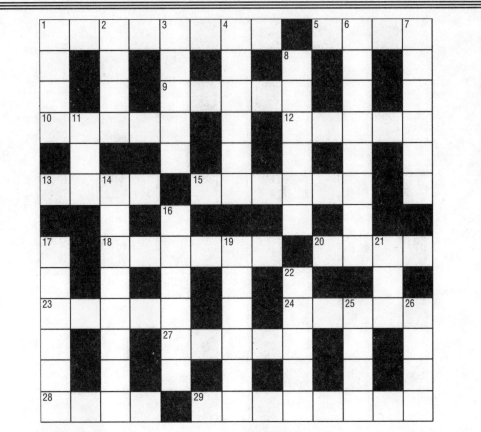

ACROSS

1 On the outside (8)
5 Audible breath (4)
9 Inexperienced (5)
10 Large African animal? (5)
12 Garden ornament (5)
13 Christmas (4)
15 Brush mark (6)
18 Speak in a vague manner (6)
20 Engrave (4)
23 Hangman's loop (5)
24 Dirt (5)
27 Blow (5)
28 Piffle (4)
29 The way in (8)

DOWN

1 Every one (4)
2 Stumble (4)
3 Fibre made from wood pulp (5)
4 Charm against evil spirits (6)
6 Rude, disrespectful (8)
7 Fair and just (6)
8 Alcoholic drink (6)
11 Debtor's note (1, 1, 1)
14 Highest court of appeal (3, 5)
16 Result (6)
17 Large sea-bird (6)
19 Stretch of salt water (6)
21 Lacerate (3)
22 Later (5)
25 French city (4)
26 Detest (4)

The Biggest Crossword Book In The World

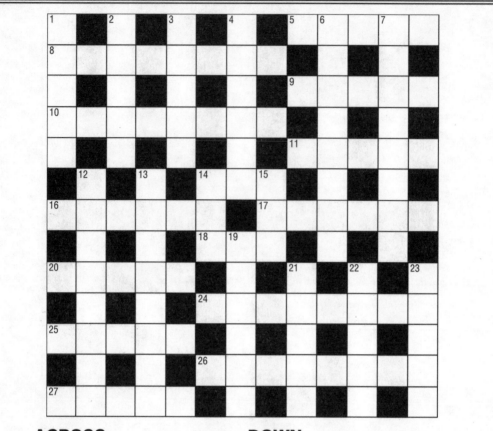

ACROSS

5 Hint (5)
8 The clothing business (3, 5)
9 Objectionable (5)
10 Very big (8)
11 Exotic dance (5)
14 Poem (3)
16 Accountant's book (6)
17 Idea, opinion (6)
18 Non-venomous snake (3)
20 Value (5)
24 Capital of Nepal (8)
25 Caribbean country (5)
26 Tepid (8)
27 Thin (5)

DOWN

1 Small bay (5)
2 Ice-house (5)
3 Chief (5)
4 Sir - - - Hillary, Everest climber (6)
6 Put in a logical way (8)
7 Class, group (8)
12 Embellish (8)
13 Excited (8)
14 Sphere, globe (3)
15 Greek letter (3)
19 Hard to understand (6)
21 Cinder (5)
22 Massage (5)
23 Model (5)

The Biggest Crossword Book In The World

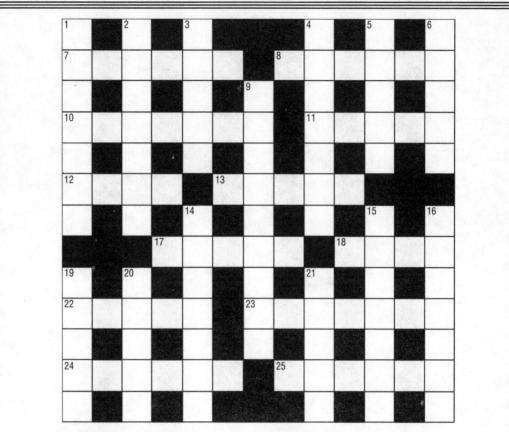

ACROSS

7 Willing to obey (6)
8 Citrus fruit (6)
10 Lowest quantity (7)
11 Fortune-telling card (5)
12 Required achievement (4)
13 Foolish (5)
17 Satan (5)
18 Put by for a rainy day (4)
22 Stringed instrument (5)
23 Uninformed (7)
24 Budgie food (6)
25 Biting comedy (6)

DOWN

1 Unyielding (7)
2 Landscape (7)
3 Liquid mud (5)
4 Hard and fragile (7)
5 Conductor, - - - Previn (5)
6 Liner's bunk (5)
9 Keen for success (9)
14 Regain (7)
15 German state (7)
16 Soccer umpire (7)
19 Atomic weapon (1-4)
20 Cousin's father (5)
21 Film, - - - *Attraction* (5)

ACROSS

1 Shaggy-haired oxen (5)
4 Very irate (7)
8 Item of jewellery (7)
9 Comedian, - - - Milligan (5)
10 Grave (4)
11 Skill (3)
12 Hostile (4)
15 Rehearsal (3, 3)
16 Respectful, urbane (6)
19 Italian city with leaning tower (4)
21 Snooker rod (3)
22 Kiln for drying hops (4)
26 Set of hotel rooms (5)
27 Russian ruler's wife (7)
28 Difficulty (7)
29 Build (5)

DOWN

1 Lamb's cry (5)
2 Rough cider (7)
3 Horny fingertip growth (4)
4 Number symbol (6)
5 Coarse file (4)
6 Pungent vegetable (5)
7 Fruitless (7)
13 Container (3)
14 Dance (3)
15 Set down (7)
17 John Lennon song (7)
18 Push about (6)
20 Irish county (5)
23 Proposal of success (5)
24 Flavoursome plant (4)
25 Speed contest (4)

The Biggest Crossword Book In The World

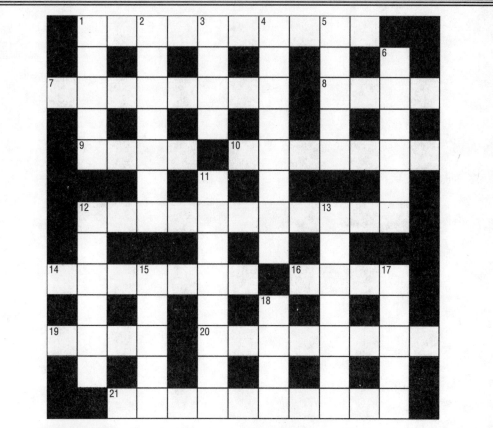

ACROSS

- **1** Container (10)
- **7** Plaice, eg (8)
- **8** Crooked (4)
- **9** Insolent (4)
- **10** Wiped out, erased (7)
- **12** Imagine (11)
- **14** Quack remedy (7)
- **16** Witty saying (4)
- **19** Tidings (4)
- **20** Clothes shop (8)
- **21** Elvis hit, - - - *Hotel* (10)

DOWN

- **1** Governor, chief (5)
- **2** Refuge (7)
- **3** Couple, two (4)
- **4** Physically powerful (8)
- **5** Depart, go (5)
- **6** European country (6)
- **11** Long green salad item (8)
- **12** Former American President (6)
- **13** Insulting (7)
- **15** Flavour (5)
- **17** Courage (5)
- **18** Restrain (4)

The Biggest Crossword Book In The World

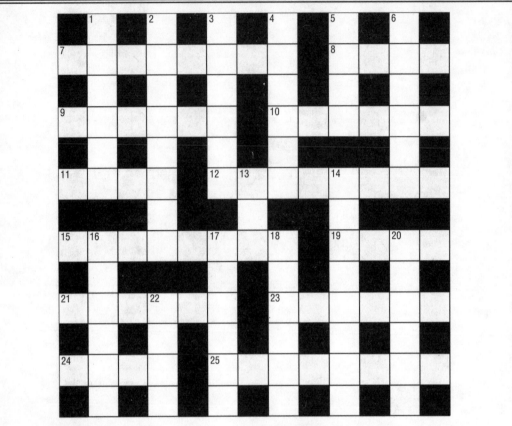

ACROSS

7 Sumptuous (8)
8 Book of the Bible (4)
9 Fearful (6)
10 Unrefined (6)
11 Surfeit (4)
12 Brought up, raised (8)
15 Subordinate event (8)
19 Thought (4)
21 Stringed instrument (6)
23 Prairie-wolf (6)
24 Poker stake (4)
25 Islands noted for wool
and ponies (8)

DOWN

1 Foreman, boss (6)
2 Cripple (8)
3 Concealed (6)
4 Splinter (6)
5 Fruit skin (4)
6 Thick oily substance (6)
13 Flying saucer (1, 1, 1)
14 Clown's bike (8)
16 Large lizard (6)
17 Worry (6)
18 Bowler's target (6)
20 Scope, range (6)
22 Layer (4)

The Biggest Crossword Book In The World

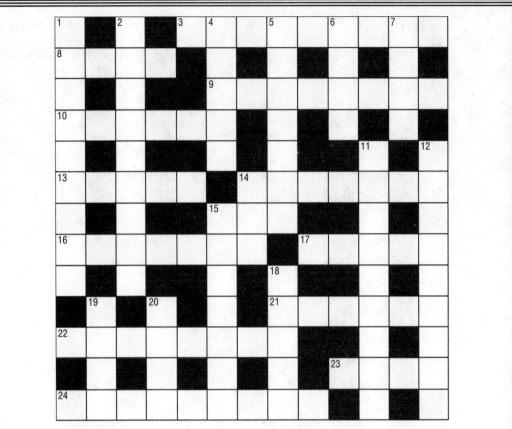

ACROSS

3 Top blanket (9)
8 Snail without a shell (4)
9 Outlaw (8)
10 Shop stewards call? (3-3)
13 Fruit of the oak tree (5)
14 Northern Scandinavia (7)
15 Chum (3)
16 Shade of green (7)
17 Repeatedly (5)
21 *Sister Act* star,
   - - - Goldberg (6)
22 Squid (8)
23 Song from an opera (4)
24 Article of trade (9)

DOWN

1 Snowballed (9)
2 Vehicle with
   caterpillar tracks (9)
4 Soil (5)
5 Ancient timepiece (7)
6 Great anger (4)
7 Assistant (4)
11 Jocky Wilson's target (9)
12 Exactly alike (9)
14 Young man (3)
15 Notice for public
   display (7)
18 Speedy (5)
19 Simon - - -, TV and
   radio presenter (4)
20 Moderately hot (4)

The Biggest Crossword Book In The World

ACROSS
1 Feel (5)
4 Large steak (1-4)
10 Large wall painting (5)
11 German town (7)
12 Brutal, cruel (8)
13 Sway loosely (4)
15 Stomach ache (11)
19 Spun thread (4)
20 Acquired (8)
23 Not on either side (7)
24 Interior design (5)
25 Pretend (5)
26 Stairpost (5)

DOWN
2 American talk show host,
- - - Winfrey (5)
3 Capital of
South Carolina (8)
5 Curve (4)
6 Ivor - - -, composer (7)
7 Range (5)
8 Flash of lightning (11)
9 Chart (5)
14 Sit with a leg
either side (8)
16 Nourish (7)
17 Spotted carnivore (5)
18 Decorate (5)
21 Suitable place in life (5)
22 Ship's prison (4)

The Biggest Crossword Book In The World

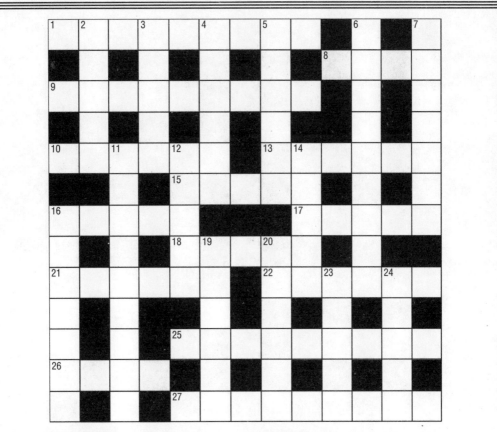

ACROSS

1 Capital of Scotland (9)
8 Hand warmer (4)
9 Fine porcelain (4, 5)
10 Mr Hyde's doctor? (6)
13 Landed property (6)
15 Idolise (5)
16 Obstructs (5)
17 Card game (5)
18 Ketchup (5)
21 System (6)
22 Stem (6)
25 Facial hair (9)
26 Church recess (4)
27 Stammered (9)

DOWN

2 Low dull sound (5)
3 In want (5)
4 Maintain (6)
5 Light orange-brown colour (6)
6 Very profitable (9)
7 Unusual (7)
11 Ken Dodd comes from here (6, 3)
12 Cowboy's rope (5)
14 Drain (5)
16 Funny (7)
19 Floating aimlessly (6)
20 Condition (6)
23 Journey plan (5)
24 Burn slightly (5)

The Biggest Crossword Book In The World

ACROSS
1 SAS motto (3, 5, 4)
9 Part of a sword (5)
10 Noisy argument (5)
11 Engage in winter sports (3)
12 Equal stakes (5)
13 Vague (7)
15 Herald's jacket (6)
17 Combination of karate and judo (4, 2)
20 Month (7)
23 Peter - - -, snooker player (5)
25 Troops (3)
26 Ward off (5)
27 Pig food (5)
28 *GMTV* presenter (6, 6)

DOWN
2 Equine animal (5)
3 Item of furniture (7)
4 Pungent red salad vegetable (6)
5 Curved sword (5)
6 Sci-fi author, - - - Asimov (5)
7 British hurdler (5, 7)
8 Loving (12)
14 Brown (3)
16 Bustling activity (3)
18 Tool (7)
19 Northern Ireland county (6)
21 Heat unit (5)
22 Drum major's stick (5)
24 Golf shot (5)

The Biggest Crossword Book In The World

ACROSS

7 Wholesale trader (8)
8 Roman garment (4)
9 Dale - - -, TV star (6)
10 Lover's town,
- - - Green (6)
11 Surmise (5)
12 Groom's mate (4, 3)
15 Rotted (7)
17 Bestow (5)
20 Expression (6)
22 Regular behaviour (6)
23 Walking stick (4)
24 Without warning (8)

DOWN

1 Trust (8)
2 Harm (6)
3 Shrewd, clever (5)
4 Walk unsteadily (7)
5 Urban road (6)
6 Restaurant critic,
- - - Ronay (4)
13 Delightful (8)
14 Travel backwards (7)
16 Rouse (6)
18 Aromatic kernel (6)
19 TV presenter,
- - - Mostue (5)
21 Warmth (4)

The Biggest Crossword Book In The World

ACROSS

1 Annual steeplechase at Aintree (5, 8)
7 Web-footed, long-necked birds (5)
8 Women's eyelash make-up (7)
9 In the neighbourhood (7)
10 Walk at leisurely pace (5)
11 Track competitor (7)
17 Collection of wives? (5)
18 Show devotion to (7)
20 Woman's bedroom (7)
21 *Memphis - - -*, war film (5)
22 Otherwise (13)

DOWN

1 Fancy-man (6)
2 Organisation (6)
3 Live (5)
4 Fleeting moment (7)
5 Adjacent (6)
6 Demagogue (6)
8 Pilgrim Father's ship (9)
12 Embroidery frame (7)
13 Fear, aversion (6)
14 Increase suddenly (6)
15 Defer indefinitely (6)
16 Prompt (6)
19 Jewish doctor of law (5)

The Biggest Crossword Book In The World

ACROSS

1 Active and nimble (4)
4 Central American canal (6)
8 International football competition (5, 3)
9 Protein-rich bean (4)
10 Shape, form (5)
11 Template (7)
13 Source (6)
15 Partially fermented fodder crop (6)
17 Immortal (7)
19 Long-handled spoon (5)
22 Pitch tents (4)
23 Infinite time (8)
24 Nearer (6)
25 Stench (4)

DOWN

2 Snapshot (5)
3 Christmas cake (4, 3)
4 Agreement, treaty (4)
5 Favouritism towards own family (8)
6 Perry - - -, TV lawyer (5)
7 Secretarial skill (6)
12 Teeth? (8)
14 Bob Marley's music? (6)
16 Student (7)
18 Part of a jacket (5)
20 Metric measure (5)
21 Twelve months (4)

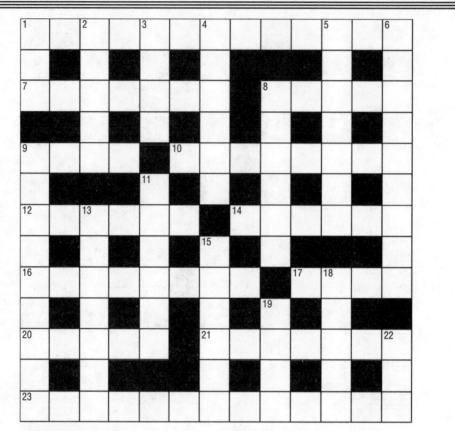

ACROSS

1 *Top Gun* actress (5, 8)
7 Fit of temper (7)
8 Try to turn out (5)
9 Crossbar on a ladder (4)
10 Large grey mammal (8)
12 Ravenous (6)
14 Robber (6)
16 Charles - - -,
French singer (8)
17 Lord (4)
20 Beer mug (5)
21 Make bigger (7)
23 Army rank (5, 8)

DOWN

1 Set of tools (3)
2 Former Soviet leader (5)
3 English racecourse (4)
4 Do as asked (6)
5 Tight-fitting garment (7)
6 Eyewitness (9)
8 Tall tree (6)
9 Practice session (9)
11 Andre - - -, conductor (6)
13 Hard-wearing cotton
fabric (7)
15 Dinner jacket (6)
18 Mistake (5)
19 Prune with shears (4)
22 Jellied fish? (3)

The Biggest Crossword Book In The World

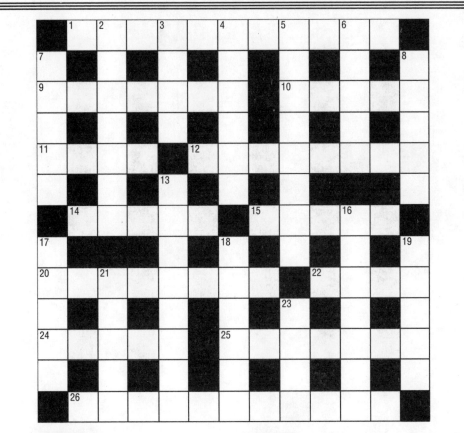

ACROSS

1 *Whistle Down the Wind* actress (6, 5)
9 Tropical fruit (7)
10 Cloud of bees (5)
11 Lengthy epic (4)
12 Uncertain (8)
14 Hoard (5)
15 Threatening look (5)
20 Lazy person (8)
22 Charm (4)
24 Market-place (5)
25 Ghost (7)
26 Singer, eg (11)

DOWN

2 Surrounded by (7)
3 Borrowed sum (4)
4 Beefeaters (6)
5 Inborn impulse (8)
6 South American beast of burden (5)
7 Wild flower (5)
8 Void (5)
13 Card game (8)
16 Grapple (7)
17 Flee to wed (5)
18 Miss Piggy, eg (6)
19 Proof of payment on a letter (5)
21 Long for (5)
23 Indonesian holiday isle (4)

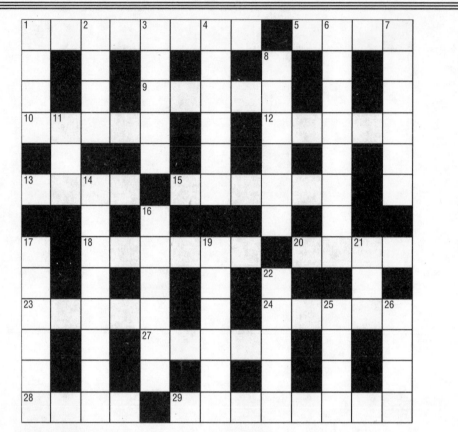

ACROSS

1 Shell fragments (8)
5 Difficult journey (4)
9 American Indian warrior (5)
10 Try-out (5)
12 Driver's accommodation (5)
13 Inform (4)
15 Choose (6)
18 Delay, loiter (6)
20 Steep rock (4)
23 Evade work (5)
24 Ancient (5)
27 Sports team (5)
28 Gain (4)
29 Television news and information service (8)

DOWN

1 Put in order (4)
2 Indian queen (4)
3 Artist, - - - Picasso (5)
4 Pass (time) (6)
6 Fizzy drink (4, 4)
7 Murderer (6)
8 Be left behind (6)
11 Regret (3)
14 Imaginery country in Gullivar's Travels (8)
16 Use capital (6)
17 Engine part (6)
19 Make certain (6)
21 Affirmative vote (3)
22 Make rotten (5)
25 Musical quality (4)
26 Powdery dirt (4)

The Biggest Crossword Book In The World

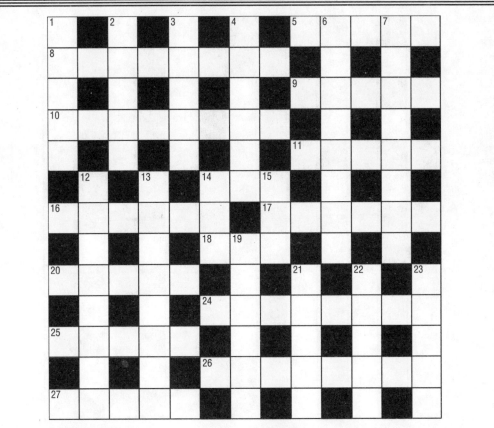

ACROSS

5 Ballroom dance (5)
8 Eye doctor (8)
9 Musical drama (5)
10 Spice (8)
11 Wireless (5)
14 Body of water (3)
16 Oscar winning film starring Ben Kingsley (6)
17 Gloomy (6)
18 Danger colour (3)
20 Woven cloth (5)
24 Reason, need (8)
25 Unadorned (5)
26 University term (8)
27 Ship's propeller (5)

DOWN

1 Freshwater fish (5)
2 Acrobatic action (5)
3 Vamoose (5)
4 Word of honour (6)
6 Expression of approval (8)
7 Fatal (8)
12 American car (8)
13 Glue (8)
14 Knight's title (3)
15 Join (3)
19 Go beyond (6)
21 Danny - - -, television and radio presenter (5)
22 Unclean (5)
23 Access (5)

The Biggest Crossword Book In The World

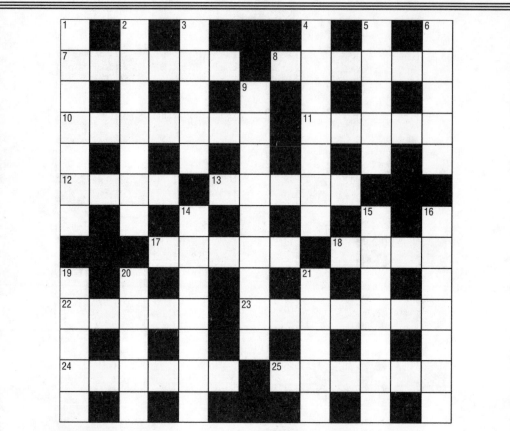

ACROSS

7 Metal plating (6)
8 Mushroom, eg (6)
10 A love affair (7)
11 Malice (5)
12 Large water jug (4)
13 Bend, bow (5)
17 British-based charity (5)
18 Actor, - - - Bridges (4)
22 Unclouded (5)
23 Burn to ashes (7)
24 Andre - - -,
   tennis player (6)
25 Obsessive enthusiast (6)

DOWN

1 Accumulated (7)
2 Prime Minister (7)
3 Make improvements (5)
4 Facial photograph (3, 4)
5 Another time (5)
6 Large variety of daisy (5)
9 International cricket
   game (4, 5)
14 Put into words (7)
15 Edible jelly (7)
16 Transgression (7)
19 Small fragment (5)
20 Hinder (5)
21 Hit song for Frankie
   Goes to Hollywood (5)

The Biggest Crossword Book In The World

ACROSS

1 Dogma (5)
4 Foolish person (7)
8 Regular design (7)
9 Interlace (5)
10 Bloke (4)
11 Fare-paying passenger vehicle (3)
12 Cry noisily (4)
15 Quiet (6)
16 Raved (6)
19 Desk light (4)
21 Astern (3)
22 Dell (4)
26 Italian explorer, - - - Polo (5)
27 Scott novel (7)
28 Make ineffective (7)
29 Huge mythical being (5)

DOWN

1 Subject for argument (5)
2 Sport similar to basketball (7)
3 Woody plant (4)
4 Nonsense (6)
5 Domestic hen (4)
6 City in Nebraska (5)
7 Irritated (7)
13 *Fifteen to - - -*, TV quiz (3)
14 Receipt (3)
15 Biblical king (7)
17 Windpipe (7)
18 Model (6)
20 Ethical (5)
23 Wield (5)
24 UN chief, - - - Annan (4)
25 Sudden pain (4)

The Biggest Crossword Book In The World

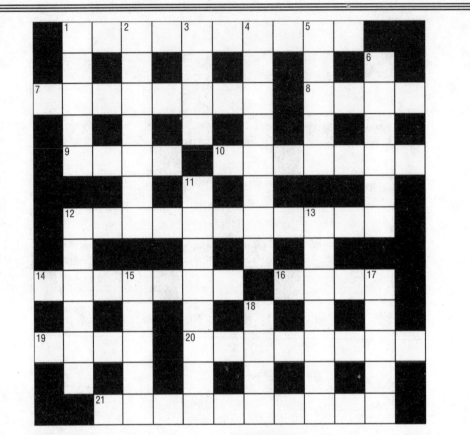

ACROSS
1 Batman? (5, 5)
7 Make up item (3, 5)
8 Cage (4)
9 Frisky short-haired
mammal (4)
10 Liberation (7)
12 Difficult situation (11)
14 Success (7)
16 Retain (4)
19 Capital of Switzerland (4)
20 Eating disorder (8)
21 Romantic note (4, 6)

DOWN
1 Fetch (5)
2 Improve (7)
3 Prince Harry's school (4)
4 Native of Vienna? (8)
5 Mother-of-pearl (5)
6 Withdraw
gracefully (3, 3)
11 Reproduce, copy (8)
12 Like better (6)
13 Himalayan mountain (7)
15 Language (slang) (5)
17 Before (5)
18 Unemployment
benefit (4)

The Biggest Crossword Book In The World

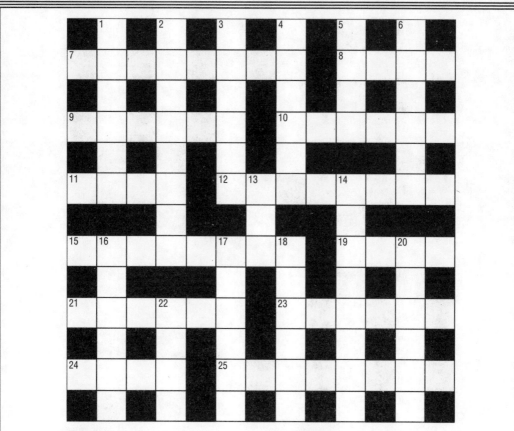

ACROSS

7 Rich (4-2-2)
8 Handle roughly (4)
9 Tim - - -, British
 tennis player (6)
10 Spouted vessel (3-3)
11 Water from the clouds (4)
12 Baptise (8)
15 Spanish girl (8)
19 America's Buckeye
 state (4)
21 Walt Disney's duck (6)
23 Travelling bag (6)
24 Composer,
 - - - Novello (4)
25 Conforming (8)

DOWN

1 Politician,
 - - - Gorman (6)
2 Spanish dance (8)
3 High-quality brandy (6)
4 Stand aimlessly (6)
5 Actress,
 - - - Thompson (4)
6 Our continent (6)
13 Strike (3)
14 Burn slowly (8)
16 Develop naturally (6)
17 Third largest ocean (6)
18 Commercial (6)
20 Crazy (6)
22 Breezy (4)

The Biggest Crossword Book In The World

ACROSS

3 Alternative traffic route (9)
8 Backless shoe (4)
9 Cut of meat (4, 4)
10 Ill, sick (6)
13 Cutlery item (5)
14 Entrance (7)
15 Noah's vessel (3)
16 Very old (7)
17 Plaintive cry (5)
21 Regard as the same (6)
22 Fixed, unchanging (8)
23 German river (4)
24 Revolt (9)

DOWN

1 Complaint handler (9)
2 Not a fast person! (9)
4 Suggest (5)
5 Reserve for a definite purpose (7)
6 Cult (4)
7 Woodwind instrument (4)
11 Handy (9)
12 Children's TV programme (4, 5)
14 Curved line (3)
15 Overseas letters (3, 4)
18 Underground railway system (5)
19 Coupling (4)
20 Water-surrounded land (4)

The Biggest Crossword Book In The World

ACROSS

1 Of the sun (5)
4 Shabby-looking (5)
10 Rebuke (5)
11 Perusing (7)
12 Daphne Du Maurier novel (3, 5)
13 Revise text (4)
15 *It'll Be Alright on the Night* presenter (5, 6)
19 Injury (4)
20 Boundary of playing area (8)
23 Unadulterated (food) (7)
24 Hazardous (5)
25 Setting (5)
26 Horse (5)

DOWN

2 Tree symbolising peace (5)
3 Alcoholic drink before a meal (8)
5 Dash, flair (4)
6 Waste away (7)
7 Sharp (5)
8 Evidence of ability (11)
9 Striped quartz (5)
14 John Wayne film (4, 4)
16 Irregular (7)
17 Safari animal (5)
18 African country (5)
21 Give out (5)
22 Magnetic metal (4)

ACROSS

1 Savage (9)
8 Large pond (4)
9 Mafia boss (9)
10 Flammable gas (6)
13 Shed for horses (6)
15 Ire (5)
16 Military shop (inits)
17 Modify (5)
18 Snake's poison (5)
21 Parent (6)
22 Creepy-crawly creature (6)
25 Tobacco product (9)
26 Person or country on same side (4)
27 Initial advantage (4, 5)

DOWN

2 Overhead (5)
3 British film and TV award (5)
4 Decomposed (6)
5 Unwilling (6)
6 Thick paper (9)
7 Intensely passionate (7)
11 Sincere (9)
12 Simple, innocent (5)
14 Vagrant (5)
16 Virtually nothing (7)
19 Judge's robe fur (6)
20 Lee Harvey - - -, alleged killer of President Kennedy (6)
23 Chemically unreactive (5)
24 Go in (5)

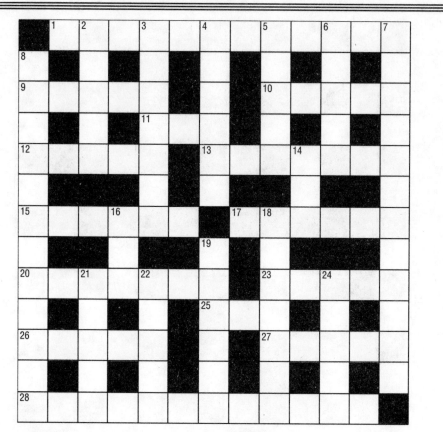

ACROSS

1 Two-tiered bus (6, 6)
9 German submarine (1-4)
10 Slices of meat (5)
11 Farm animal (3)
12 Unfeeling (5)
13 Disease (7)
15 Contract writer (6)
17 American state (6)
20 Cold drink (4, 3)
23 Greek letter (5)
25 Fishing stick (3)
26 Large gimlet (5)
27 Select clique (5)
28 Prince Edward (4, 2, 6)

DOWN

2 Aroma (5)
3 Brutal murderer (7)
4 Small pincered insect (6)
5 Outdo (5)
6 Currency unit of Norway (5)
7 Revived (12)
8 Confirm (12)
14 Currently (3)
16 Linking word (3)
18 Composer, Wolfgang - - - Mozart (7)
19 Implement used to break up clods of earth (6)
21 Impatient (5)
22 Body (5)
24 Dignity (5)

The Biggest Crossword Book In The World

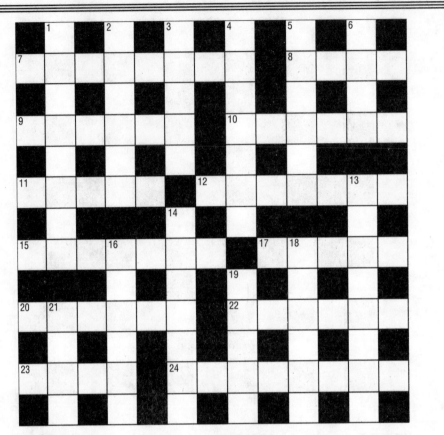

ACROSS

7 With no fixed abode (8)
8 Frozen rain (4)
9 Figure of speech (6)
10 Indian tribe (6)
11 Collier (5)
12 Dizzy feeling (7)
15 Army officer (7)
17 Furious (5)
20 Free, release (6)
22 Say again (6)
23 Curved (4)
24 Occur at the
same time (8)

DOWN

1 Certain, sure (8)
2 Purify (6)
3 Actor, - - - Barkworth (5)
4 Prisoner on the run (7)
5 Hinder (6)
6 Express a desire (4)
13 Creator of the
English clown (8)
14 Grating (7)
16 Impartial decision (6)
18 Peruvian llama (6)
19 Ancient Celtic priest (5)
21 Masticate (4)

The Biggest Crossword Book In The World

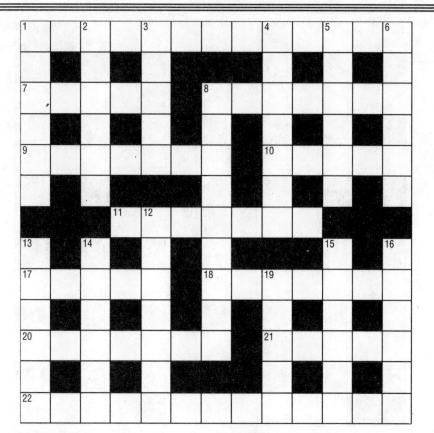

ACROSS

1 Commercial (13)
7 Royal symbol (5)
8 Cooking utensil (7)
9 Plan (7)
10 Celtic language (5)
11 Former English county (7)
17 Country west of Togo (5)
18 Encourage (7)
20 American golfer (3, 4)
21 Hard stone (5)
22 Housing (13)

DOWN

1 Receive (6)
2 Caribbean witchcraft (6)
3 Scope (5)
4 Published issue (7)
5 Cream-filled chocolate cake (6)
6 Cross and irritable (6)
8 Celestial body (9)
12 Source of nuclear energy (7)
13 Thriller writer, Dame - - - Christie (6)
14 Paving material (6)
15 Skimpy bathing costume (6)
16 Setting agent in ripe fruit (6)
19 Capital of Bulgaria (5)

The Biggest Crossword Book In The World

ACROSS

1 Disturbance (4)
4 Straight line from the centre (6)
8 Aubergine (8)
9 Writing table (4)
10 North American Indian's tent (5)
11 Sour liquid used as a condiment (7)
13 Formal offer to supply goods at stated price (6)
15 Breathe out (6)
17 Cry of disapproval (7)
19 Reduce (fear) (5)
22 Back part of the foot (4)
23 Rubbing (8)
24 Foul smelling (6)
25 Travel by bicycle (4)

DOWN

2 Fireplace (5)
3 The best player (3, 4)
4 Rove (4)
5 Delayed (8)
6 Needless (5)
7 Attack violently (6)
12 Fruitful (8)
14 In high spirits (6)
16 Pistol case (7)
18 Actress, - - - Imrie (5)
20 Audibly (5)
21 Feathered vertebrate (4)

The Biggest Crossword Book In The World

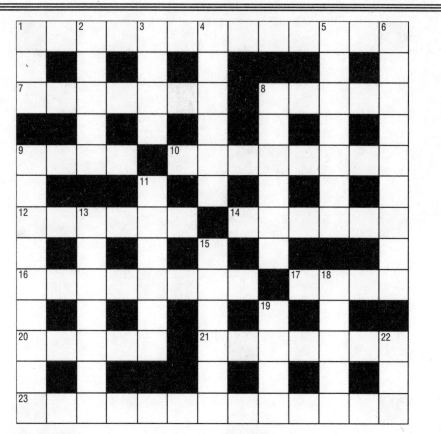

ACROSS

1 Alternative to glasses (7, 6)
7 Writer, - - - Kipling (7)
8 Swelling (5)
9 Hebridian island (4)
10 Definite (5-3)
12 Snoopy creator (6)
14 Chaotic (6)
16 Superior in quality (2-6)
17 High point (4)
20 Mythical giant (5)
21 Cause agony to (7)
23 Port official (7, 6)

DOWN

1 Vehicle (3)
2 Big Ears' friend (5)
3 Desert dweller (4)
4 Walk with unsteady steps (6)
5 Seek business (7)
6 Interesting object (9)
8 Straw hat (6)
9 Big Foot? (9)
11 Old British coin (6)
13 Cage pet (7)
15 Jockey, - - - Piggott (6)
18 Marked area for racket game (5)
19 District (4)
22 Make mistakes (3)

The Biggest Crossword Book In The World

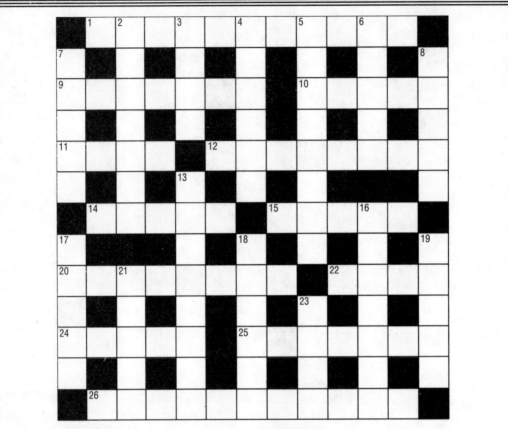

ACROSS
1 Understanding (11)
9 Comfortable chair (7)
10 French river (5)
11 Salary (4)
12 Madeleine - - -,
Former US Secretary of
State (8)
14 Freshwater fish (5)
15 Denim trousers (5)
20 Not grown up (8)
22 Gulf country (4)
24 City in Oklahoma (5)
25 Senior army officer (7)
26 Pleasantly sad? (6-5)

DOWN
2 Junior (7)
3 Leaf of a book (4)
4 Marine creature (6)
5 Made bigger (8)
6 Sugar topping (5)
7 Circus performer (5)
8 Molars (5)
13 Refuse vehicle (8)
16 Candidate (7)
17 Mental view (5)
18 Shopkeeper (6)
19 Death bell (5)
21 Many (5)
23 Gush out (4)

The Biggest Crossword Book In The World

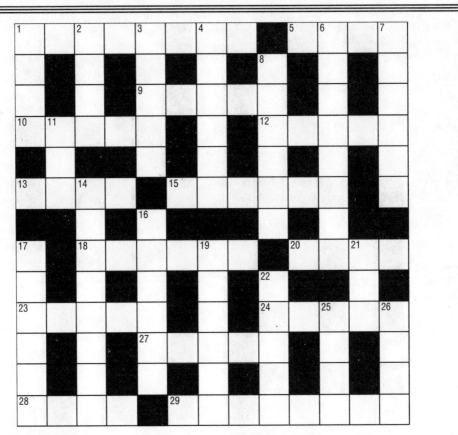

ACROSS

1 Personal beliefs (8)
5 Remove from power (4)
9 Quarrel (5)
10 Occasion (5)
12 Norwegian sea inlet (5)
13 Deride (4)
15 Japanese hostess (6)
18 Saucepan stand (6)
20 Plant germ (4)
23 Dilate (5)
24 Mythological son
of Cronus (5)
27 All (5)
28 Roald - - -, author (4)
29 Long narrow flag (8)

DOWN

1 Pass slowly out (4)
2 Inactive (4)
3 Furious (5)
4 Small fault (6)
6 Current (2-2-4)
7 Dealer (6)
8 Turn down, decline (6)
11 Wrangle (3)
14 Establish firmly (8)
16 Flour maker (6)
17 Scurried (6)
19 Skilful (6)
21 Sooner than (3)
22 Verse (5)
25 Fate, destiny (4)
26 Mix (4)

The Biggest Crossword Book In The World

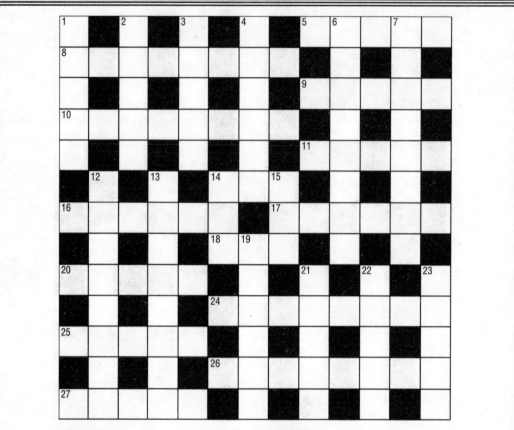

ACROSS

5 Thump (5)
8 Logical (8)
9 Publish (5)
10 Odd number (8)
11 Royal racecourse (5)
14 Wooden club used to hit ball with (3)
16 From which place? (6)
17 Jogger (6)
18 Negative vote (3)
20 Degrade (5)
24 Terrible (8)
25 Vital body organ (5)
26 Not damaged (8)
27 Distance downwards (5)

DOWN

1 Tine (5)
2 Put up with (5)
3 Artery (5)
4 Photographic device (6)
6 Rebellion (8)
7 Suppressed (8)
12 Swimming pool chemical (8)
13 Concern (8)
14 Comedian, - - - Elton (3)
15 Endeavour (3)
19 Extent (6)
21 Underground vault (5)
22 Attach, append (5)
23 Paul - - -, *Jewel in The Crown* author (5)

The Biggest Crossword Book In The World

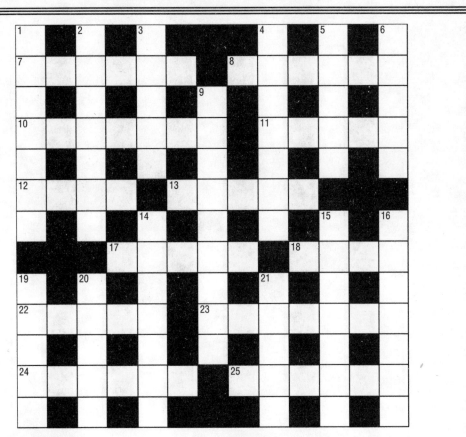

ACROSS

7 Quarrel over petty things (6)
8 Pool of rainwater (6)
10 Preacher (7)
11 Faith, loyalty (5)
12 Adam's son (4)
13 Cluster of things fastened together (5)
17 Light wood (5)
18 Bitter herb (4)
22 Company directors (5)
23 Open porch (7)
24 Syria's neighbour (6)
25 Spring up (6)

DOWN

1 Biblical character (7)
2 Child's toy (7)
3 Unimportant (5)
4 Fairness (7)
5 Stupid person (5)
6 New - - -, capital of India (5)
9 Disgusting (9)
14 Laggard (7)
15 Bill - - -, Former American President (7)
16 Boat race meeting (7)
19 Become less severe (5)
20 Heap of stones (5)
21 Moved quietly (5)

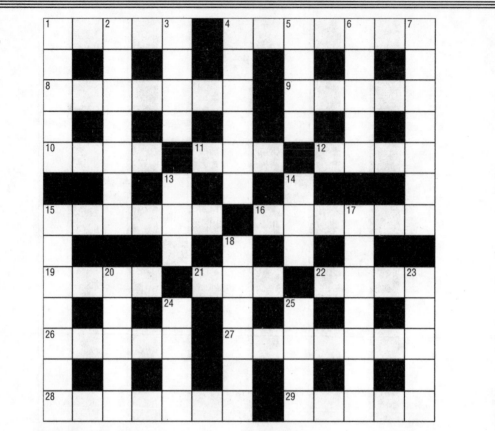

ACROSS

1 Mike - - -, American boxer (5)
4 Lose lustre (7)
8 Fighting capacity (7)
9 Rather dull (5)
10 Statistics (4)
11 Unused (3)
12 Unaided effort (4)
15 Military lookout (6)
16 Waterproof jacket (6)
19 Flat, level (4)
21 Sleep (3)
22 Waxed Dutch cheese (4)
26 Garden mollusc (5)
27 Unexpected puncture (7)
28 Remarkable (7)
29 Indian instrument (5)

DOWN

1 Lukewarm (5)
2 Decrease in size (7)
3 Require (4)
4 Decorative fringed knot (6)
5 Daring, impetuous (4)
6 American state (5)
7 Cod-like food fish (7)
13 Caustically witty (3)
14 Dynamite (1, 1, 1)
15 Cowboy's hat (7)
17 Holiday camp entertainer (7)
18 Responsible (6)
20 Bring into force (5)
23 Parking regulator (5)
24 Insincere (4)
25 TV presenter, - - - King (4)

The Biggest Crossword Book In The World

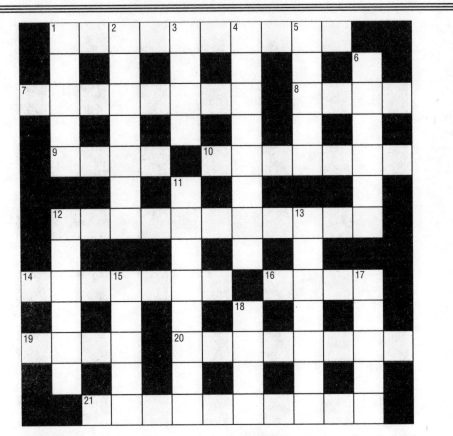

ACROSS

1 Island in the road (10)
7 Keen, acute (8)
8 Actress, - - - Bryan (4)
9 Beast's den (4)
10 Law enforcement officer (7)
12 Information superhighway (3, 8)
14 A deadly poison (7)
16 Overbalance (4)
19 Tear with teeth (4)
20 Style (8)
21 Not moving (10)

DOWN

1 Of the kidneys (5)
2 Make practical use of (7)
3 Irish house of parliament (4)
4 Relatives (8)
5 Below (5)
6 Money gained (6)
11 Secondary (8)
12 Dick - - -, outlaw (6)
13 Canadian waterfall (7)
15 Throw out (5)
17 Fortuitous (5)
18 Nought (4)

The Biggest Crossword Book In The World

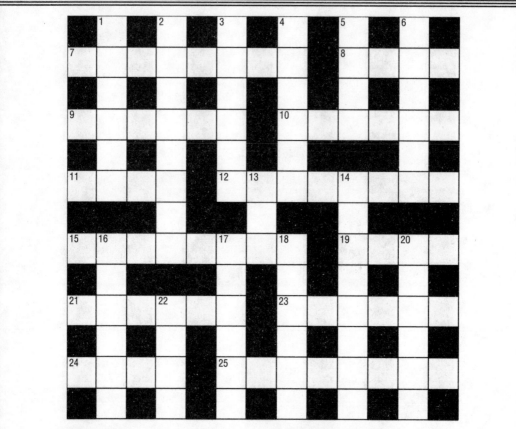

ACROSS
7 Stoppered bottle (8)
8 Hemispherical roof (4)
9 Disposition (6)
10 Holiday (6)
11 Couch, settee (4)
12 Mistress of
Charles II (4, 4)
15 Aardvark, eg (8)
19 Parched (4)
21 Hugh - - -,
comedy actor (6)
23 Light shoe (6)
24 Long, straight cut (4)
25 Earth movement (8)

DOWN
1 Water-craft (6)
2 Drench (8)
3 Spread widely (6)
4 Cunning, wily (6)
5 Brim, border (4)
6 Forge worker (6)
13 Day before an event (3)
14 Russian policy
of openness (8)
16 Almost (6)
17 One of the rings on
a dartboard (6)
18 Take exception to (6)
20 Slanting type (6)
22 Duty list (4)

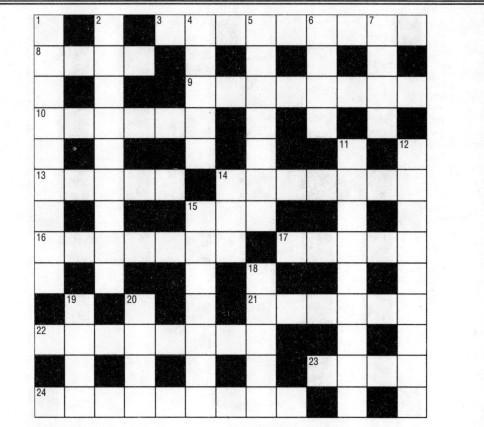

ACROSS

3 Airfield (9)
8 Lecherous look (4)
9 Salvage (8)
10 Dead body (6)
13 Greek philosopher (5)
14 Soothing song (7)
15 Object (3)
16 Watch (7)
17 Bohemian dance (5)
21 Small restaurant (6)
22 Copy, echo (8)
23 German Mrs (4)
24 Finished (9)

DOWN

1 British seaside resort (9)
2 Creamy sauce made from egg yolks (9)
4 Lesser white heron (5)
5 Most favourable (7)
6 Horizontal bar (4)
7 Change position (4)
11 Exaggerated account (4, 5)
12 Religious building (9)
14 Fib (3)
15 Mean, norm (7)
18 Overweight (5)
19 Roman emperor (4)
20 Snare (4)

The Biggest Crossword Book In The World

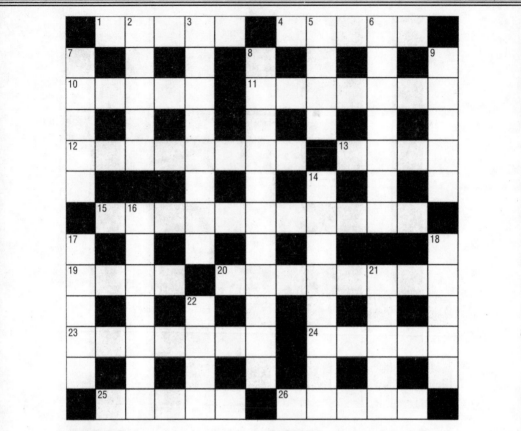

ACROSS

1 Stupid (5)
4 N American Indian tribe (5)
10 Partly divided (5)
11 Decide (7)
12 Table tennis (4-4)
13 Earth (4)
15 British TV actor (5, 6)
19 Squirrel's nest (4)
20 Soldier who led the elephants over the Alps (8)
23 Synthetic product (7)
24 Short-lived fashion (5)
25 Blend (5)
26 Naval force (5)

DOWN

2 Bertie - - -, Irish PM (5)
3 Figure of speech (8)
5 Popular childrens game (1-3)
6 Horned horse (7)
7 Range (5)
8 Financial support (11)
9 Steps over a fence (5)
14 Unemotional (8)
16 Lift up (7)
17 Very skilful (5)
18 Make different (5)
21 Pair (5)
22 Stock market speculator (4)

The Biggest Crossword Book In The World

ACROSS

1 Fourth largest city in England (9)
8 Roof-covering (4)
9 Second stage of man (6, 3)
10 Tequila country! (6)
13 Jacques - - -, French president (6)
15 Flowering plant (5)
16 Ice cream dessert (5)
17 Single-handed (5)
18 Clip hair (5)
21 Distinction (6)
22 Position (6)
25 Game for one person (9)
26 Camera's eye (4)
27 Coming to the throne (9)

DOWN

2 Large crowd (5)
3 Toadstools etc. (5)
4 Compartment in a refrigerator (6)
5 Heirloom (6)
6 Small soft duck feathers (9)
7 Medium (7)
11 Percussion instrument (9)
12 Proceed with ease (5)
14 Vital organ (5)
16 Marvel (7)
19 Courageous (6)
20 Have ambition (6)
23 Accumulate (5)
24 Rare object (5)

The Biggest Crossword Book In The World

ACROSS

1 Perfume (3, 2, 7)
9 Romantic poet (5)
10 Distributed cards (5)
11 Ventilate (3)
12 Personal servant (5)
13 Sluggishness, laziness (7)
15 On dry land (6)
17 Fashion designer, - - - Rhodes (6)
20 Give details of (7)
23 Roughly (5)
25 Twosome (3)
26 Honorary prize (5)
27 Hysteria (5)
28 Oscar-winning actress (4, 8)

DOWN

2 Of the ears (5)
3 Alms-giver (7)
4 PM's wife, - - - Blair (6)
5 Shelf (5)
6 Hard work (5)
7 Wasteful spending (12)
8 Exceptional (5, 7)
14 Flow (3)
16 Liquid fuel (3)
18 New alcoholic drink (7)
19 Natural blue dye obtained from a plant (6)
21 Sacred song (5)
22 Examination of accounts (5)
24 Beatles' drummer, - - - Starr (5)

The Biggest Crossword Book In The World

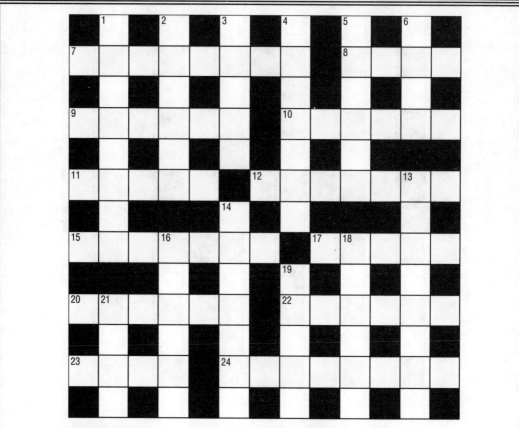

ACROSS

7 Shows (8)
8 Vegetable (4)
9 Beautiful (6)
10 Look after (6)
11 Glazier's fixing paste (5)
12 Contrition (7)
15 Excess of liabilities (7)
17 Alloy (5)
20 Golfer, - - - Palmer (6)
22 Roof material (6)
23 Floor-length skirt (4)
24 Scrooge's first name (8)

DOWN

1 Publicity (8)
2 Turn aside (6)
3 Record material (5)
4 Got free (7)
5 Drunk! (6)
6 Average (4)
13 Grabbed (8)
14 Violinist (7)
16 Sarcastic (6)
18 Hard white coating
   on a tooth (6)
19 Guide, control (5)
21 Back part (4)

The Biggest Crossword Book In The World

ACROSS

1 Dedication (13)
7 Rotund (5)
8 Rough sketch (7)
9 Increased threefold (7)
10 Secret hiding place (5)
11 Infuriated (7)
17 Spanish holiday island (5)
18 Collection of books (7)
20 Group of heavy guns (7)
21 Come to (5)
22 Former James Bond actor (7, 6)

DOWN

1 Stand-in (6)
2 Wig (6)
3 Drive off (5)
4 Item, object (7)
5 Stupid behaviour (6)
6 Required (6)
8 The Central Criminal Court (3, 6)
12 Tidiest (7)
13 Morsel (6)
14 Casualty (6)
15 Empty (6)
16 Crushing snake (6)
19 Asian country (5)

The Biggest Crossword Book In The World

ACROSS

1 Road hump to control speed (4)
4 Baby swan (6)
8 High status (8)
9 Television award (4)
10 Theatrical entertainment (5)
11 Dignified, lofty (7)
13 Serious (6)
15 Drink of the gods (6)
17 Plug, bung (7)
19 Cropped up (5)
22 Bundle (4)
23 Close examination (8)
24 Short sleep (6)
25 Went by bicycle (4)

DOWN

2 Concur (5)
3 Position of body (7)
4 Adam and Eve's son (4)
5 Welcome (8)
6 Choose by ballot (5)
7 Aviator, - - - Earhart (6)
12 Clive - - -, TV presenter (8)
14 Expenditure (6)
16 Person in charge of an art gallery (7)
18 Good, genuine (5)
20 Church council (5)
21 Hold tight (4)

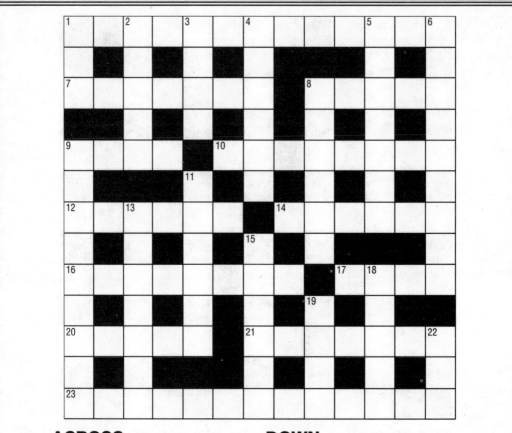

ACROSS

1 Uneasy (13)
7 Disturb (7)
8 Polite (5)
9 Electrical cable (4)
10 Grow, increase (8)
12 Tall cylindrical headgear (3, 3)
14 Accompany (6)
16 Sudden occurrence (8)
17 Bobbin, spool (4)
20 Sovereign's rule (5)
21 Not straightforward (7)
23 London street market (9, 4)

DOWN

1 Uncle Sam's country (1, 1, 1)
2 Bell sound (5)
3 Flesh (4)
4 Ukranian city (6)
5 Show of boldness (7)
6 Basic (9)
8 Lightly scattered (6)
9 Exhausted (3, 2, 4)
11 Head of nursing staff (6)
13 Film, - - - *Games* (7)
15 Building with panoramic view (6)
18 Lloyd-Webber musical (5)
19 Trade centre (4)
22 Watch closely (3)

The Biggest Crossword Book In The World

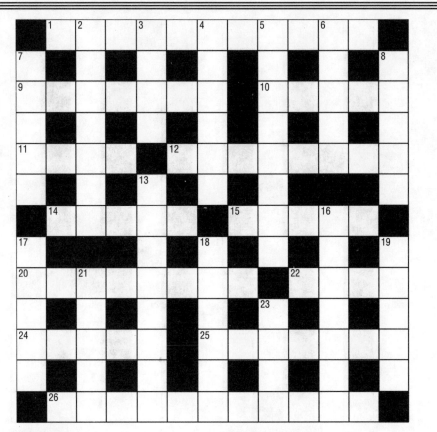

ACROSS

1 Resound, echo (11)
9 Profound hurt (7)
10 Flower with large spikes (5)
11 Seduce (4)
12 Supersonic passenger jet (8)
14 Thick, deep-pile fabric (5)
15 Corn thresher (5)
20 Popular breed of dog (8)
22 Outstanding bill (4)
24 Diving apparatus (5)
25 Appease (7)
26 Churchill actor (6, 5)

DOWN

2 Venue of the Portugese Grand Prix (7)
3 Academic test (4)
4 Inhabitant of Brittany (6)
5 Reading of register (4, 4)
6 Drunkard (5)
7 Eucalyptus eating 'bear' (5)
8 Bury (5)
13 Caper, fling (8)
16 European country (7)
17 Camera bulb (5)
18 Cambodian Communist leader (3, 3)
19 Sloping sharply (5)
21 Frank - - -, heavyweight boxer (5)
23 Father (4)

The Biggest Crossword Book In The World

ACROSS

1 Cud-chewing animal (8)
5 TV presenter,
- - - Harris (4)
9 Soft fruit (5)
10 Show excessive
enthusiasm (5)
12 Israeli Prime Minister,
- - - Meir (5)
13 Throw up, lob (4)
15 Pluto, eg (6)
18 Tax (6)
20 Large seaweed (4)
23 Roused (5)
24 Beaten contestant (5)
27 Relative darkness (5)
28 Sleepy (4)
29 Car safety strap (4, 4)

DOWN

1 Highway (4)
2 Departmental note (4)
3 Fine, self-sacrificing (5)
4 Conventional (6)
6 Egg dish (8)
7 Rummage (for food) (6)
8 Past, former (6)
11 River, - - - Grande (3)
14 French resort (2, 6)
16 Clergyman (6)
17 Dreaded (6)
19 Conclusion (6)
21 Golfer, - - - Westwood (3)
22 Fold (5)
25 Dimensions (4)
26 Yell violently (4)

The Biggest Crossword Book In The World

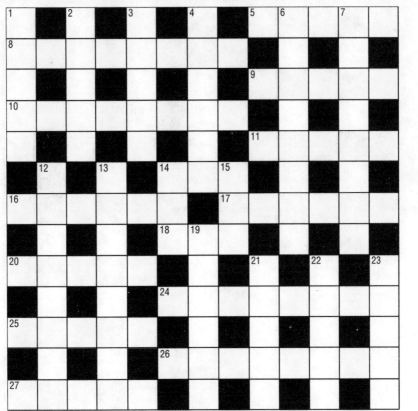

ACROSS

5 Cape (5)
8 Foolish talk (8)
9 Coming afterwards (5)
10 Stronghold (8)
11 Harbour platform (5)
14 Comedian,
    - - - Dennis (3)
16 Observe (6)
17 Personal integrity (6)
18 The light hours (3)
20 Abolish (5)
24 Piece of furniture for
   hanging clothes on (8)
25 Justify (5)
26 Medicinal plant (4, 4)
27 Train driver's union (5)

DOWN

1 Jeer (5)
2 Priest's title (5)
3 Desolate, bare (5)
4 Wrangle (6)
6 Aversion (8)
7 Generation (3-5)
12 English ball game (8)
13 Statuette (8)
14 Conducted (3)
15 Timid (3)
19 Suitable for growing
   crops in (6)
21 Lopsided (5)
22 Garden barriers (5)
23 Absolutely perfect (5)

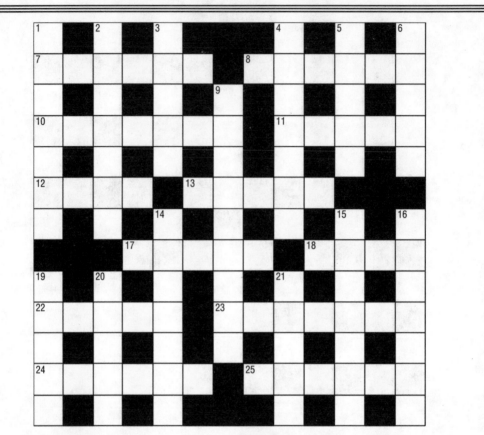

ACROSS

7 Scandinavian country (6)
8 Well-being (6)
10 Obedient (7)
11 Short and broad (5)
12 Coax away from (4)
13 Piece of turf (5)
17 Wandering tribesman (5)
18 Heathland (4)
22 Maxim (5)
23 Joan of Arc's city (7)
24 Forerunner (6)
25 Describe exactly (6)

DOWN

1 Paddy - - -, politician (7)
2 London football club (4, 3)
3 Cricketer, - - - Boycott (5)
4 Emotional strain (7)
5 Bread ingredient (5)
6 Slide (5)
9 Crocodile relative (9)
14 Scientific rule (7)
15 The North Star (7)
16 Joint of meat (7)
19 Cleanse (5)
20 Sign of the zodiac (5)
21 Tenpin bowling lane (5)

The Biggest Crossword Book In The World

ACROSS
1 Say, speak (5)
4 Rare (7)
8 Breed of cat (7)
9 Bus station (5)
10 Cash register (4)
11 Chewing sweet (3)
12 American tribe (4)
15 Not completely (6)
16 Insatiable (6)
19 Noisy conflict (4)
21 Married lady (3)
22 TV presenter,
 - - - Roslin (4)
26 Hero (5)
27 Sign of honour (7)
28 Forceful (7)
29 Sigmund - - -,
 psychiatrist (5)

DOWN
1 Emotionally
 distressed (5)
2 Fishing boat (7)
3 Marsh grass (4)
4 Beneficial, of help (6)
5 Unfasten (4)
6 Top of a shoe (5)
7 Raffle (7)
13 Pub drink (3)
14 Mining extract (3)
15 Narrow minded (2-5)
17 Displaced person (7)
18 Reviewer (6)
20 Grand Prix driver,
 - - - Prost (5)
23 Give up control (5)
24 Luncheon meat (4)
25 Slight quarrel (4)

The Biggest Crossword Book In The World

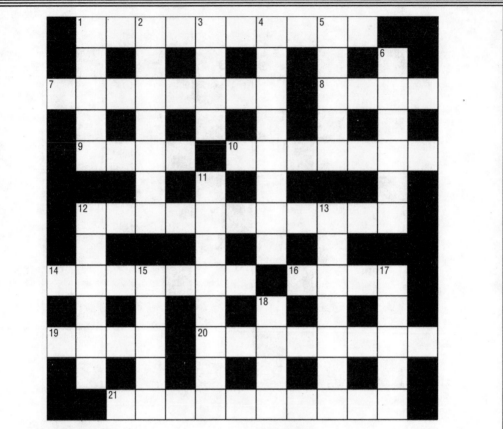

ACROSS

1 Norwegian explorer (4, 3, 3)
7 Smarten up (8)
8 Cry of despair (4)
9 Radiate (4)
10 Unsightly (7)
12 Failure (11)
14 Alistair - - -, author (7)
16 Facial feature (4)
19 Choir voice (4)
20 Equals (8)
21 Legally bestowed property (10)

DOWN

1 Banish, expel (5)
2 First letter (7)
3 Froglike amphibian (4)
4 Telescope part (8)
5 Obliterate (5)
6 Ringed planet (6)
11 Hungarian capital (8)
12 Poor, wretched (6)
13 Mimic, copy (7)
15 Baggy (5)
17 Perfume (5)
18 Rough fibre (4)

The Biggest Crossword Book In The World

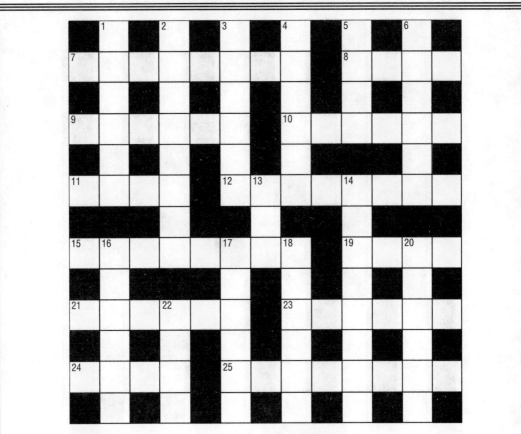

ACROSS

7 Envy (8)
8 Previous name for Republic of Ireland (4)
9 Flowering plant (6)
10 Vicious-tempered person (6)
11 Ink stain (4)
12 Pattern (8)
15 Blind alley (3-2-3)
19 Mute (4)
21 In short supply (6)
23 Stefan - - -, Swedish tennis player (6)
24 Sprinkle from a perforated container (4)
25 Edible snail (8)

DOWN

1 Top up (6)
2 Budgeted (8)
3 Familiar (2, 4)
4 Procedure (6)
5 Precious (4)
6 Culpable (6)
13 Period of time (3)
14 Flying insect (8)
16 Mischievous child (6)
17 Kebab spike (6)
18 Squeeze firmly together (6)
20 Looking-glass (6)
22 Book of the bible (4)

The Biggest Crossword Book In The World

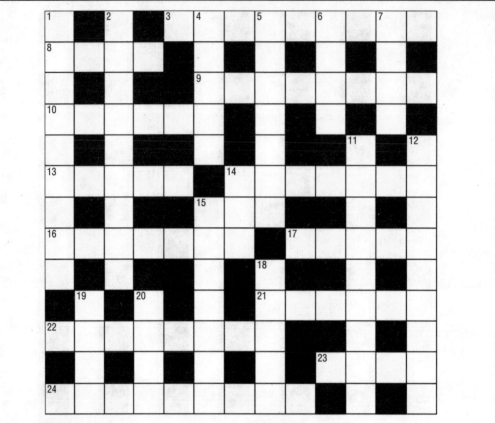

ACROSS

3 Lawyer (9)
8 Navigation float (4)
9 Fire raiser (8)
10 Carry out (6)
13 Point opposite south (5)
14 Percussion instrument (7)
15 Miserable (3)
16 Line that touches a curve (7)
17 Communicate by letter (5)
21 Disfigure (6)
22 Indian meal side-dish (8)
23 Retained (4)
24 Europe, eg (9)

DOWN

1 Swear word (9)
2 Banana shaped missile (9)
4 Speak at length (5)
5 In place of (7)
6 Scottish isle (4)
7 British river (4)
11 Kindled (9)
12 Cinema worker (9)
14 Thin rug (3)
15 Welsh mountain (7)
18 Paperwork (5)
19 Tramp (4)
20 Pimple (4)

The Biggest Crossword Book In The World

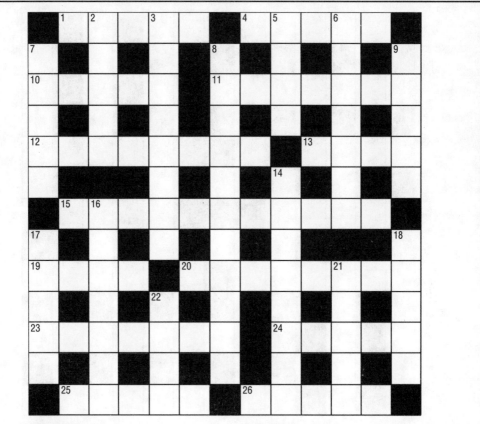

ACROSS

1 Seashore (5)
4 Well-groomed (5)
10 Displayed (5)
11 Intense delight (7)
12 Exciting, tense (8)
13 Small bundle of straw (4)
15 American film star (4, 7)
19 Old brandy (4)
20 Precise (8)
23 Clothing (7)
24 Small crown (5)
25 Join on to make larger (5)
26 Improvised (2, 3)

DOWN

2 Eat away (5)
3 Analyse (8)
5 Lean to one side (4)
6 Inspect (7)
7 Wedding official (5)
8 Give and receive mutually (11)
9 Slender girl (5)
14 Altered slightly (8)
16 Strong feeling (7)
17 *Ebony And - - -*, hit song for Paul McCartney and Stevie Wonder (5)
18 Carrying chair (5)
21 Memorable American battle (5)
22 Richard - - -, *Pretty Woman* actor (4)

ACROSS

1 Cushioned (9)
8 Frighten away birds (4)
9 Controller (9)
10 Attribute (6)
13 Portable computer (6)
15 Mutineer (5)
16 Run after (5)
17 Brag (5)
18 Oriental rice dish (5)
21 Street performer (6)
22 Smear (6)
25 Route to follow (9)
26 Bloodthirsty (4)
27 Magician's cry (3, 6)

DOWN

2 Shatter, explode (5)
3 Japan's second city (5)
4 Noel Coward comedy,
  - - - Spirit (6)
5 Compass pointer (6)
6 Method of
  rapid writing (9)
7 Driver's compartment (7)
11 Convey from one place
  to another (9)
12 Thin pancake (5)
14 Book of photographs (5)
16 Garden vegetable (7)
19 Eddie - - -,
  racing driver (6)
20 Dozing (6)
23 Unfasten (5)
24 Tile jointing cement (5)

The Biggest Crossword Book In The World

ACROSS
1 American singer (5, 7)
9 Aircraft door (5)
10 Indira Gandhi's son (5)
11 Scottish racecourse (3)
12 Pulsate (5)
13 Brimstone (7)
15 Fantastic cave (6)
17 Remove colour (6)
20 Indigestion remedy (7)
23 In the countryside (5)
25 Pig (3)
26 Capital of Vietnam (5)
27 Roof overhang (5)
28 Remembering (12)

DOWN
2 Discourage (5)
3 Dwell in (7)
4 Programme of training (6)
5 Yellowish-pink (5)
6 Indian prince (5)
7 However, yet (12)
8 David Bailey, eg (12)
14 Pastry-topped dish (3)
16 Brewed beverage (3)
18 Biggest (7)
19 Stick (to) (6)
21 Mixer for gin? (5)
22 Make cold (5)
24 Split (5)

The Biggest Crossword Book In The World

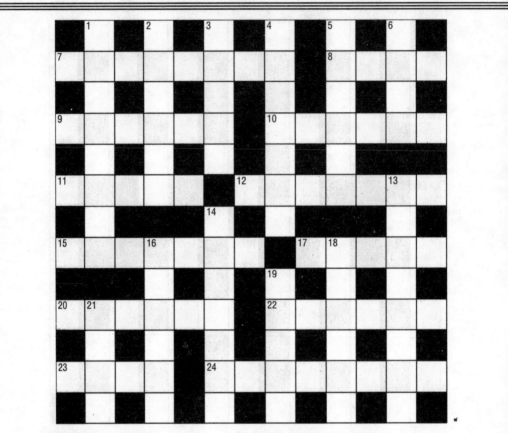

ACROSS

7 Month of the year (8)
8 Small, sheltered bay (4)
9 Bewail (6)
10 Pleasurable trip (6)
11 Student's mark (5)
12 Violent tropical storm (7)
15 Notable (7)
17 Earth (5)
20 Take out a policy (6)
22 Powerful racing car (3, 3)
23 Spanish artist (4)
24 English hill range (8)

DOWN

1 Star-shaped figure (8)
2 Soul mate (6)
3 Fry quickly in a little fat (5)
4 Word meaning the same as another (7)
5 One kind of whisky (6)
6 Stratford's river (4)
13 Spectator (8)
14 Rough appearance (7)
16 Chewy sweet (6)
18 Soup ingredient? (6)
19 Express gratitude (5)
21 Midday (4)

The Biggest Crossword Book In The World

ACROSS
1 Patriotic song (4, 9)
7 Military government (5)
8 Obvious (7)
9 Somerset village (7)
10 Chocolate powder (5)
11 Actress, - - - Monroe (7)
17 Live (5)
18 Row of houses (7)
20 Speech impediment (7)
21 Tennis player,
 - - - Ivanisevic (5)
22 Go for it! (4, 3, 6)

DOWN
1 Decline (6)
2 Yearned (6)
3 Facial hair (5)
4 Lawlessness (7)
5 Subtle difference
 in meaning (6)
6 Missing (6)
8 Advocate (9)
12 Undertake (7)
13 Fast social group? (3, 3)
14 Seize control (of a
 vehicle) (6)
15 Charity benefactor (6)
16 Meeting for
 spirit contact (6)
19 Royal, kingly (5)

The Biggest Crossword Book In The World

ACROSS
1 Noisy (4)
4 Training bullets (6)
8 Responsive (8)
9 Lure (4)
10 Prepare to pray (5)
11 Superficial (7)
13 Glenn - - -, football manager (6)
15 Regular payment to an employee (6)
17 Official document (7)
19 Teacher (5)
22 Exhaled (4)
23 Strongest (8)
24 Tense (2, 4)
25 Computer floppy (4)

DOWN
2 Pacific, eg (5)
3 Laid down (7)
4 French cheese (4)
5 Gemstone (8)
6 Capital of Afghanistan (5)
7 Energy, activity (6)
12 Joined together again (8)
14 ITV teletext service (6)
16 Chortled (7)
18 Mountain ash (5)
20 Fertile spot in the desert (5)
21 Deceive (4)

The Biggest Crossword Book In The World

ACROSS

1 Shakespeare line (2, 2, 2, 3, 2, 2)
7 Cattle thief (7)
8 Separated (5)
9 Victim (4)
10 Two-humped camel (8)
12 Easy, graceful (6)
14 Spanish dictator (6)
16 Replied (8)
17 Self-admiring (4)
20 Empty (5)
21 Laurence - - -, film legend (7)
23 Looking back in time (13)

DOWN

1 Dangerous tobacco constituent (3)
2 Moisten with hot fat during cooking (5)
3 Sole (4)
4 European country (6)
5 Formal speech (7)
6 Rock star (5, 4)
8 Major road (6)
9 Venomous snake (4, 5) **11** Junior doctor (6)
13 Arrogant person (7)
15 Get back (6)
18 Legal excuse (5)
19 Bluish-white metal (4)
22 Cereal (3)

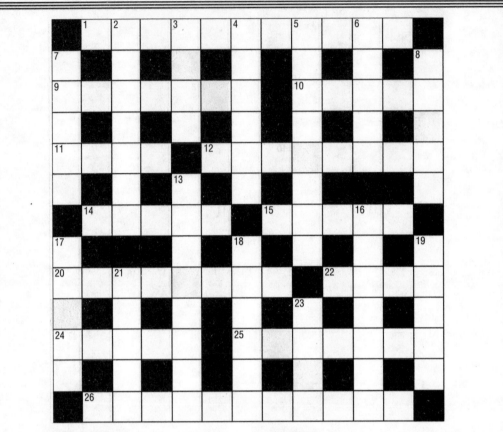

ACROSS
1 Comedy actor (6, 5)
9 Tenor, - - - Pavarotti (7)
10 Dig (5)
11 Strong flavour (4)
12 Mountain peak (8)
14 Frank Sinatra song (2, 3)
15 Throng, mass (5)
20 Eastern (8)
22 Interesting quality (4)
24 Small drum (5)
25 Surgeon's knife (7)
26 In preparation (11)

DOWN
2 Creepy (7)
3 Thin (4)
4 Somerset town (6)
5 Plain (8)
6 Ancient memento (5)
7 Lighting war (5)
8 Smooth (5)
13 Reddish brown bird (5, 3)
16 Talk in hushed tones (7)
17 Porch (5)
18 Money paid to release a hostage (6)
19 Nimble (5)
21 Part of a target (5)
23 Minor chessman (4)

The Biggest Crossword Book In The World

ACROSS

1 Elegant, stylish (8)
5 Cartoon bunny (4)
9 River estuary (5)
10 Native New Zealander (5)
12 Faulty (5)
13 George Bernard - - - Irish dramatist (4)
15 Dashboard (6)
18 Shrill cry (6)
20 Famous Brazilian footballer (4)
23 Lure, entice (5)
24 Tony - - -, Prime Minister (5)
27 Illicitly distilled spirit (5)
28 Submit to authority (4)
29 Novices (8)

DOWN

1 Metric unit of weight (4)
2 Bullets, etc. (4)
3 Pixie-like (5)
4 TV presenter, - - - Jonsson (6)
6 Last (8)
7 Quarter-year period (6)
8 Opportunity (6)
11 Smoker's debris (3)
14 Gather together (8)
16 Full of bubbles (6)
17 Vegetable (6)
19 Uncover (6)
21 Garland (3)
22 Detest (5)
25 Efficient (4)
26 Curved chest bones (4)

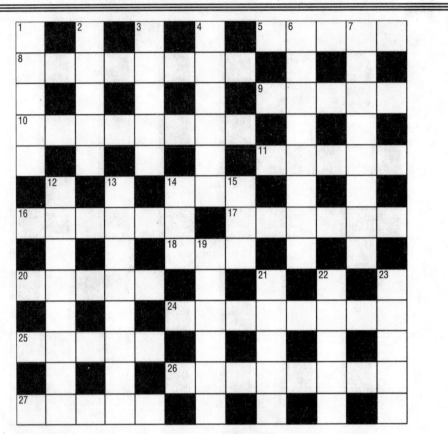

ACROSS

5 Throw (5)
8 A left-handed boxer (8)
9 Waste material spread around plants (5)
10 Warranted, earned (8)
11 Emulsion, eg (5)
14 Have food (3)
16 Bay tree leaves (6)
17 Self-confidence, savoir-faire (6)
18 Still (3)
20 Harbour (5)
24 Disapproved (8)
25 Drab (5)
26 Monument (8)
27 Gaddafi's country (5)

DOWN

1 Stage whisper (5)
2 Courageous (5)
3 County (5)
4 Creamy cake (6)
6 Praiseworthy (8)
7 Popular title (8)
12 Type of pasta (8)
13 Amicable (8)
14 Sneaky (3)
15 Tap lightly (3)
19 Number of players in a football team (6)
21 Metallic mixture (5)
22 Attribute (5)
23 Grown-up (5)

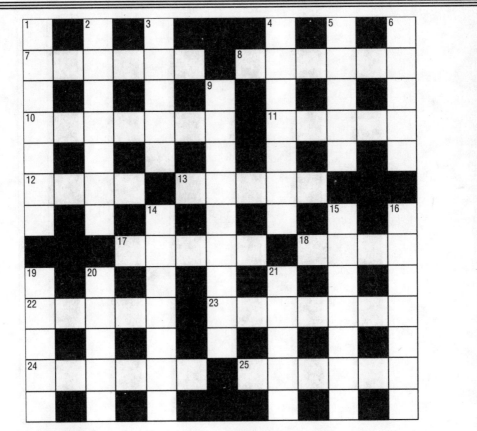

ACROSS

7 International agreement (6)
8 Man's heavy double-breasted overcoat (6)
10 Devon holiday resort (7)
11 Punctuation mark (5)
12 Wicked (4)
13 Mountain song (5)
17 Outspoken (5)
18 *Billy - - -*, comic novel (4)
22 Beau (5)
23 Very stupid (7)
24 Soothe, calm (6)
25 Insult (6)

DOWN

1 Speak with difficulty (7)
2 Lie of the land (7)
3 Solidly built (5)
4 Mass of ice (7)
5 Tread heavily (5)
6 Wide (5)
9 Love of fires (9)
14 Shock (7)
15 Grand National venue (7)
16 Go before (7)
19 Gradient, incline (5)
20 Expel from property (5)
21 Short space of time? (5)

ACROSS

1 Debris (5)
4 Thick bed cover (7)
8 Rocket (7)
9 Prestigious car, - - - Martin (5)
10 Leave out (4)
11 Seat in a church (3)
12 German man (4)
15 Plan (6)
16 Ceremonial (6)
19 Sad colour (4)
21 Assist (3)
22 Damp and cold (4)
26 Increase (5)
27 Lying in court (7)
28 Extremely bad (7)
29 Adjust slightly (5)

DOWN

1 Shakespeare character (5)
2 Suffolk town (7)
3 Cut (4)
4 Beer maker (6)
5 At a distance (4)
6 Agony aunt, - - - Boyle (5)
7 Coiling shoot (7)
13 Aviator, - - - Johnson (3)
14 Female pig (3)
15 Russian region (7)
17 Size, quantity (7)
18 Drive away (6)
20 Togetherness (5)
23 Eskimo canoe (5)
24 Regard (4)
25 Legal document (4)

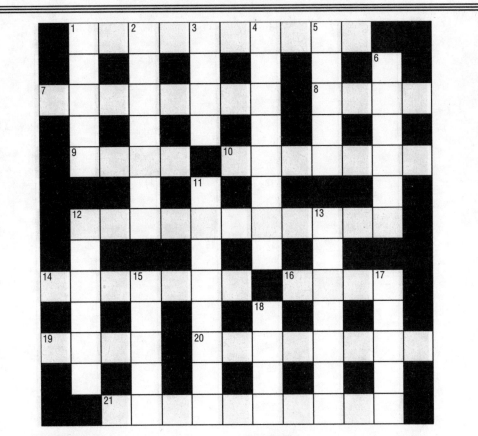

ACROSS

1 Property (4, 6)
7 Remove (8)
8 Connection (4)
9 Sitcom, - - - *Decreasing Circles* (4)
10 Suggest (7)
12 Jubilant (4, 3, 4)
14 Cowboy film (7)
16 In poor taste (4)
19 Petticoat (4)
20 Enrolled (8)
21 Put into a trance (10)

DOWN

1 European river (5)
2 Gain by ability (7)
3 Deserve (4)
4 Foiled (8)
5 Spring flower (5)
6 Concord (6)
11 Caviar fish (8)
12 Frankly (6)
13 Aristotle - - -, shipping magnate (7)
15 Slightly intoxicated (5)
17 Wicked person (5)
18 Congealed lump of blood (4)

The Biggest Crossword Book In The World

ACROSS

7 Max - - -,
   British singer (8)
8 Aberdeen airport (4)
9 Drawing instrument (6)
10 National song (6)
11 Sign (4)
12 Ill-fated BBC
   soap opera (8)
15 Degree holder (8)
19 Church dignitary (4)
21 Steam (6)
23 Shock (6)
24 Sponsor (4)
25 Marine mammal (8)

DOWN

1 London theatre (6)
2 Spider (8)
3 Sophisticated (6)
4 Country surrounded
   by water (6)
5 Mine entrance (4)
6 Thin layer of cement
   on a floor (6)
13 Illuminated (3)
14 Cooling device for
   a car engine (8)
16 Former US president (6)
17 Unexpected (6)
18 Get by threat (6)
20 Very nearly (6)
22 Classic Epsom race (4)

The Biggest Crossword Book In The World

ACROSS
3 Clearly (9)
8 Dish of reheated leftovers (4)
9 Kent ferry port (8)
10 Chevron (6)
13 Doubter (5)
14 Somerset - - -, British novelist (7)
15 Afflict (3)
16 Suitor (7)
17 Raise on a winch (5)
21 David - - -, politician (6)
22 Publican (8)
23 Tennis player, - - - Kournikova (4)
24 Break (9)

DOWN
1 Medical practitioner (9)
2 Study of heavenly bodies (9)
4 Soft, felt cap (5)
5 Debauched (7)
6 Encourage (4)
7 Behind schedule (4)
11 Exciting (9)
12 Capital of The Netherlands (9)
14 Troubled Russian space station (3)
15 Pressurised can (7)
18 Revise (5)
19 *Wizard of Oz* character (4)
20 Golfer, - - - Ballesteros (4)

The Biggest Crossword Book In The World

ACROSS

1 Ron - - -, *Oliver!* actor (5)
4 Bony case that houses the brain (5)
10 Less (5)
11 Expression of regret (7)
12 Fictional detective, - - - Holmes (8)
13 Show of hands (4)
15 Secure (11)
19 Contest for two (4)
20 Unknown person (8)
23 Inactive drug (7)
24 Computer letter (1, 4)
25 Shatter (5)
26 Make amends (5)

DOWN

2 Small weight (5)
3 Reveal (8)
5 Fort - - -, American gold store (4)
6 Warning cry! (4, 3)
7 Tennis shot (5)
8 Estimate (11)
9 Welsh county (5)
14 Close by (8)
16 Alfresco (4, 3)
17 Foster permanently (5)
18 Quaintly amusing (5)
21 Wheat, eg (5)
22 Greek cheese (4)

The Biggest Crossword Book In The World

ACROSS

1 Active (9)
8 Greenish-blue (4)
9 Unsophisticated, crude (9)
10 Fully recovered (6)
13 Electricity generator (6)
15 Fracas (5)
16 Slow learner (5)
17 Clamour (5)
18 Automaton (5)
21 Soft, gentle breeze (6)
22 Medical centre (6)
25 Usually (9)
26 Wingless insect (4)
27 Figurine (9)

DOWN

2 Ward worker (5)
3 Send (5)
4 Complete (6)
5 Attack (6)
6 Legendary king of Cyprus (9)
7 Fence in (7)
11 Kitchen gadget (3, 6)
12 Board used for shaping nails (5)
14 Barbra Streisand film (5)
16 Fall into a light sleep (4, 3)
19 The East (6)
20 The supernatural (6)
23 Empty, senseless (5)
24 Small bay (5)

The Biggest Crossword Book In The World

ACROSS

1 Harrison Ford film (7, 5)
9 Flower (5)
10 John - - -, musician (5)
11 Become old (3)
12 Vital body part (5)
13 Military stripe (7)
15 Dethrone (6)
17 Spanish ships sunk by Drake (6)
20 Wrapped (7)
23 Slow (5)
25 Spoil (3)
26 Black wood (5)
27 Young eel (5)
28 Superstitious tradition (3, 5, 4)

DOWN

2 Beside (5)
3 European country (7)
4 Purpose (6)
5 Bird (5)
6 Engine (5)
7 British actress (8, 4)
8 Coldest possible temperature (8, 4)
14 Force, energy (3)
16 Model, - - - Herzigova (3)
18 Pull back (7)
19 Regard with esteem (6)
21 Obscure, darken (5)
22 Johanna - - -, *Heidi* author (5)
24 Challenger (5)

The Biggest Crossword Book In The World

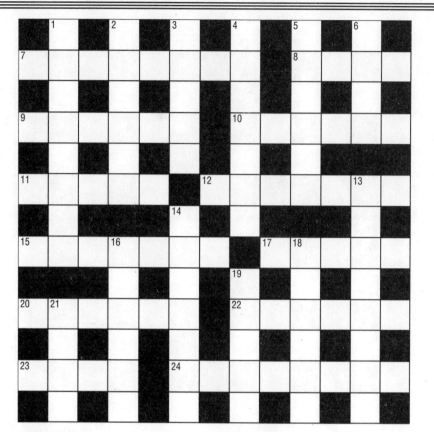

ACROSS
7 Widespread outbreak (8)
8 Flying toy (4)
9 Control with authority (6)
10 Part of the eye (6)
11 Circumference (5)
12 Italian car manufacturer (7)
15 Answered (7)
17 Inferior specimen (5)
20 Plane with no engine (6)
22 Dog's house (6)
23 Virginia - - -, tennis player (4)
24 Annoy, pester (8)

DOWN
1 Facing (8)
2 Season of four weeks before Christmas (6)
3 Jeffrey Archer novel, *First - - - Equals* (5)
4 Run away (7)
5 Ice dancer (6)
6 Daze (4)
13 Casino game (8)
14 New member (7)
16 Climbing apparatus (6)
18 Fancy (6)
19 Female garment (5)
21 Fertile soil (4)

The Biggest Crossword Book In The World

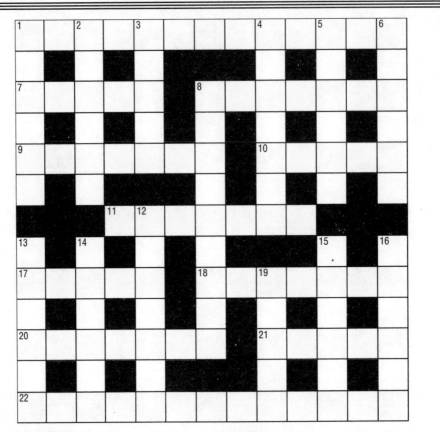

ACROSS
1 Alternative medic? (13)
7 Purify (5)
8 Long-necked animal (7)
9 Boxer, - - - Holyfield (7)
10 Type of lizard (5)
11 Fine plain-weave cotton (7)
17 Leg bone (5)
18 Yearly grant (7)
20 Belated (7)
21 Association for smart Alecs! (5)
22 Become involved (3, 2, 2, 3, 3)

DOWN
1 Cider ingredient (6)
2 Fictional (6)
3 Capsize (5)
4 Erect (7)
5 Contaminate (6)
6 Minor quake (6)
8 Develop (9)
12 Pantomime character (7)
13 Mighty (6)
14 Lacking (6)
15 Capital of Austria (6)
16 Cruel despot (6)
19 Legendary maiden (5)

The Biggest Crossword Book In The World

ACROSS
1 Stun (4)
4 The - - - Tower, Paris landmark (6)
8 Religious teaching (8)
9 Pretentious person (4)
10 African animal (5)
11 Hint (7)
13 State without proof (6)
15 Count (6)
17 City noted for it's Hanging Gardens (7)
19 Party (5)
22 Largest island in the West Indies (4)
23 In an excited state (8)
24 Belgian port (6)
25 On top of (4)

DOWN
2 Bright blue (5)
3 Sanction (7)
4 Author, - - - Blyton (4)
5 Ladylike (8)
6 Artist's picture stand (5)
7 Snooker player, - - - O'Sullivan (6)
12 Fizzy drink (8)
14 Group of sports clubs (6)
16 Distinguished musician (7)
18 Irish poet, Nobel prize winner in 1923 (5)
20 Female relation (5)
21 Walk slowly (4)

The Biggest Crossword Book In The World

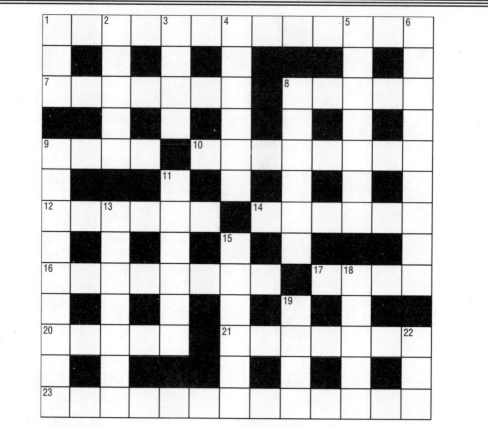

ACROSS

1 Free (13)
7 British colony (7)
8 Provide food (5)
9 Jazz singer,
- - - Fitzgerald (4)
10 American actor (3, 5)
12 Thick seafood soup (6)
14 Georgio - - -, fashion
designer (6)
16 Recall (8)
17 Small nail (4)
20 Protective garment (5)
21 Passage (7)
23 Actress who became a
US ambassador (7, 6)

DOWN

1 Young lion (3)
2 *Postcards from the Edge*
actress, - - - Streep (5)
3 Rough person (4)
4 Lea (6)
5 Insect's feeler (7)
6 Comparison (9)
8 Stick together (6)
9 Abash (9)
11 Gather up (energy) (6)
13 Japanese warrior (7)
15 Aristocracy (6)
18 Greek fable writer (5)
19 Garden tool (4)
22 Drawn game (3)

The Biggest Crossword Book In The World

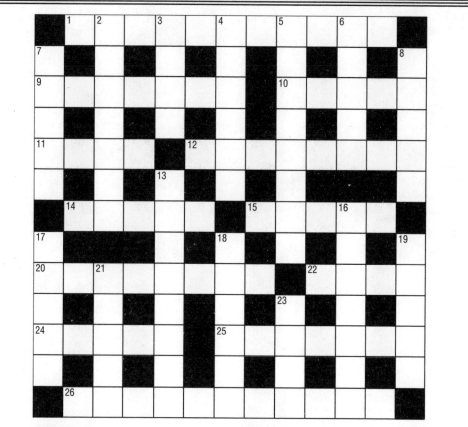

ACROSS

1 Bitter, spiteful (11)
9 Heathrow, eg (7)
10 Glisten (5)
11 Leak slowly (4)
12 Large rocks (8)
14 Ascend (5)
15 Employees (5)
20 Radiant (8)
22 Flower holder (4)
24 Numeral (5)
25 Sing-along entertainment (7)
26 Outdoor music festival (11)

DOWN

2 Fruit drink (7)
3 Portrait (4)
4 Choice (6)
5 Protect against the cold (8)
6 Join forces (5)
7 Convenient (5)
8 Stop (5)
13 Derives (8)
16 Taste (7)
17 Curved part of a trombone (5)
18 Bird with a distinctive cry (6)
19 Social outcast (5)
21 Powerful person (5)
23 Child's cot (4)

The Biggest Crossword Book In The World

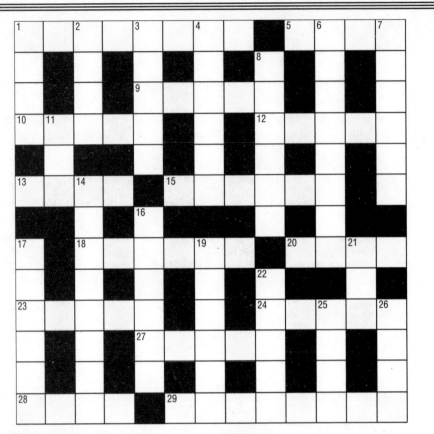

ACROSS

1 Extension (8)
5 Calf's flesh (4)
9 Irritable (5)
10 Germaine - - -, feminist (5)
12 Foe (5)
13 Celestial body (4)
15 Back out of (a promise) (6)
18 Country invaded by Iraq in 1990 (6)
20 Sudden quick movement (4)
23 Kofi - - -, United Nations chief (5)
24 Marsh (5)
27 Hit with the fist (5)
28 Snake's sound (4)
29 Recent arrival (8)

DOWN

1 All ears (4)
2 Plunge into water (4)
3 Stay briefly (5)
4 Slow to understand (6)
6 And so on (2, 6)
7 Solicitor (6)
8 Lace hole (6)
11 Rodent (3)
14 American state (8)
16 Two tens (6)
17 Shortfall (6)
19 Protected against disease (6)
21 Crash against (3)
22 Children's charity (5)
25 Tiny particle (4)
26 Mediocre (4)

The Biggest Crossword Book In The World

ACROSS

5 Love (5)
8 Type of exercise (8)
9 Strength (5)
10 Backwards and forwards (2, 3, 3)
11 Water-power (5)
14 TV presenter, - - - Lynam (3)
16 Military greeting (6)
17 George Orwell novel, - - - *Farm* (6)
18 Intuition? (1, 1, 1)
20 Singer, - - - Parton (5)
24 Guarantee (8)
25 French composer (5)
26 American government (8)
27 Motive, purpose (5)

DOWN

1 Festive occassion (5)
2 Trance (5)
3 Dwelling (5)
4 Increase gradually (6)
6 Preserve (8)
7 Disruption (8)
12 Complete view (8)
13 Construction site workers (8)
14 Chester's river (3)
15 Plant juice (3)
19 Patch of shade (6)
21 Leftovers (5)
22 Mountain range (5)
23 Romany traveller (5)

The Biggest Crossword Book In The World

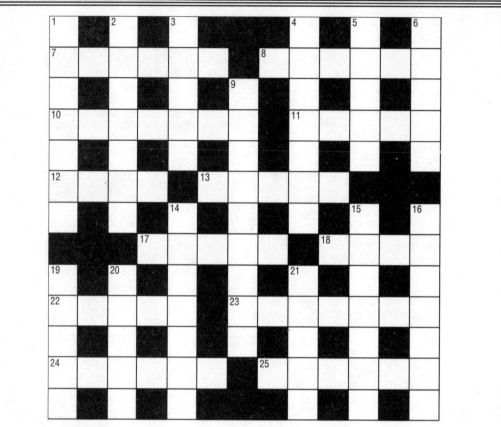

ACROSS

7 Sound of thunder (6)
8 Happily (6)
10 Junior embassy official (7)
11 Brownish-yellow (5)
12 Narrow valley with a stream (4)
13 Refund (5)
17 Top of the milk (5)
18 Purpose (4)
22 Female (5)
23 Capacious bag (7)
24 Crude dwelling (6)
25 Chinese self-defence (3, 3)

DOWN

1 Set out according to a plan (7)
2 Not included (7)
3 Timepiece (5)
4 Yearbook (7)
5 Sun-dried brick (5)
6 Wales (5)
9 Supposed thought-communication (9)
14 Hard rock (7)
15 Equilibrium (7)
16 Win back (7)
19 Wind round (5)
20 Daub (5)
21 False name (5)

The Biggest Crossword Book In The World

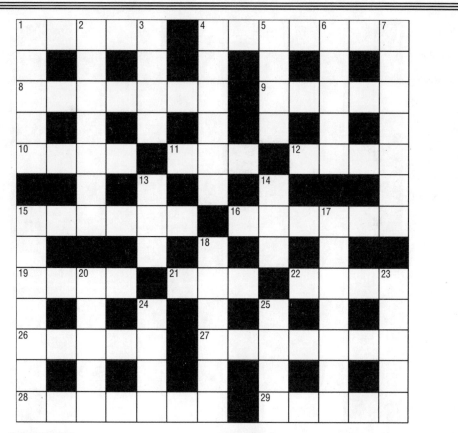

ACROSS

1 Provide entertainment (5)
4 Acrobat (7)
8 Alan - - -, footballer (7)
9 Hand digit (5)
10 Excursion (4)
11 Sum total (3)
12 Business transaction (4)
15 Sweet sound (6)
16 Pleasure boat
   harbour (6)
19 Fleshy root (4)
21 Not in (3)
22 Elderly (4)
26 Country singer,
   - - - Wynette (5)
27 Exceed (7)
28 Hectic routine (3, 4)
29 Song of lament (5)

DOWN

1 Valued possession (5)
2 Unbalanced (7)
3 Nobleman (4)
4 Excite (6)
5 Partner (4)
6 Wingless insect (5)
7 German measles (7)
13 Not even (3)
14 Taxi (3)
15 Gangster (7)
17 Ungrateful person (7)
18 Fight, scuffle (6)
20 Restrict (5)
23 Dim (5)
24 Indian bird which can
   mimic speech (4)
25 Real, genuine (4)

The Biggest Crossword Book In The World

ACROSS

1 Slept through winter? (10)
7 Barbara - - -, novelist (8)
8 Linger furtively (4)
9 Animal with antlers (4)
10 Climate (7)
12 Make, create (11)
14 Sum claimed as compensation (7)
16 Channel (4)
19 Malay dagger (4)
20 Speculative (8)
21 Occupation (10)

DOWN

1 Stash (5)
2 Halfway (7)
3 Gather a harvest (4)
4 Spectators (8)
5 Dazzling effect (5)
6 Wallpaper border (6)
11 In spite of expectations (5, 3)
12 Insufficient (6)
13 Four-stringed guitar (7)
15 Indian state (5)
17 Spoil (5)
18 Large number (4)

The Biggest Crossword Book In The World

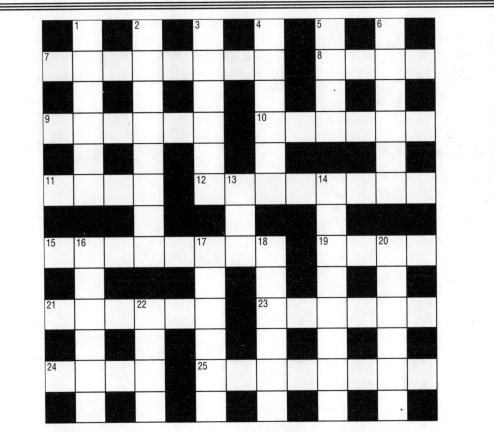

ACROSS

7 Reddish-brown wood (8)
8 Jeer, mock (4)
9 Open savoury tart (6)
10 Tree-lined street (6)
11 Practice, as a boxer (4)
12 John - - -, politician (8)
15 Determined (8)
19 Shoe protector (4)
21 Small European
   country (6)
23 Novelist, - - - Greene (6)
24 Look at lustfully (4)
25 Starter switch (8)

DOWN

1 Raise the price (6)
2 Musical composition (8)
3 Greasepaint (4-2)
4 Turn in a circle (6)
5 Monster (4)
6 Kidnap (6)
13 Nonsense (3)
14 Accident victim (8)
16 Adequate (6)
17 Ecstasy (6)
18 Locomotive (6)
20 Warrior woman (6)
22 Vertex (4)

The Biggest Crossword Book In The World

ACROSS

3 American film star (3, 6)
8 Suffer defeat (4)
9 Green petrol (8)
10 Blot (6)
13 Rabbit's cage (5)
14 Fastidious (7)
15 America's spy organisation (1, 1, 1)
16 Asian wind (7)
17 Slightest (5)
21 Sikh's headwear (6)
22 Old British coin (8)
23 Jest (4)
24 Violent political extremist (9)

DOWN

1 Swear, curse (9)
2 Aide, helper (9)
4 Of the same value (5)
5 Military force (7)
6 Large quantity of paper (4)
7 Listed object (4)
11 Cuttings file (9)
12 Spectator (9)
14 Vertical tailplane of an aircraft (3)
15 Inquest official (7)
18 Levels (5)
19 Broad (4)
20 Incitement (4)

The Biggest Crossword Book In The World

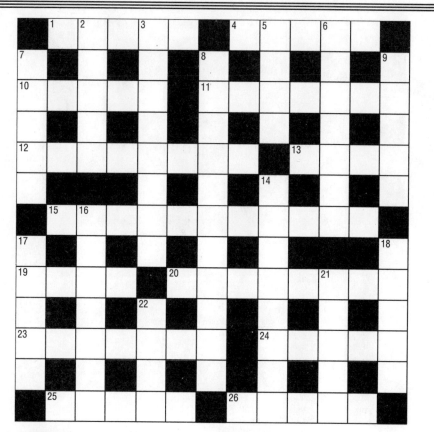

ACROSS

- **1** Tricky problem (5)
- **4** Gallantry award (5)
- **10** Toy with another's affections (5)
- **11** Aperture, breach (7)
- **12** Dutiful (8)
- **13** Actress, - - - Collins (4)
- **15** *The French Connection* actor (4, 7)
- **19** Dinosaur (1-3)
- **20** Intrude (8)
- **23** Instruct (7)
- **24** Picture (5)
- **25** Summarise (5)
- **26** Torn narrow strip (5)

DOWN

- **2** Utter an opinion (5)
- **3** Interweaved (8)
- **5** Adam's garden (4)
- **6** America's 'Copper State' (7)
- **7** Under way (5)
- **8** Writing instrument (8, 3)
- **9** Representative (5)
- **14** Minor battle (8)
- **16** Perform (7)
- **17** Hard alloy (5)
- **18** Bed linen (5)
- **21** Knowing (5)
- **22** Festive occasion (4)

The Biggest Crossword Book In The World

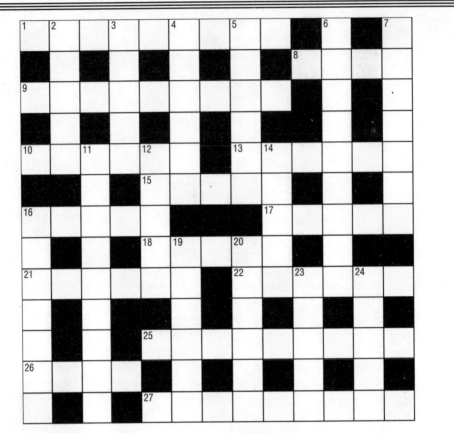

ACROSS

1 Arm of the Mediterranean (6, 3)
8 Heal (4)
9 Traditional British lunch (5, 4)
10 Anna - - -, *Black Beauty* author (6)
13 Type of ape (6)
15 Arabian country (5)
16 Retinue (5)
17 Aromatic spice (5)
18 Farewell (5)
21 A paradox (6)
22 Distant planet (6)
25 Apparent worth (4, 5)
26 Perform in the street? (4)
27 Loud-hailer (9)

DOWN

2 Draw forth (5)
3 Follow on (5)
4 Little bite (6)
5 Appear, arise (6)
6 *EastEnders'* actress (4, 5)
7 Punishment (7)
11 Tiredness (9)
12 Desmond - - -, TV presenter (5)
14 Cause to happen (5)
16 As a result of (7)
19 Harm (6)
20 Cry of Archimedes (6)
23 Embarrass (5)
24 Reversal of political policy (1-4)

The Biggest Crossword Book In The World

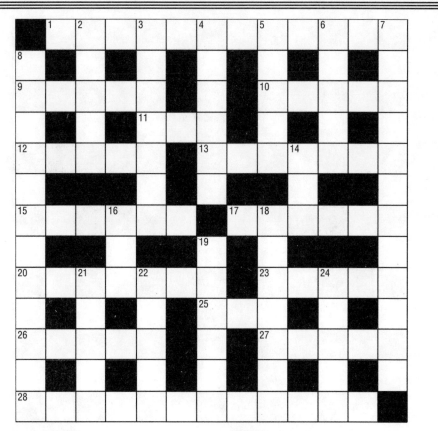

ACROSS

1 Befitting (12)
9 Red-hot (5)
10 Heartbeat (5)
11 Crisp lettuce (3)
12 Young salmon (5)
13 Huntsman's cry (5-2)
15 Popular 'whodunit' board game (6)
17 Ballet dancer, - - - Nureyev (6)
20 Wrap up (7)
23 Spanish hors d'oeuvre (5)
25 Civil award (1, 1, 1)
26 Explode (5)
27 Indian currency (5)
28 Current champions (5-7)

DOWN

2 Force open (5)
3 Thrown out (7)
4 Reliable (6)
5 Urge forward (5)
6 Embed (5)
7 Scottish comedian (6, 6)
8 *EastEnders* actress (3, 2, 7)
14 Cover (3)
16 West country river (3)
18 Spoke (7)
19 Son of Zeus (6)
21 Leap (5)
22 Woodwork machine (5)
24 Scottish musician (5)

The Biggest Crossword Book In The World

ACROSS
7 Increased in size (8)
8 Sharp, sour (4)
9 Three times as many (6)
10 Singer, - - - Clark (6)
11 Cuban dictator, - - - Castro (5)
12 Space to stretch out? (7)
15 Irish county (7)
17 Youth in training (5)
20 Dignified and imposing (6)
22 Jane's jungle friend (6)
23 Rant (4)
24 Capital of Jamaica (8)

DOWN
1 Drive out (evil spirits) (8)
2 Black and white bird (6)
3 Venomous snake (5)
4 Multisocket plug (7)
5 Stocking support (6)
6 Bottom part of a window (4)
13 Telephonist (8)
14 Leon - - -, Russian rebel (7)
16 US tap (6)
18 From side to side (6)
19 Allotted amount of time (5)
21 American state (4)

The Biggest Crossword Book In The World

ACROSS
1 Stimulation (13)
7 Provide medical attention (5)
8 Rich (7)
9 Dry white wine (7)
10 Theatrical show (5)
11 Everywhere (3, 4)
17 Important (5)
18 Pete - - -, tennis player (7)
20 Pain-killing drug (7)
21 Oyster's gem (5)
22 Tony Hancock sketch (3, 5, 5)

DOWN
1 Attract by exciting hope or desire (6)
2 Roman ruler (6)
3 To such time as (5)
4 Model (7)
5 Lengthen (6)
6 Elizabeth - - -, movie legend (6)
8 American state (9)
12 From the sides (7)
13 Overcome with amazement (6)
14 Human-beings (6)
15 Initiate into the priesthood (6)
16 Inn's stableman (6)
19 Motorized bicycle (5)

The Biggest Crossword Book In The World

ACROSS

1 Out of danger (4)
4 Audience's cry
for more (6)
8 Soft kind of wool (8)
9 Earth used to
make bricks (4)
10 Sham attack (5)
11 Seasoned sausage (7)
13 Best (6)
15 Longest British river (6)
17 Image (7)
19 Dutch cheese (5)
22 Fleshy stone-fruit (4)
23 European sea (8)
24 Idle talk (6)
25 Volcano in Sicily (4)

DOWN

2 Degrade (5)
3 Improve (7)
4 Sword (4)
5 Deep chasm (8)
6 Pleated frilling (5)
7 Work (6)
12 Sci-fi film starring
Harrison Ford (4, 4)
14 Spear of frozen water (6)
16 Break (agreement) (7)
18 Musical time (5)
20 Think fit (5)
21 Plummet (4)

The Biggest Crossword Book In The World

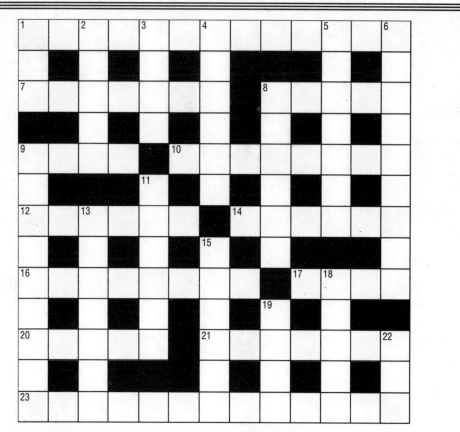

ACROSS
1 Linger (13)
7 Funnel-shaped flower (7)
8 Copper alloy (5)
9 Tiny amount (4)
10 Periodical publication (8)
12 Small rodent (6)
14 Withdraw, pull back (6)
16 Skittles (8)
17 Flat paving stone (4)
20 Open to view (5)
21 London cricket ground (3, 4)
23 July 15th (2, 8, 3)

DOWN
1 Personal Equity Plan (3)
2 Eight-piece band (5)
3 Lodger's dues (4)
4 German POW camp (6)
5 One of the deadly sins (7)
6 Seasonal chocolate gift (6, 3)
8 Man's jacket (6)
9 Cleverly contrived (9)
11 Clinging marine creature (6)
13 Park wardens (7)
15 Seize (6)
18 Extremely angry (5)
19 Blood-carrying tube (4)
22 Set down (3)

284

The Biggest Crossword Book In The World

ACROSS
1 South coast resort (6, 5)
9 Roy - - -, singer (7)
10 European country (5)
11 Part of the school year (4)
12 Indian chief (8)
14 Bridle straps (5)
15 The present age (5)
20 Welsh town (4, 4)
22 Shoe-string (4)
24 Tree of Lebanon (5)
25 Disobedient (7)
26 British actor (6, 5)

DOWN
2 John - - -, dramatist (7)
3 Bird's home (4)
4 French artist (6)
5 Clint - - -, US film star (8)
6 Not suitable (5)
7 Legal expenses (5)
8 Soldier from Australia or New Zealand (5)
13 All existing things (8)
16 Muslim leader (3, 4)
17 Dame Judi - - -, actress (5)
18 Ample supplies (6)
19 English diary writer (5)
21 Emblem (5)
23 Sound of a happy cat (4)

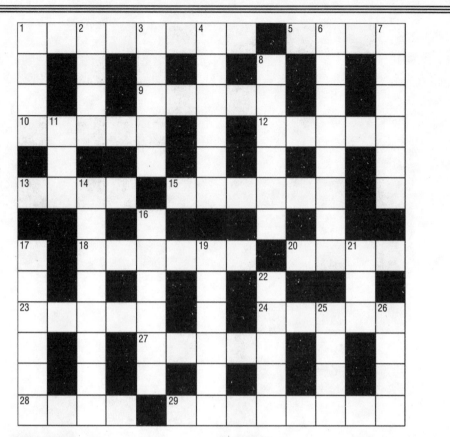

ACROSS

1 Pittiless (8)
5 Area of London (4)
9 Australian TV presenter, - - - James (5)
10 Animal charity (inits) (5)
12 Glare (5)
13 Peck (4)
15 Eventual failure (6)
18 Sheen (6)
20 Remain (4)
23 Blaspheme (5)
24 Dismay (5)
27 Main French river port (5)
28 Capital of Peru (4)
29 Loosen (8)

DOWN

1 Laugh loudly (4)
2 Ram down (concrete) (4)
3 Nearby pub (5)
4 Private get-together (6)
6 Decorative item (8)
7 Most senior (6)
8 *Men Behaving Badly* star, - - - Ash (6)
11 Country, - - - Lanka (3)
14 Tanning room (8)
16 Behind at sea (6)
17 Wild dog (6)
19 Come back (6)
21 Farmhouse cooker (3)
22 Chinese 'bear' (5)
25 Cheeky, saucy (4)
26 Garden grass (4)

The Biggest Crossword Book In The World

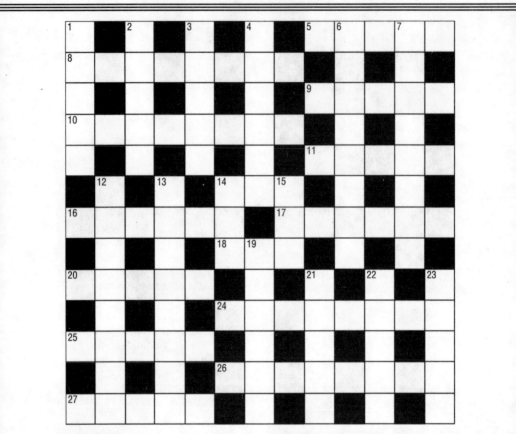

ACROSS

5 Bitter (5)
8 Item of clothing (8)
9 Cereal crop (5)
10 Spanish tourist resort (8)
11 Planet's path (5)
14 Mischievous child (3)
16 Thought (6)
17 Senior Girl Guide (6)
18 Lock-opener (3)
20 Financially ruined (5)
24 Man notorious for seducing women (8)
25 Female fox (5)
26 Obstruction (8)
27 Open-mouthed (5)

DOWN

1 Rascal, rogue (5)
2 Smug smile (5)
3 Variety of poplar (5)
4 Skiing race over a winding course (6)
6 Easily followed (8)
7 Pictured in the mind (8)
12 Troubling (8)
13 Medicine to cure depression (4-2-2)
14 Writing fluid (3)
15 Meddle (3)
19 Make possible (6)
21 First woman MP, - - - Astor (5)
22 Brief attack (5)
23 Pole for tossing (5)

The Biggest Crossword Book In The World

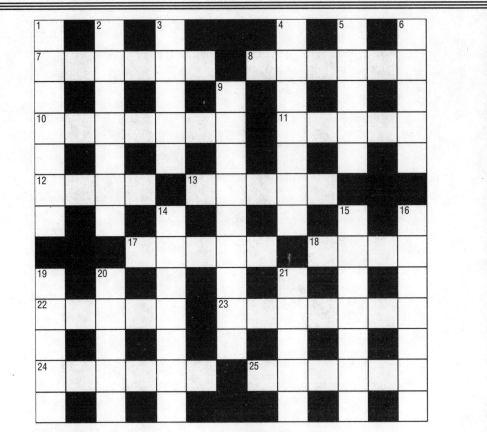

ACROSS

7 Phrase (6)
8 Toasted roll (6)
10 Ruth - - -, crime writer (7)
11 Trap (5)
12 Barrel-like container (4)
13 Scatter loosely (5)
17 Hot steam bath (5)
18 Afresh (4)
22 Serious (5)
23 Kiev's country (7)
24 Recommendation (6)
25 Distinct from (6)

DOWN

1 Large bird (7)
2 Narrow margin
    of victory (2, 1, 4)
3 Express contempt (5)
4 Estimated (7)
5 Less valuable parts
    of the carcass (5)
6 Beginning (5)
9 Metallic element (9)
14 Patron saint of Ireland (7)
15 Dull (7)
16 Add sugar (7)
19 Nile dam (5)
20 Higher (than) (5)
21 Salute (5)

The Biggest Crossword Book In The World

ACROSS

1 Sudden roll or pitch (5)
4 Bouncy, breezy (7)
8 Curving inwards (7)
9 Illegal act (5)
10 Players on same side (4)
11 Matador's shout (3)
12 Pierce with a horn (4)
15 Small racing vehicle (2-4)
16 Edible seed of a nut (6)
19 Long cod (4)
21 Substance made by bees (3)
22 Glaswegian? (4)
26 Fairly big (5)
27 Underwater missile (7)
28 Precisely (7)
29 Bathroom fitment (5)

DOWN

1 Authorised (5)
2 Pillage, plunder (7)
3 Listen to (4)
4 Insect with hard wing cover on its back (6)
5 Expression of pain (4)
6 Comrade? (5)
7 **Former** home of Southampton FC (3, 4)
13 Weep (3)
14 Hack, lop (3)
15 Part of ancient Palestine (7)
17 Centre (7)
18 Larder (6)
20 John Major's wife (5)
23 Prickly part of a plant (5)
24 Throb rhythmically (4)
25 Snatch (4)

The Biggest Crossword Book In The World

ACROSS

1 Group of Caribbean islands (4, 6)
7 Travel document (8)
8 Group of three (4)
9 Cure (4)
10 Foot lever (7)
12 Thoughtful (11)
14 Animal with a striped tail (7)
16 Prosperity (4)
19 Dramatic part (4)
20 Oxford college (3, 5)
21 Edward's lover (3, 7)

DOWN

1 Indignation (5)
2 Withstand (7)
3 False god (4)
4 Discouraged (8)
5 Crowd actor (5)
6 Jockey, - - - Carson (6)
11 Dual purpose specs (8)
12 Coloured wax pencil (6)
13 Affectionate (7)
15 Applaud (5)
17 Juicy fruit (5)
18 Thin, slight (4)

The Biggest Crossword Book In The World

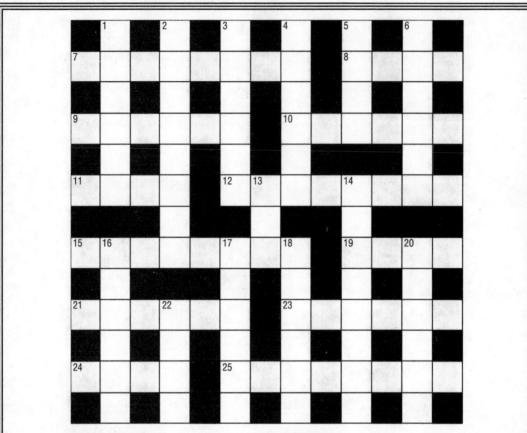

ACROSS

7 Protect from harm (8)
8 Funeral pile (4)
9 Reach destination (6)
10 Servant (6)
11 Greek B (4)
12 Disregards (8)
15 Power (8)
19 Sketch (4)
21 Handle (6)
23 Boris Becker's sport (6)
24 Aspect (4)
25 Go through (8)

DOWN

1 Origin (6)
2 Guess (8)
3 TV oaf (2, 4)
4 Post-flight tiredness (3, 3)
5 Long adventure film (4)
6 Eager, zealous (6)
13 Newt (3)
14 Put in peril (8)
16 Appalling (6)
17 Ethnic area (6)
18 Hired assassin (3, 3)
20 In the middle of (6)
22 Chopped (4)

The Biggest Crossword Book In The World

ACROSS

3 Faulty (9)
8 Stern (4)
9 Country residence of the Prime Minister (8)
10 Town of St Francis (6)
13 Gardening string (5)
14 Bravery (7)
15 Deceive (3)
16 Art museum (7)
17 Jack in the pack (5)
21 Send in all directions (6)
22 Thrive, prosper (8)
23 Small American coin (4)
24 Flying machine (9)

DOWN

1 Benefit (9)
2 Boxer's protection (9)
4 Rodrigo Diaz de Vivar? (2, 3)
5 Football club from Liverpool (7)
6 Hooligan (4)
7 Modify (4)
11 Highly-trained ambulanceman (9)
12 *Tomorrow - - -,* Bond film (5, 4)
14 Bashful (3)
15 Very important (7)
18 Drained of colour (5)
19 Run away (4)
20 Board game (4)

The Biggest Crossword Book In The World

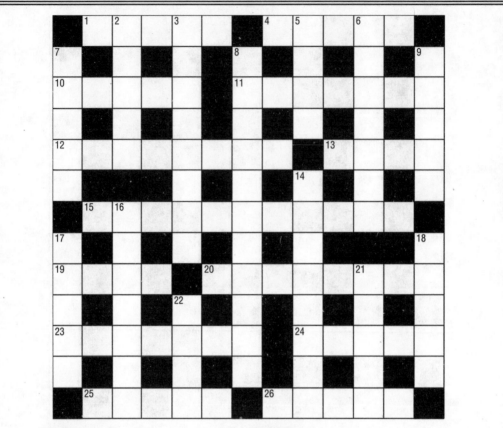

ACROSS

1 Jeans material (5)
4 English artist (5)
10 Loft room (5)
11 Japanese art of flower arranging (7)
12 Fused together (8)
13 Flightless bird (4)
15 Safety hat (5, 6)
19 Depend (4)
20 Protective clothing (8)
23 Missing race horse (7)
24 Shopping extravaganza (5)
25 Fred - - -, English tennis player (5)
26 London cricket ground (5)

DOWN

2 Praise (5)
3 Rise in size (8)
5 Working cattle (4)
6 Come to understand (7)
7 Untrue (5)
8 *Dangerfield* actor (5, 6)
9 Herb used in cooking (5)
14 In the open air (8)
16 Alleviate (7)
17 Grip firmly (5)
18 Chelmsford's county (5)
21 Shockingly vivid (5)
22 Gelatine obtained from seaweed (4)

The Biggest Crossword Book In The World

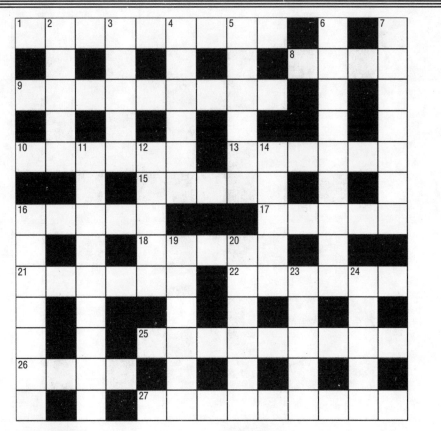

ACROSS

1 *Brookside's* Beth Jordache (4, 5)
8 Silent acting (4)
9 Dreary routine (9)
10 Become embittered (6)
13 Robust (6)
15 Large flat fish (5)
16 Property document (5)
17 Author, - - - Dahl (5)
18 Deep chasm (5)
21 Scapegoat (6)
22 Traditional story (6)
25 River between Mexico and USA (3, 6)
26 Biting insect (4)
27 American state (9)

DOWN

2 Impudence (5)
3 Expect (5)
4 Perceive, notice (6)
5 Enrol (6)
6 Sleep through winter (9)
7 Postponed (7)
11 Lead from the front (9)
12 Short written work (5)
14 Tight-lipped (5)
16 Placido - - -, Spanish tenor (7)
19 Mark left by a blow to the skin (6)
20 Advertising phrase (6)
23 Informer (slang) (5)
24 Gentle poke (5)

The Biggest Crossword Book In The World

ACROSS
1 High-spirited (12)
9 Grasp firmly (5)
10 Show the way (5)
11 Female sheep (3)
12 Official request (5)
13 Strong wind storm (7)
15 Compost (6)
17 Rallying call (3, 3)
20 Illness, sickness (7)
23 Small but tasteful (5)
25 Anger (3)
26 Follow (5)
27 Navigation method (5)
28 Proved (12)

DOWN
2 Deceitful person (5)
3 Imperial ruler (7)
4 Fast ballroom dance (6)
5 Jam ingredient (5)
6 The heath genus (5)
7 Kevin Costner film (3, 9)
8 Provided with lodgings (12)
14 And not (3)
16 Purpose (3)
18 Canadian province (7)
19 Mediterranean port (6)
21 Muscular contraction (5)
22 Tired (3, 2)
24 Court official (5)

The Biggest Crossword Book In The World

ACROSS

7 Lack of energy (8)
8 Rubbish tip (4)
9 Extreme enthusiast (6)
10 Mean (6)
11 Likewise (5)
12 Carve figures on
a surface (7)
15 Tarnish (7)
17 Missile projected
from a bow (5)
20 Acid fruit (6)
22 Head protector (6)
23 Keep out of sight (4)
24 Charade (8)

DOWN

1 Corrective (8)
2 Wooden house (6)
3 Beast (5)
4 Cleanliness (7)
5 Newspaper chief (6)
6 So be it! (4)
13 Cruelty (8)
14 Proof of payment (7)
16 Jog along (6)
18 Easing of pain
or pressure (6)
19 Very steep (5)
21 Body of soldiers (4)

The Biggest Crossword Book In The World

ACROSS

1 Home of the crown jewels (5, 2, 6)
7 Mark - - -, *Huckleberry Finn* author, (5)
8 Three-pronged spear (7)
9 Drastic (7)
10 Large, stout (5)
11 Electrical path (7)
17 Rough in voice (5)
18 Moral (7)
20 River mouth (7)
21 Remove all accessories (5)
22 Important political directive (5, 4, 4)

DOWN

1 Be about to fall (6)
2 Abundance (6)
3 Wash through (5)
4 Paper-folding art (7)
5 French ferry port (6)
6 Gossip (6)
8 Disloyalty (9)
12 Fill with air (7)
13 King of Wessex from 802 (6)
14 Great Train robbery film (6)
15 Burn slightly (6)
16 Blunder (4, 2)
19 Speed (5)

The Biggest Crossword Book In The World

ACROSS
1 Verse (4)
4 Fully developed (6)
8 JM Barrie character (5, 3)
9 Throwing line in a game of darts (4)
10 Salary (5)
11 Final part of a race (4, 3)
13 Reaping implement (6)
15 Hate, abhor (6)
17 Observed (7)
19 Young person (5)
22 Comedy actor, - - - Wilder (4)
23 Honest (8)
24 Soviet leader (6)
25 Healthy looking (4)

DOWN
2 Greek O (5)
3 American actress (3, 4)
4 Sulk (4)
5 Octopus arm (8)
6 Bird's perch (5)
7 Knife cover (6)
12 Column support (8)
14 Henry - - -, former boxer (6)
16 One more (7)
18 Clumsy (5)
20 Solicits custom (5)
21 Scottish stream (4)

The Biggest Crossword Book In The World

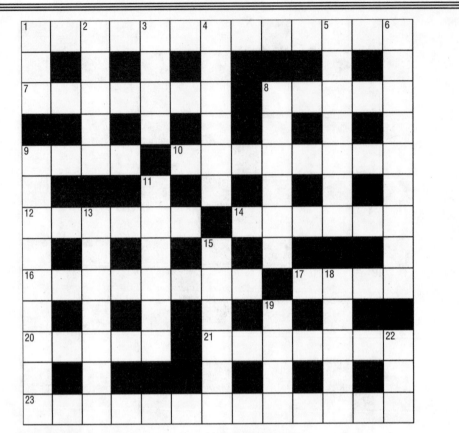

ACROSS

1 Thinking intensely (13)
7 Part of a stove (7)
8 Pudding (5)
9 Eyelid sore (4)
10 First public performance (8)
12 Occasional worker (6)
14 *Jungle Book* character (6)
16 Grateful (8)
17 Mixture of smoke and fog (4)
20 Coalition (5)
21 Self-supporting stockings (4, 3)
23 Police department (7, 6)

DOWN

1 Tooth on a wheel (3)
2 Loud (5)
3 Whirlpool (4)
4 Hypothetical situation (6)
5 Type of lettuce (7)
6 Assembly (9)
8 Emblem (6)
9 Pruning shears (9)
11 Serviette (6)
13 Coastal resort (7)
15 Dry measure of eight gallons (6)
18 Grieve for (5)
19 Become less distinct (4)
22 Musical note (3)

The Biggest Crossword Book In The World

ACROSS
1 Endangered (11)
9 Rower (7)
10 Small woody plant (5)
11 Scalp covering (4)
12 Lodgers (8)
14 Mood (5)
15 Frighten (5)
20 Sudden fit of temper (8)
22 A narcotic drug (4)
24 Holy book (5)
25 Provide assistance (4, 3)
26 Noisy ghost (11)

DOWN
2 Before this time (7)
3 Splendour (4)
4 Haphazard (6)
5 Teach (8)
6 Uncanningly disturbing (5)
7 Strong coffee (5)
8 Use wrongly (5)
13 Cheeky (8)
16 Unruly (7)
17 Pastime (5)
18 Line on a weather map (6)
19 Outstanding bills (5)
21 Something not allowed (5)
23 Adhesive (4)

The Biggest Crossword Book In The World

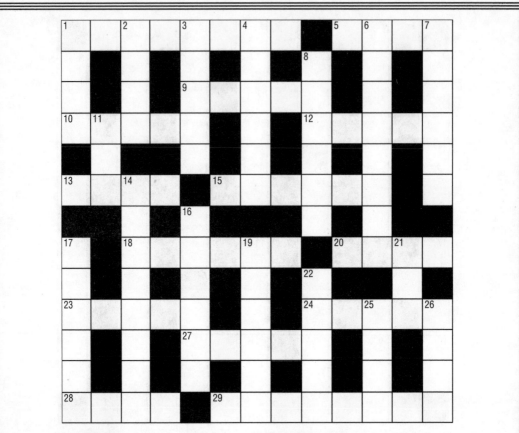

ACROSS

1 Tacit, not overtly stated (8)
5 Female spouse (4)
9 Michael Caine film (5)
10 Fourth month (5)
12 Capital of Bangladesh (5)
13 Pull suddenly (4)
15 Charm (6)
18 Short-sighted (6)
20 Model or pattern (4)
23 Tiny particle (5)
24 Slope (5)
27 Fit out (5)
28 Town on the Isle of Wight (4)
29 Close-fitting leg covering (8)

DOWN

1 Notion (4)
2 Dispense (4)
3 Rome's country (5)
4 Tell (6)
6 Foot soldiers (8)
7 Avoid (6)
8 Interfere with (6)
11 Part of a referee's whistle (3)
14 Totalled (8)
16 Long-tailed primate (6)
17 Pearl producer (6)
19 Abuse (6)
21 Quip (3)
22 Savoury jelly (5)
25 Averse (4)
26 Garden basket (4)

The Biggest Crossword Book In The World

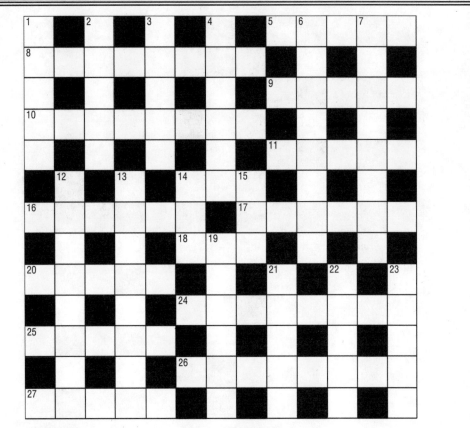

ACROSS

5 Soft leather (5)
8 Part of the galaxy (5, 3)
9 Fasten (5)
10 Gossip service on the phone (8)
11 Refracting glass (5)
14 Lingerie item (3)
16 Bureau (6)
17 Real, genuine (6)
18 Rubbish (3)
20 Tenancy contract (5)
24 Recurring at short intervals (8)
25 *Tarzan* author, - - - Rice Burroughs (5)
26 Vagrant (8)
27 One of the deadly sins (5)

DOWN

1 Slap, blow (5)
2 Dwell on with satisfaction (5)
3 Ride a bike (5)
4 Flag (6)
6 Underlying (motives) (8)
7 Modified racing car (8)
12 Culprit (8)
13 Medical treatment (5, 3)
14 Have a wager (3)
15 Relevant (3)
19 Antenna (6)
21 Indian woman (5)
22 High-quality tea (5)
23 Scrutinise (5)

The Biggest Crossword Book In The World

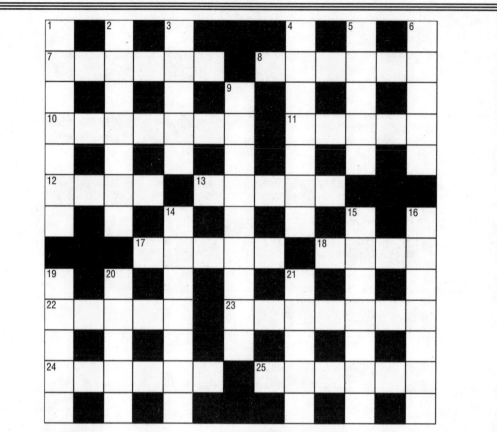

ACROSS

7 Burrowing rodent (6)
8 Steven Redgrave's sport (6)
10 Against the law (7)
11 Musical instrument (5)
12 Short turned-up nose (4)
13 Danger signal (5)
17 Accusation (5)
18 Greek spirit (4)
22 Acting platform (5)
23 Form a mental picture (7)
24 Concurred (6)
25 King who tried to turn back the tide (6)

DOWN

1 Versus (7)
2 Show approval (7)
3 Pretend (5)
4 Cinema-goer's snack (7)
5 Name (5)
6 Eskimo's ice hut (5)
9 Second World War battle (2, 7)
14 Small earring (7)
15 Suspect (7)
16 Nevertheless (7)
19 Acting award (5)
20 Convey (5)
21 Of the pope (5)

The Biggest Crossword Book In The World

ACROSS

1 German sausage (5)
4 Spanish drink (7)
8 Sudden desire (7)
9 George Cross island (5)
10 Narrow (4)
11 Hair cream (3)
12 Two-masted ship (4)
15 Amphibious rodent (6)
16 Basketball team,
  - - - Globetrotters (6)
19 Spandau jail's last
  prisoner (4)
21 Consumed (3)
22 Pond fish (4)
26 Astound, surprise (5)
27 A riding-school (7)
28 Jotting block (7)
29 Appointment (5)

DOWN

1 Arm joint (5)
2 Exact copy (7)
3 Lean (4)
4 Hi-fi system (6)
5 Title (4)
6 Monarch (5)
7 Alloy of metals (7)
13 Precious stone (3)
14 Old horse (3)
15 Tiny nation in the
  Arabian Gulf (7)
17 Theft (7)
18 Thread (6)
20 Quick-witted (5)
23 Cairo's country (5)
24 Trickle (4)
25 Extensive (4)

The Biggest Crossword Book In The World

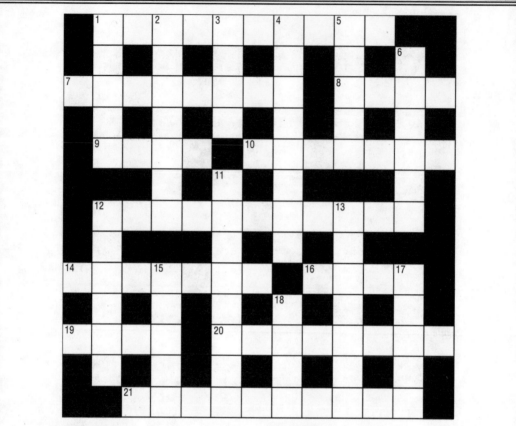

ACROSS

1 Section of a store (10)
7 Gags (8)
8 Extremely (4)
9 Stained (4)
10 Formal document (7)
12 Schwarzenegger film (5, 6)
14 Sarcastic, cutting (7)
16 Reverberation (4)
19 Eager (4)
20 Enough (8)
21 Capital of New Zealand (10)

DOWN

1 Dehydrated (5)
2 Hinder effectually (7)
3 Instrument of torture (4)
4 Annoying behaviour (8)
5 Melina Mercouri film, - - - *on Sunday* (5)
6 Terrible trial (6)
11 Wholly (3, 2, 3)
12 Tantalising riddle (6)
13 Report, description (7)
15 Sound judgement (5)
17 Frequently (5)
18 Old advert sign gas (4)

ACROSS

7 Round (8)
8 Sandy - - -, golfer (4)
9 Touch (6)
10 Tatty (6)
11 Solitary (4)
12 Corn chip (8)
15 Wobbled (8)
19 Young horse (4)
21 Motionless (6)
23 Mix, blend (6)
24 Amount wagered (4)
25 Full of incident (8)

DOWN

1 The emperor of Japan (6)
2 Rigorous examination (4, 4)
3 Customer (6)
4 Art rubber (6)
5 Urgent request (4)
6 Worldwide (6)
13 Have debts (3)
14 Without limits (8)
16 Degree (6)
17 Tennis bat (6)
18 Young lady (6)
20 Whole-hearted (3-3)
22 Stepped layer (4)

The Biggest Crossword Book In The World

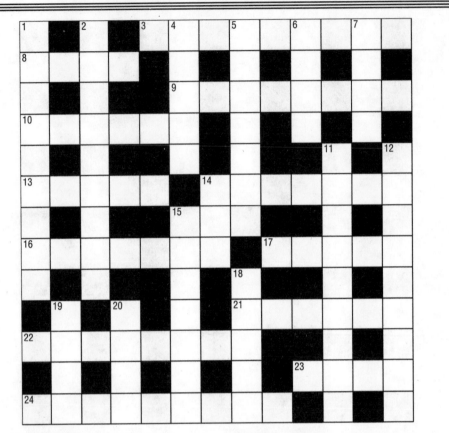

ACROSS

3 Wholly committed (9)
8 Surrender (4)
9 Lake District village (8)
10 Fairground game (6)
13 Greek island (5)
14 Breed of dog (7)
15 Metal container (3)
16 Came into view (7)
17 Movable joint (5)
21 Disturbance (6)
22 Take away (8)
23 Diesel oil (4)
24 Mouth organ (9)

DOWN

1 Game played on skates (3, 6)
2 Deferred (9)
4 British composer (5)
5 From Rome or Turin? (7)
6 Fighting force (4)
7 Greyish-yellow (4)
11 Robert Louis Stevenson novel (9)
12 Disgusting attack (9)
14 Crazy (3)
15 Positive (7)
18 Large lorry (5)
19 Hawaiian dance (4)
20 Part of a plant (4)

The Biggest Crossword Book In The World

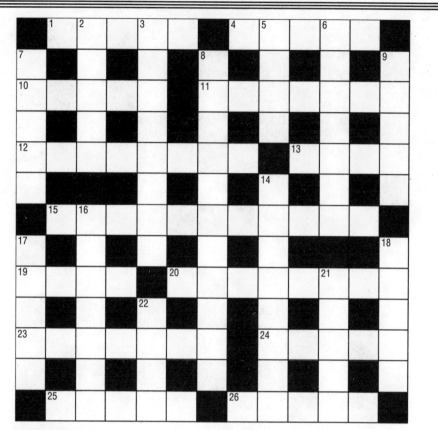

ACROSS

1 Lucifer (5)
4 Irrigation channel (5)
10 Work (dough) (5)
11 Officially supervise (7)
12 Settle in
  another country (8)
13 Wait patiently (4)
15 Last chance to pay (5, 6)
19 Mountain range (4)
20 Skin cream (8)
23 Eighth sign of
  the zodiac (7)
24 Crest of land (5)
25 Difficult, severe (5)
26 Prime number (5)

DOWN

2 Jean - - -,
  racing driver (5)
3 Senior councillor (8)
5 Mountain goat (4)
6 Rim of a
  snooker table (7)
7 Winter sportsman (5)
8 Spanish tourist
  area (5, 3, 3)
9 Bar for exerting
  pressure (5)
14 *Peter Pan* author (1, 1, 6)
16 Make better (7)
17 Fall in behaviour (5)
18 Fisherman's basket (5)
21 Move in a furtive
  manner (5)
22 Wide boy, black
  marketeer (4)

The Biggest Crossword Book In The World

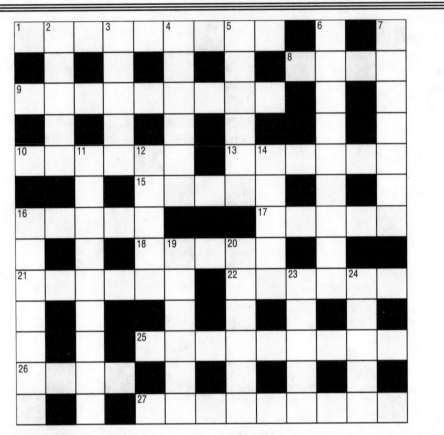

ACROSS

1 Second President of the United States (4, 5)
8 Opinion (4)
9 Horribly distorted (9)
10 Defer indefinitely (6)
13 Theatrical straight man (6)
15 Tree of the birch family (5)
16 Essential (5)
17 In front (5)
18 Scientist, Sir - - - Newton (5)
21 List of things to be dealt with (6)
22 Item of furniture (6)
25 Admin (9)
26 Snug (4)
27 Worried (9)

DOWN

2 Talk show host, - - - Winfrey (5)
3 South African province (5)
4 Sacha - - -, French singer (6)
5 Creamy dessert (6)
6 Deceitful (9)
7 Welsh county (7)
11 Enthusiast (9)
12 Sound (5)
14 Find (5)
16 Bridge over a valley (7)
19 Ferocious (6)
20 Upward slope (6)
23 Skyscraper (5)
24 Eagle's nest (5)

The Biggest Crossword Book In The World

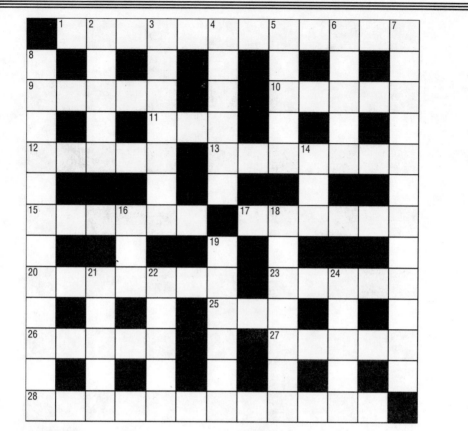

ACROSS

1 *Anna Lee* star (6, 6)
9 Chinese criminal society (5)
10 Dance party (5)
11 Canine (3)
12 Seated enclosure for sports events (5)
13 Dried bean (7)
15 Root vegetable (6)
17 Igloo dweller (6)
20 Refrain from (7)
23 Minister of a synagogue (5)
25 Watering-place (3)
26 Japanese fencing (5)
27 Crash (a vehicle) (5)
28 Beatles No 1 (6, 2, 4)

DOWN

2 Type of corn (5)
3 Libyan leader (7)
4 Nothing (6)
5 Henry VIII's dynasty (5)
6 Film, - - - *Instinct* (5)
7 Defects (12)
8 Confining garment (12)
14 Annoy (3)
16 Fish trap (3)
18 Wallpaper remover (7)
19 Put between (6)
21 Relating to sound waves (5)
22 Love deeply (5)
24 Make of goods (5)

The Biggest Crossword Book In The World

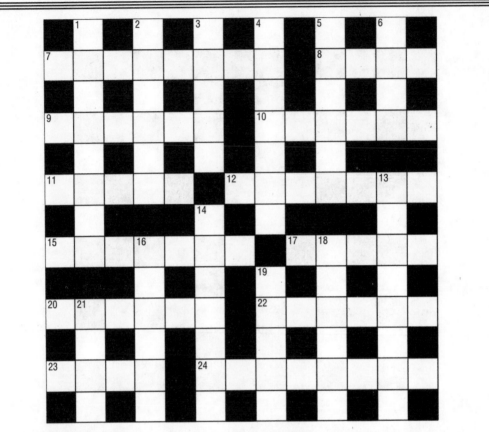

ACROSS

7 Capital of South Australia (8)
8 Shrub (4)
9 Moral goodness (6)
10 Artist's workplace (6)
11 Baby, grand eg (5)
12 Crook (7)
15 Eternal (7)
17 Fleshy fruit (5)
20 Long, narrow arm of the Indian Ocean (3, 3)
22 Calm (6)
23 Floor covering (4)
24 Escape clause? (8)

DOWN

1 Appreciative (8)
2 Enid - - -, author (6)
3 French composer (5)
4 Regular payment to retired people (7)
5 Ridiculous (6)
6 Sparkling wine (4)
13 Awkward, clumsy (8)
14 Violent attack (7)
16 Period of instruction (6)
18 Lack of enthusiasm (6)
19 Reel (5)
21 Viking, - - - the Red (4)

The Biggest Crossword Book In The World

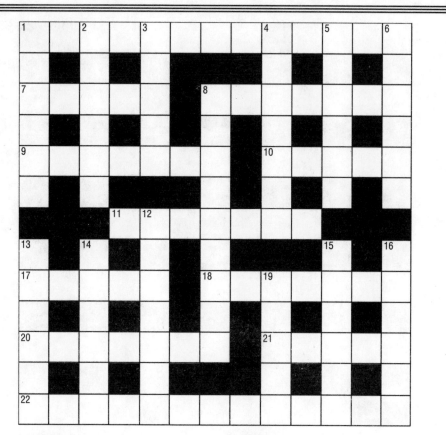

ACROSS
1 Reckless (13)
7 Three-wheeled cycle (5)
8 Commonplace (7)
9 Very fast animal (7)
10 Company of soldiers (5)
11 South African
conflict (4, 3)
17 Strength (5)
18 An anniversary (7)
20 Body organ (7)
21 Fifty-fifty bet (5)
22 Yellowish-brown
mottled cat (13)

DOWN
1 Entire (6)
2 Brought up (6)
3 Nodded off (5)
4 Frank - - -, singer (7)
5 Signal fire (6)
6 Free from obligation (6)
8 Indian prince (9)
12 Aromatic herb (7)
13 Sideshoot (6)
14 Metal clothing (6)
15 Record cover (6)
16 Stoat-like mammal (6)
19 Sanctify (5)

The Biggest Crossword Book In The World

ACROSS

1 Imran - - -, Pakistan cricketer (4)
4 Sing (6)
8 Salad item (8)
9 Simmer (4)
10 Hindu recluse (5)
11 Built up (7)
13 Extreme condition (6)
15 American state (6)
17 Public sale (7)
19 Cross (5)
22 Highland Gaelic (4)
23 As a rule (8)
24 Mr Hyde's doctor? (6)
25 Not hard (4)

DOWN

2 Dog-like animal (5)
3 Nought (7)
4 Sheep's fleece (4)
5 Reserved (8)
6 Narrow, intense light beam (5)
7 Rely (6)
12 US lawyer (8)
14 French museum and art gallery (6)
16 Good viewing point (7)
18 Topic (5)
20 Regulations (5)
21 Spoken test (4)

The Biggest Crossword Book In The World

ACROSS

1 *Dirty Dancing* actor (7, 6)
7 Get in touch with (7)
8 Mouth of a river (5)
9 Quite hot (4)
10 Where Napoleon lost to the Duke of
Wellington (8)
12 Accounts book (6)
14 Church caretaker (6)
16 Male horse (8)
17 Burden (4)
20 Home of Glasgow Rangers (5)
21 James Bond's favourite tipple (7)
23 Government official (4, 9)

DOWN

1 Polyvinyl chloride (1, 1, 1)
2 Choir singer (5)
3 Iran's neighbour (4)
4 Soldier's holdall (6)
5 Christmas cake (4, 3)
6 Inspired with love (9)
8 Vehicle fuel (6)
9 American film star (4, 5)
11 Involuntary response (6)
13 Technical drawing (7)
15 Of the whole universe (6)
18 Seance board (5)
19 Fish-eating eagle (4)
22 Very cold (3)

The Biggest Crossword Book In The World

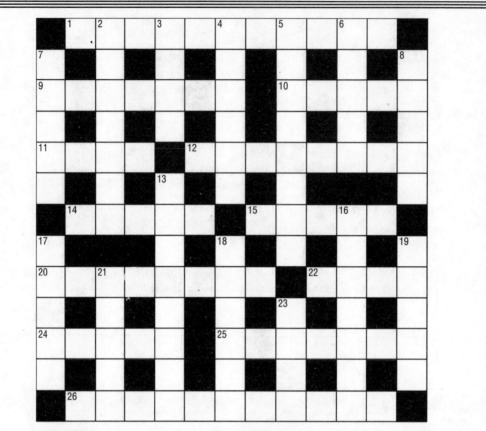

ACROSS
1 Senior naval officer (4, 7)
9 Apparent (7)
10 British airport (5)
11 Metal money (4)
12 Medieval entertainer (8)
14 Listened to (5)
15 Tribal badge (5)
20 Falling back (8)
22 Quip (4)
24 Beauty parlour (5)
25 Pantomime character (3, 4)
26 Doubt (11)

DOWN
2 Large building (7)
3 Smell strongly (4)
4 Hold in custody (6)
5 Deceptive appearance (8)
6 Church table (5)
7 Hussy (5)
8 Small hill (5)
13 Jilly Cooper novel (8)
16 Tasteful in dress (7)
17 Confidence (5)
18 Baby (6)
19 Book of maps (5)
21 Hurdler, - - - Jackson (5)
23 Medium sized (4)

The Biggest Crossword Book In The World

ACROSS

1 Cosmetic pincers (8)
5 Mother of Jesus (4)
9 Citrus fruit (5)
10 Frenzied (5)
12 Knot in a tree (5)
13 *EastEnders*' actor,
- - - Woodyatt (4)
15 Murderer (6)
18 Breakfast food (6)
20 Book of the Old
Testament (4)
23 Gold purity standard (5)
24 Very kind person (5)
27 Principle, belief (5)
28 Irish county (4)
29 Poisonous (8)

DOWN

1 Rain heavily (4)
2 Food taster,
- - - Ronay (4)
3 Nothing! (5)
4 Italian holiday resort (6)
6 Rocky island in San
Francisco Bay (8)
7 Daffodil colour (6)
8 Swamp (6)
11 Join on (3)
14 Precision (8)
16 Charming (6)
17 Household cleaner (6)
19 Take retaliation (6)
21 Feel sorrow (3)
22 Proportion (5)
25 Dole cheque (4)
26 Girl (4)

The Biggest Crossword Book In The World

ACROSS

5 Dwell (5)
8 Soft, comfortable shoes (8)
9 Horse-drawn vehicle (5)
10 Alienate (8)
11 Dirty (5)
14 Harden (3)
16 Pocket of air (6)
17 Irregular (6)
18 Movement of tide (3)
20 Breed of dog (5)
24 Gash, slit (8)
25 Flavoursome (5)
26 Energetic (8)
27 Deduce (5)

DOWN

1 Large showy daisy (5)
2 Quick, agile (5)
3 Floral display (5)
4 Capital of Czech Republic (6)
6 Wrist jewellery (8)
7 Thick sandwich (8)
12 German motorway (8)
13 Missing person (8)
14 Catch sight of (3)
15 Container (3)
19 Gangster (6)
21 Hairy oxen (5)
22 Short pin supporting something that turns (5)
23 Grind (teeth) together (5)

The Biggest Crossword Book In The World

ACROSS

7 Well paid company boss? (3, 3)
8 Celestial body (6)
10 Lean and scrawny (7)
11 Sling (5)
12 Pack of cards (4)
13 Happen again (5)
17 Humped mammal (5)
18 Plays a role (4)
22 Scottish river (5)
23 Put on a list (7)
24 Wood (6)
25 Part of the eye (6)

DOWN

1 Football rule (7)
2 Draw (7)
3 Dance (5)
4 Quiet (7)
5 Metric measurement (5)
6 Edible sea crustacean (5)
9 Dorset resort (4, 5)
14 Narrowed to a point (7)
15 Deeds (7)
16 Gloria - - -, singer (7)
19 Severe, intense (5)
20 Small breed of animal (5)
21 Cruel person (5)

The Biggest Crossword Book In The World

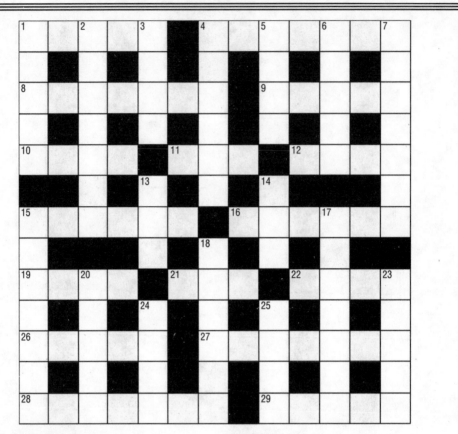

ACROSS

1 Knight's spear (5)
4 Low, cushioned backless seat (7)
8 Annul, repeal (7)
9 Bid (5)
10 Employ for wages (4)
11 Commercial vehicle (3)
12 Minicab (4)
15 Prison resident (6)
16 Feeding dish (6)
19 Edward - - -, British artist and poet (4)
21 Comedian, - - - Mayall (3)
22 Wind instrument (4)
26 Sing softly (5)
27 Garden plant (7)
28 Kitchen appliance (7)
29 Aromatic herb (5)

DOWN

1 Deciduous tree (5)
2 Patent medicine (7)
3 North African chieftain (4)
4 Lancashire town (6)
5 Gentle gallop (4)
6 Sicilian secret society (5)
7 Norfolk city (7)
13 Pigpen (3)
14 Sphere (3)
15 Forbidden (7)
17 South American country (7)
18 Child (6)
20 Distinct smell (5)
23 Alert (5)
24 Hair tangle (4)
25 Lose weight (4)

The Biggest Crossword Book In The World

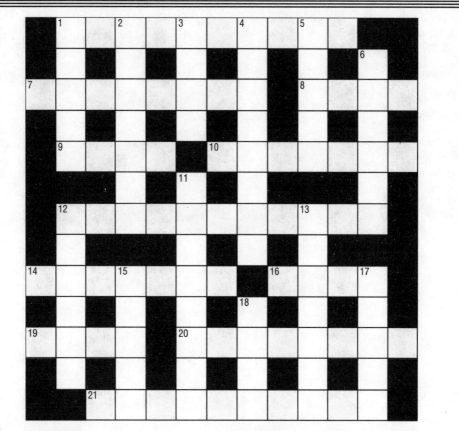

ACROSS

1 Foxy puppet (5, 5)
7 Indian food cooked in a clay oven (8)
8 Softly-spoken actor, - - - Baldwin (4)
9 Moment (4)
10 Fostered permanently (7)
12 For ever (11)
14 Armed contest (7)
16 Irish novelist, - - - Murdoch (4)
19 Singlet (4)
20 Part of a word (8)
21 Household pest (10)

DOWN

1 Strong gust (5)
2 Motorcycle seat for passenger (7)
3 Swag, booty (4)
4 Arctic source of milk, flesh and hide (8)
5 Top of the head (5)
6 Cure (6)
11 Hockey-like game (8)
12 Earnest entreaty (6)
13 Chris - - -, radio and TV star (7)
15 Michael Douglas film, - - - *Attraction* (5)
17 Work out (5)
18 And (4)

The Biggest Crossword Book In The World

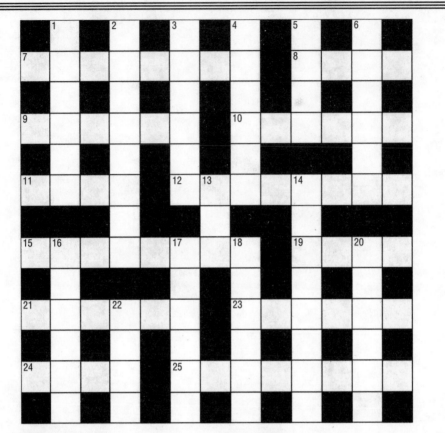

ACROSS

7 Renegade (8)
8 Biblical character (4)
9 Daintily odd (6)
10 Dinner jacket (6)
11 German river (4)
12 Always (8)
15 Sets right (8)
19 Container weight (4)
21 Lock securely (6)
23 Strip of material (6)
24 Void (4)
25 Pistol (8)

DOWN

1 Shared (6)
2 Bridge builder (8)
3 Calm (6)
4 Sculpted work (6)
5 Quartz (4)
6 Food cupboard (6)
13 Doctor who cares for pets (3)
14 Store, postpone (8)
16 Obscure (6)
17 Main court at Wimbledon (6)
18 Try hard (6)
20 Gary - - -, TV chef (6)
22 Loss or damage from a disaster (4)

The Biggest Crossword Book In The World

ACROSS

3 Proposed as candidate (9)
8 Summer month (4)
9 Obstructed (8)
10 Distant cold period (3, 3)
13 Candid (5)
14 Cravat (7)
15 Piece of turf (3)
16 Bound by oath (7)
17 Graph (5)
21 Nick Faldo, eg (6)
22 Commonwealth country (8)
23 Worry unduly (4)
24 In rebellion (9)

DOWN

1 American footballer cleared of murdering his wife (1, 1, 7)
2 Exposed (9)
4 Alternative (5)
5 Disregarded (7)
6 Yemen port (4)
7 Pitcher (4)
11 Shakespeare's birthplace (9)
12 Manual skill (9)
14 Sign of approval (3)
15 Navigation aid (7)
18 Once more (5)
19 Part of a skeleton (4)
20 Capital of Norway (4)

The Biggest Crossword Book In The World

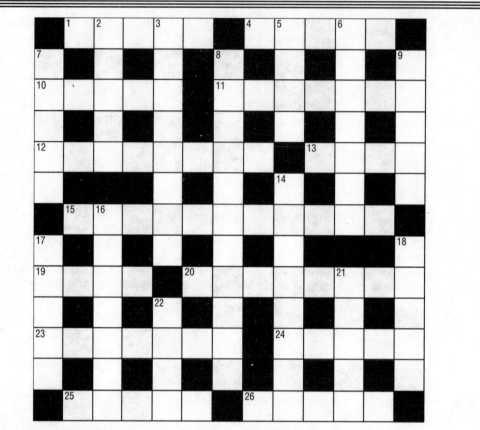

ACROSS

1 Arctic sledgedog (5)
4 Diaper (5)
10 Happen (5)
11 Stockings, etc (7)
12 Game bird with
a bright plumage (8)
13 Prohibit (4)
15 John Cleese's
former wife (6, 5)
19 Tough timber (4)
20 Recognise (8)
23 Set of clothes worn by
soldiers etc. (7)
24 Drama set to music (5)
25 Excessive (5)
26 Open box (5)

DOWN

2 Male relative (5)
3 Paraffin (8)
5 Recess in a church (4)
6 Fictitious reason (7)
7 Sporty car (5)
8 *Beyond The* - - -,
Mad Max film (11)
9 Power line support (5)
14 Heavy fall of rain (8)
16 Prolonged applause (7)
17 Support, prop (5)
18 Bob - - -, US singer
and poet (5)
21 Motionless (5)
22 Soya curd (4)

The Biggest Crossword Book In The World

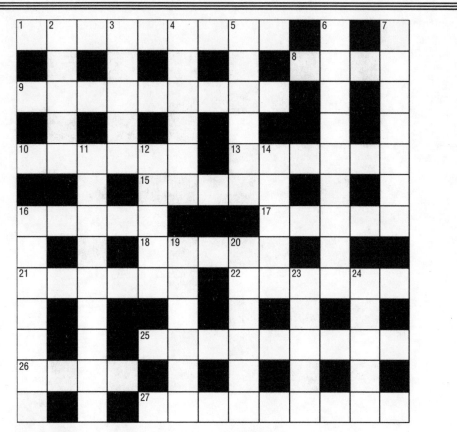

ACROSS

1 Napoleon's wife (9)
8 Sign of sulking (4)
9 French cathedral (5, 4)
10 Timber structure
to stop beach erosion (6)
13 Mel Gibson film,
- - - Weapon (6)
15 Reference list at
back of book (5)
16 Straighten up (5)
17 Cold, chilly (5)
18 Tent made of
skins etc. (5)
21 Medieval warrior (6)
22 Sheep's coat of wool (6)
25 Instrument to
measure atmosphere (9)
26 Ceremony (4)
27 In great need (9)

DOWN

2 Particular smell (5)
3 Before due time (5)
4 Concealed (6)
5 Sprightly (6)
6 Slave (9)
7 Falkland Islands port (7)
11 Start from new (9)
12 Last Beethoven
symphony (5)
14 Force out (5)
16 Bungling (7)
19 Odourless gas (6)
20 Physical exertion (6)
23 Put on pressure (5)
24 Part of the body (5)

The Biggest Crossword Book In The World

ACROSS

1 Directions, orders (12)
9 Prevent (5)
10 Commerce (5)
11 Digit (3)
12 Regal (5)
13 Ultraviolet light (3, 4)
15 Melancholy (6)
17 Virginal (6)
20 Competent (7)
23 Midday meal (5)
25 Santa's helper (3)
26 Telegraph code (5)
27 Part of Great Britain (5)
28 Irritating (12)

DOWN

2 Very poor (5)
3 Gossip (7)
4 Troubled state (6)
5 Greek god (5)
6 City in Nebraska (5)
7 Long horse race (12)
8 Former Goon (5, 7)
14 Grazing land (3)
16 Crushing snake (3)
18 Simpleton (7)
19 Goalie (6)
21 Waterproof jacket (5)
22 Highpitched sound (5)
24 Synthetic fabric (5)

The Biggest Crossword Book In The World

ACROSS

7 Forefather (8)
8 Flying animal (4)
9 Receive willingly (6)
10 Gary - - -, golfer (6)
11 Fret (5)
12 Practical and careful (7)
15 Progress (7)
17 Garment for the upper part of a body (5)
20 Straight and upright (6)
22 Ice cream dessert (6)
23 Hillside (4)
24 Water-based paint (8)

DOWN

1 Humorous tale (8)
2 Thin layer of wood (6)
3 Condition (5)
4 Make ready (7)
5 On (an aircraft) (6)
6 Gratis (4)
13 Story teller (8)
14 Loitered (7)
16 English county (6)
18 Sincere (6)
19 Magazine edition (5)
21 Quality (4)

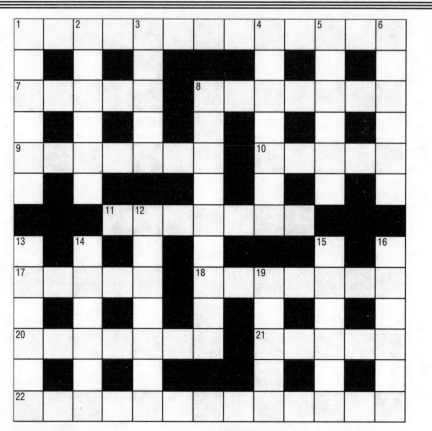

ACROSS

1 *Batman* actor (5, 3, 5)
7 Chief ballerina (5)
8 Operator? (7)
9 Breastbone (7)
10 Hit (5)
11 Absurd statement (7)
17 Image (5)
18 Moment (7)
20 Unspecified person (7)
21 Asil - - -,
  businessman (5)
22 On the way (2, 3, 8)

DOWN

1 Office worker (6)
2 Unmarried woman (6)
3 Strong desire (5)
4 Ancient walled city (7)
5 Liam - - -,
  Irish-born actor (6)
6 Upper council (6)
8 Express concisely (9)
12 Dreaded (7)
13 Andre - - -,
  tennis player (6)
14 Fate, destiny (6)
15 Ben Kingsley film (6)
16 Deprive of food (6)
19 Scorch (5)

The Biggest Crossword Book In The World

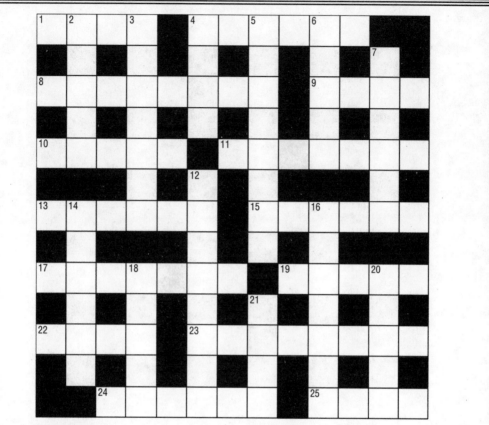

ACROSS

1 Average (4)
4 American coin (6)
8 Military flag (8)
9 Brook (4)
10 Go away (5)
11 Warned (7)
13 Respect (6)
15 Consent (6)
17 Oprah - - -,
   talk show host (7)
19 Pocket (5)
22 Defensive ditch
   round a castle (4)
23 Expression of
   gratitude (5, 3)
24 Vigour, drive (6)
25 Runner's part of
   a racetrack (4)

DOWN

2 Spirit measure (5)
3 Official command (7)
4 Undiluted (4)
5 Robbie Coltrane's
   favourite car (8)
6 Bit of dying fire (5)
7 Part of a television (6)
12 Term at university (8)
14 Electric lamp inventor (6)
16 Swimmer's
   breathing tube (7)
18 Japanese bed (5)
20 Jester (5)
21 Circumspect (4)

The Biggest Crossword Book In The World

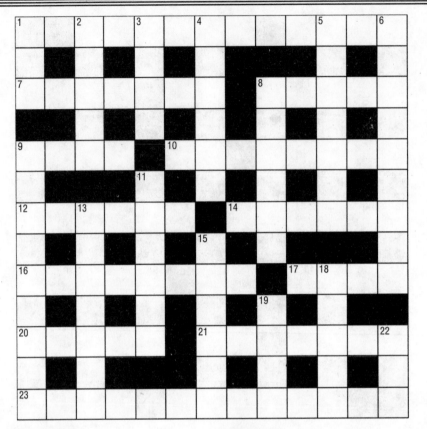

ACROSS

1 American Soul singer (6, 7)
7 The Mother of all Battles? (4, 3)
8 Snapshot (5)
9 Loud explosive noise (4)
10 The - - - of Venice, Shakespeare play (8)
12 Small handcart (6)
14 Mother - - -, Nobel prize winner (6)
16 Contest in law (8)
17 Creep forward (4)
20 Shred (cheese) (5)
21 Determined (7)
23 Expert at sums (13)

DOWN

1 Excavated (3)
2 Manmade fibre (5)
3 Nothing in Yorkshire! (4)
4 Employee (6)
5 Quarantine, segregate (7)
6 Ken Dodd's birthplace (6, 3)
8 Striker (6)
9 Chewing sweet (6, 3)
11 Dance? (6)
13 Withdraw (7)
15 Canadian capital (6)
18 Military shop (5)
19 Salvador - - -, Spanish artist (4)
22 Two times five (3)

The Biggest Crossword Book In The World

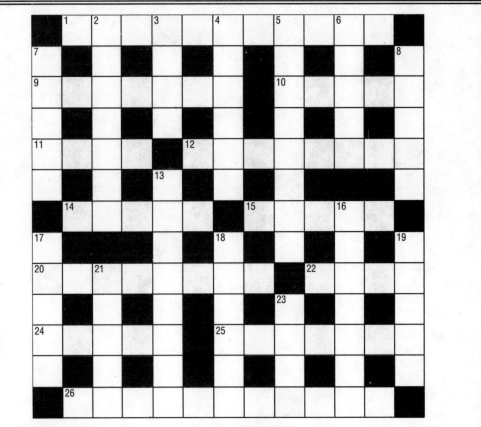

ACROSS

1 Ex England football manager (5, 6)
9 Tempted (7)
10 In existence (5)
11 Sign of weeping (4)
12 Filbert (8)
14 Foul smell (5)
15 Sugar pincers (5)
20 Flowering plant (8)
22 Edging stone (4)
24 Make, form (5)
25 Plunder (7)
26 Twin-peaked cap (11)

DOWN

2 Withdraw (7)
3 *The Seven Year - - -*, Monroe film (4)
4 Hold for ransom (6)
5 Evita? (3, 5)
6 Sigourney Weaver film (5)
7 Pier (5)
8 Trifling (5)
13 Uninvited visitor (8)
16 Bomb thrown by hand (7)
17 Spherical glass vessel (5)
18 Kermit the Frog, eg (6)
19 Church building (5)
21 Salt water (5)
23 Israeli national airline (2-2)

The Biggest Crossword Book In The World

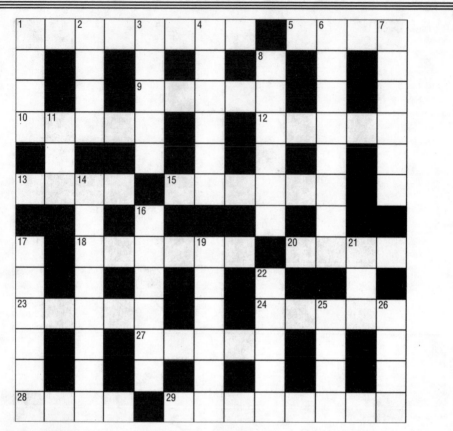

ACROSS

1 Household servant (8)
5 African country (4)
9 *The Sound of - - -,* Julie Andrews film (5)
10 Paris subway (5)
12 Out of condition (5)
13 Lowest point (4)
15 Harsh (6)
18 Small village (6)
20 Self-satisfied (4)
23 Outbreak (5)
24 Put one's name down (5)
27 Use a car ? (5)
28 British playwright, Sir - - - Coward (4)
29 Not as good (8)

DOWN

1 The Last Judgement (4)
2 Greatest (4)
3 Simple fellow? (5)
4 Interior (6)
6 School holiday (4, 4)
7 Colin - - -, crime writer (6)
8 Shrewdness (6)
11 Before (3)
14 Repeat aloud (8)
16 Hamper (6)
17 Engine part (6)
19 Banner (6)
21 Alien craft (1, 1, 1)
22 Hissing birds (5)
25 Life-saving charity (1, 1, 1, 1)
26 Gloomy (weather) (4)

The Biggest Crossword Book In The World

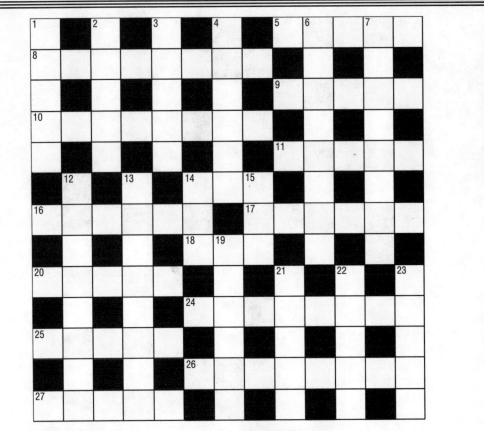

ACROSS

5 Fatigued (5)
8 Juvenile (5-3)
9 Pedigree, family (5)
10 Feelings (8)
11 Striped stone (5)
14 Adieu (3)
16 Heart disorder (6)
17 Restricted quota (6)
18 For each (3)
20 French painter (5)
24 Rocky - - -, boxer (8)
25 Tell tales (5)
26 Without hope (8)
27 An enemy of Dr Who (5)

DOWN

1 Boring tool (5)
2 Utter fool (5)
3 Celtic priest (5)
4 Business (6)
6 Water (land) (8)
7 Chance to vote (8)
12 Habitual
 sleeplessness (8)
13 Able to read and write (8)
14 Large soft roll (3)
15 Go wrong (3)
19 Happy (6)
21 Scamper (5)
22 Capital of Morocco (5)
23 Funniest card
 in the pack ? (5)

The Biggest Crossword Book In The World

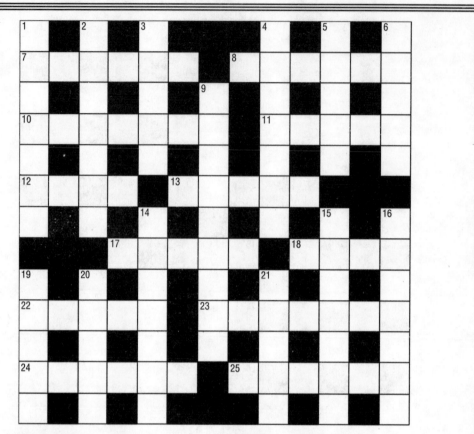

ACROSS

7 Third largest Italian city (6)
8 Kernel (6)
10 Rich red colour (7)
11 Tennis star, - - - Agassi (5)
12 Civil disorder (4)
13 Leisurely walk (5)
17 Hard outer casing (5)
18 Keen interest (4)
22 Main artery (5)
23 Slimmer (7)
24 Opinion (6)
25 Burning fiercely (6)

DOWN

1 Legendary horse (7)
2 Peach-like fruit (7)
3 Lavish meal (5)
4 Within the law (7)
5 Derogatory (5)
6 Early anaesthetic (5)
9 Hostility (9)
14 Large wave (7)
15 Cushion seat(7)
16 Race official (7)
19 Taxi driver (5)
20 Cook on a barbecue (5)
21 Dance involving a low bar (5)

The Biggest Crossword Book In The World

ACROSS

1 French river (5)
4 Trunks (7)
8 Haphazard (7)
9 Flow regulator (5)
10 Knitting stitch (4)
11 Lair (3)
12 Study hard (4)
15 Highland language (6)
16 In foreign parts (6)
19 Blast of wind (4)
21 Confer knighthood upon (3)
22 Russian ruler (4)
26 Door lock (5)
27 Wine smell (7)
28 Cell under ground (7)
29 Estimate (5)

DOWN

1 Keen, acute (5)
2 Dip (7)
3 Uniform (4)
4 Jockey, - - - Piggott (6)
5 Elasticity (4)
6 Give leave (5)
7 Opted (7)
13 Louse egg (3)
14 Serious crime (1, 1, 1)
15 Laughed nervously (7)
17 Difficult to see (7)
18 South African city (6)
20 Glossy silk fabric (5)
23 Council tax (5)
24 Clarified butter (4)
25 Cask stopper (4)

The Biggest Crossword Book In The World

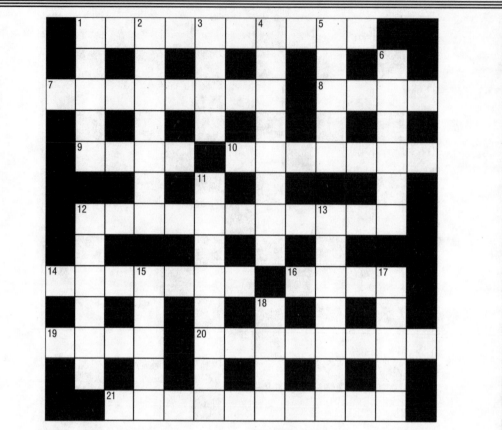

ACROSS

1 Exciting, unusual (10)
7 Current (2, 3, 3)
8 Actress,
 - - - Barrymore (4)
9 Drag (4)
10 Companion (7)
12 Absorbing (11)
14 Newspaper (7)
16 Thick string (4)
19 Metric unit of weight (4)
20 Puts in order (8)
21 Atomic power
 station (10)

DOWN

1 Freshwater fish (5)
2 Drain (7)
3 Cheese wrapped
 in wax (4)
4 Small mammal (8)
5 Beneath (5)
6 Seasoned sailor (3, 3)
11 Crucial (8)
12 Printed in sloping
 type (6)
13 Metallic period of
 history (4, 3)
15 Flee to marry (5)
17 Remove faults from (5)
18 King of Norway (4)

The Biggest Crossword Book In The World

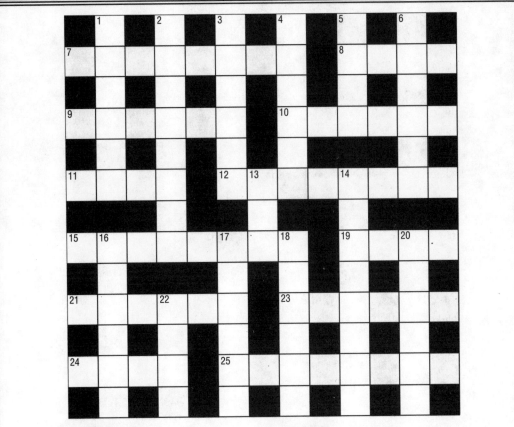

ACROSS

7 Wellknown for something bad (8)
8 Enormous pool (4)
9 Fugitive (6)
10 Get (6)
11 Make (4)
12 Rupture (8)
15 Apprehensive about (8)
19 Continent (4)
21 Agricultural implement (6)
23 Jane - - -, British novelist (6)
24 Mask (4)
25 Cut of meat (4, 4)

DOWN

1 Make certain (6)
2 Maltese capital (8)
3 Spider's trap (6)
4 On land (6)
5 Dart (4)
6 Alberto Tomba's sport (6)
13 Manage (3)
14 Hiker's bag (8)
16 Hair curler (6)
17 Breathe in (6)
18 Music industry award (6)
20 Coldest part of a refrigerator (6)
22 Hideous (4)

The Biggest Crossword Book In The World

ACROSS

3 Garden flower (9)
8 Loose outer garment (4)
9 Frightening (8)
10 Chest (6)
13 Blue - - -, naval flag (5)
14 Promise to marry (7)
15 Motor vehicle (3)
16 Tight-fitting dancers garment (7)
17 Hand tool for drilling holes (5)
21 Flavoured water ice (6)
22 Fussy (8)
23 Hindu woman's dress (4)
24 Self-appointed crime-fighter (9)

DOWN

1 Wild sour fruit (4, 5)
2 Opposition (9)
4 Diminish in strength (5)
5 English poet (7)
6 Not different (4)
7 Arm bone (4)
11 Inhabitant of the North Pole (5, 4)
12 Tribe leader (9)
14 Not good (3)
15 Country, capital Zagreb (7)
18 Berkshire racecourse (5)
19 *GI Jane* star, - - - Moore (4)
20 Wife of a rajah (4)

The Biggest Crossword Book In The World

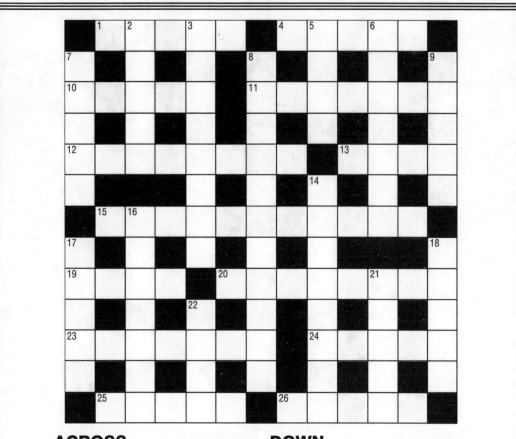

ACROSS

1 Society of tradesmen (5)
4 Set amount (5)
10 Safari animal? (5)
11 Infinite (7)
12 Chinese cooking
  ingredient (3, 5)
13 Impudence (4)
15 Thoughtful,
  considerate (11)
19 Ill will (4)
20 Frothy coffee (8)
23 Flow slowly (7)
24 Passageway between
  rows of seats
  in a church (5)
25 Small coin (5)
26 Linked series (5)

DOWN

2 Combine (5)
3 *Titanic* actor,
  - - - DiCaprio (8)
5 Official language
  of Pakistan (4)
6 Juvenile (7)
7 Worthless objects (5)
8 Classroom
  favourite (8, 3)
9 Sacred song (5)
14 Scottish holiday
  resort (8)
16 Bill (7)
17 Extent (5)
18 Kent port (5)
21 Oriental rice dish (5)
22 Hide, pelt (4)

The Biggest Crossword Book In The World

ACROSS

1 Manly (9)
8 Ripped (4)
9 Concealed (9)
10 Funeral carriage (6)
13 Actor, - - - Fox (6)
15 Puritan (5)
16 Mingle, combine (5)
17 One of the
deadly sins (5)
18 Jacket collar (5)
21 Remember (6)
22 Tension (6)
25 Quasimodo's love (9)
26 Cudgel (4)
27 White dog with
dark spots (9)

DOWN

2 Get up (5)
3 Roll of tobacco leaves for
smoking (5)
4 Wait idly (6)
5 Required (6)
6 Longing for
former times (9)
7 Curve in a river (7)
11 Extremely cruel (9)
12 Words used as charm (5)
14 Handed out
playing cards (5)
16 Rupert - - -,
media baron (7)
19 Largest American
state (6)
20 Respect (6)
23 Cook (5)
24 Asian country (5)

The Biggest Crossword Book In The World

ACROSS

1 Fighting-pole (12)
9 Up and down (5)
10 Circular reef (5)
11 Under the weather (3)
12 Device which propels a helicopter (5)
13 Protective garment (7)
15 Not any person (6)
17 Cage for sent-off sportsmen (3, 3)
20 Entertainer (7)
23 Frock (5)
25 Australian bird (3)
26 First Greek letter (5)
27 Elastic fabric (5)
28 Judy Garland's daughter (4, 8)

DOWN

2 German submarine (1-4)
3 Gone to bed (7)
4 Hire (6)
5 Musty (5)
6 Affectionate greeting (5)
7 Battle against Argentina (9, 3)
8 Hollywood actress (6, 6)
14 Managed, supervised (3)
16 French word for 'yes' (3)
18 Gratify a whim (7)
19 Kevin - - -, football manager (6)
21 Yellow gemstone (5)
22 Mass of bees (5)
24 Surpass (5)

The Biggest Crossword Book In The World

ACROSS

7 Watchful, alert (8)
8 Give out smoke (4)
9 Squanders (6)
10 Sideways drift (6)
11 Large house with gardens (5)
12 Regular action (7)
15 Australian countryside (7)
17 Part of an act (5)
20 Soft felt hat (6)
22 Restraining rope (6)
23 Female horse (4)
24 Talk (8)

DOWN

1 Layered Italian dessert (8)
2 Handgun (6)
3 Cultivated flower (5)
4 English veined cheese (7)
5 Overall impression (6)
6 Actress, - - - Samms (4)
13 Silly conduct (8)
14 Scrape with the nails (7)
16 Agent (6)
18 Small chop (6)
19 Wasp's weapon (5)
21 Style and vigour (4)

The Biggest Crossword Book In The World

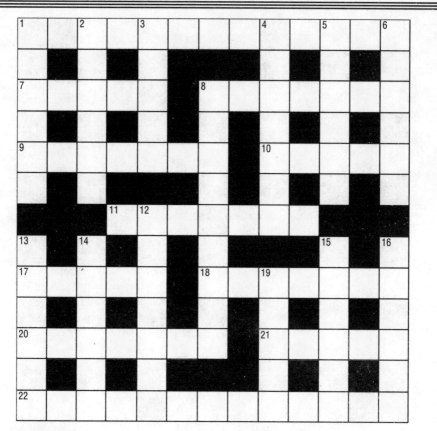

ACROSS

1 One of Henry VIII's wives (9, 4)
7 Dismissed (5)
8 Exhibition (7)
9 Forever (7)
10 *Life on - - -*, TV series (5)
11 RSPCA, eg (7)
17 Breathing apparatus of fish (5)
18 Of the eyes (7)
20 Film about the life of Mozart (7)
21 Monkey-like animal (5)
22 Killing (13)

DOWN

1 Drink made from roasted seeds (6)
2 Small tower (6)
3 Peter - - -, snooker player (5)
4 Simplest (7)
5 Entice, attract (6)
6 Musical beat (6)
8 Wildly excited (9)
12 Show compere (7)
13 Large lizard (6)
14 At all times (6)
15 Small lobster (6)
16 Old British coin (6)
19 City in Oklahoma (5)

ACROSS

- **1** Cried (4)
- **4** Hackneyed phrase (6)
- **8** Commander defeated at Waterloo (8)
- **9** Dull, heavy sound (4)
- **10** Plant's stem (5)
- **11** Reprimand (4, 3)
- **13** Deep gorge (6)
- **15** Reduce in status (6)
- **17** Jug (7)
- **19** Capital of Ecuador (5)
- **22** Money penalty (4)
- **23** Fund-raising TV programme (8)
- **24** Croaky (6)
- **25** Rim, verge (4)

DOWN

- **2** Play out a role (5)
- **3** Basket on wheels (7)
- **4** Munch (4)
- **5** Indirect accusation (8)
- **6** The Dorchester, eg (5)
- **7** Costume (6)
- **12** Creator (8)
- **14** Bitter, sharp (6)
- **16** Canadian policeman (7)
- **18** Statement of belief (5)
- **20** Thin strip of leather (5)
- **21** Besides (4)

The Biggest Crossword Book In The World

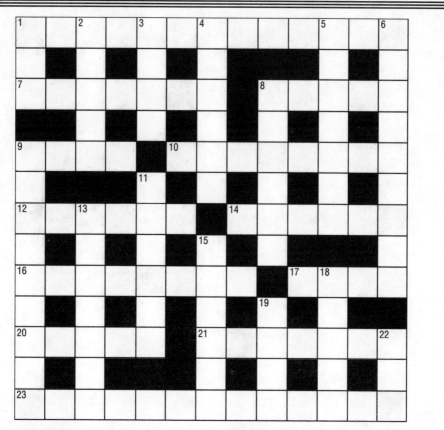

ACROSS
1 Disgraceful (13)
7 In proportion (3, 4)
8 Strain to lift (5)
9 Summon (4)
10 Drinking liquid (8)
12 Go on a journey (6)
14 Holiday destination (6)
16 Central American country (8)
17 Quarter of a pint (4)
20 Film legend, - - - Welles (5)
21 Police series set at Sun Hill (3, 4)
23 They stop progress! (7, 6)

DOWN
1 Material damage (3)
2 Move around in search of prey (5)
3 Test (4)
4 Glasslike coating (6)
5 Show of boldness (7)
6 Fundamental (9)
8 Paid attention to (6)
9 Long-bladed razor (9)
11 Small shiny decoration (6)
13 Memory loss (7)
15 Putty-like substance (6)
18 After dinner drink, - - - coffee (5)
19 Joined house (4)
22 Comedian, - - - Dennis (3)

The Biggest Crossword Book In The World

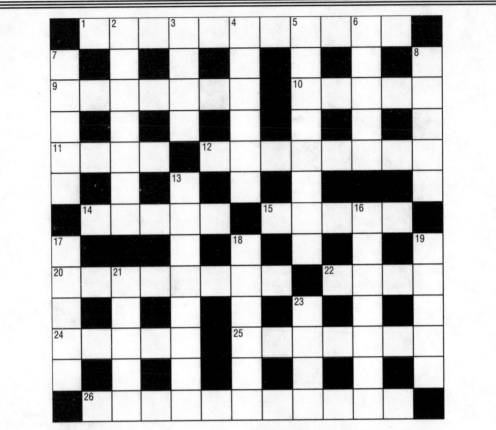

ACROSS

1 High-jumping style (7, 4)
9 Thrown out of a property (7)
10 Viscous mud (5)
11 Slide out of control (4)
12 Local (8)
14 Shabby (5)
15 Christmas tree decoration (5)
20 Musical instrument (8)
22 Jumping creature (4)
24 Small firework (5)
25 Finger protector (7)
26 *Sherlock Holmes* actor (6, 5)

DOWN

2 Opening (7)
3 West country town (4)
4 Set free (6)
5 Day of celebration (8)
6 Bulb vegetable (5)
7 Dog's lead (5)
8 Children's party dish (5)
13 Charming (8)
16 Melted cheese dish (7)
17 Light and crunchy (5)
18 Soldier on watch (6)
19 Be of the same opinion (5)
21 Slide (5)
23 Coffin stand (4)

The Biggest Crossword Book In The World

ACROSS
1 Salad item (8)
5 Blaze (4)
9 Awaken (5)
10 Body's pump (5)
12 Talk too much (5)
13 Sturdy vehicle (4)
15 Powered pleasure craft (3, 3)
18 Pail (6)
20 Public school (4)
23 Actress, - - - Keen (5)
24 Change (5)
27 Perspire (5)
28 Chances (4)
29 West Indian island (8)

DOWN
1 Hit with blunt weapon (4)
2 Fizzy drink (4)
3 Merriment (5)
4 Correspond (6)
6 Visionary (8)
7 Specialist (6)
8 Composure (6)
11 Adam's partner (3)
14 Hugged (8)
16 Obtain (data) from a computer (6)
17 Blue dye (6)
19 Captivate (6)
21 Rock rich in minerals (3)
22 Conductor's stick (5)
25 Stepped (4)
26 Foray (4)

The Biggest Crossword Book In The World

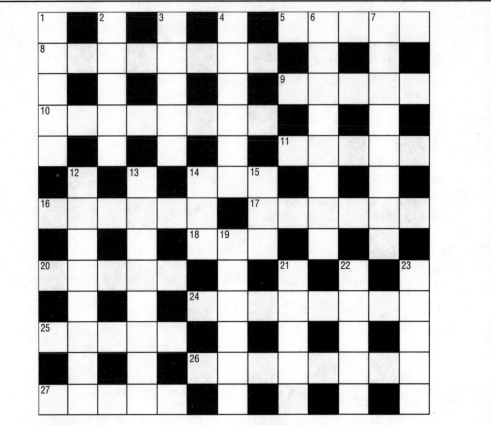

ACROSS

5 Injury (5)
8 Grand - - -, Aintree steeplechase (8)
9 Respond (5)
10 Brown spots on the skin (8)
11 Ancient Greek philosopher (5)
14 Elite regiment (1, 1, 1)
16 Distant (6)
17 Mission (6)
18 Part of a circle (3)
20 Main drain (5)
24 The Queen's Scottish home (8)
25 Tasteless liquid (5)
26 Wilful disrespect of authority (8)
27 Powerful (5)

DOWN

1 Detect a smell (5)
2 Speak (5)
3 Russian drink (5)
4 Image recorder (6)
6 D-Day codename (8)
7 Tobacco drug (8)
12 Bring into being (8)
13 Motion (8)
14 Expanse of water (3)
15 Dry (of wine) (3)
19 Purpose (6)
21 Devoid (5)
22 Gentleman of the road (5)
23 Thrill to bits (5)

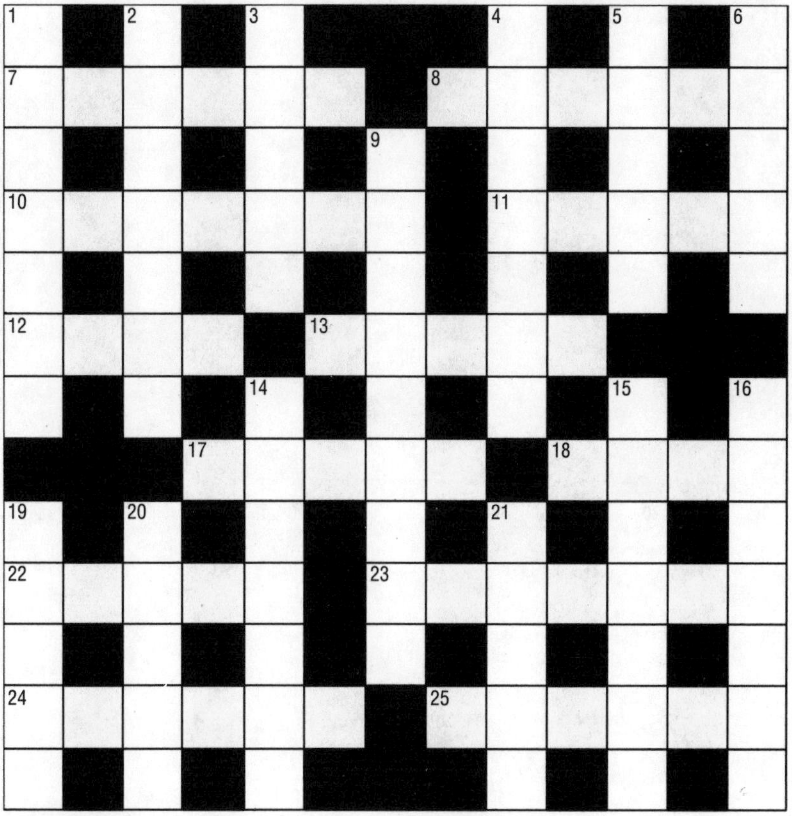

ACROSS

7 Mrs Thatcher? (6)
8 Buoyant (6)
10 Circular building (7)
11 Bedeck (5)
12 Attractive (4)
13 Feather pen (5)
17 Of a town (5)
18 Wild pig (4)
22 Monica - - -,
   tennis star (5)
23 Part of a series (7)
24 Mental institution (6)
25 Japanese robe (6)

DOWN

1 Hug (7)
2 Stir up (7)
3 Actress, - - - Rigg (5)
4 Congenial (7)
5 Punctuation mark (5)
6 Dangerous action (5)
9 Soaked (9)
14 Keep-fit exercise (5-2)
15 Biblical king (7)
16 Liberty (7)
19 Common (5)
20 Welsh county (5)
21 Copy, imitate (5)

The Biggest Crossword Book In The World

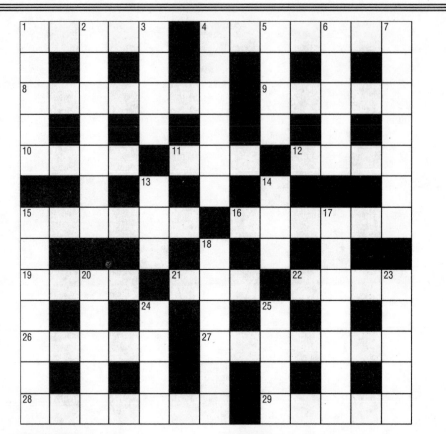

ACROSS

1 Period of rule (5)
4 Harass, nag (7)
8 Ancient paper (7)
9 Former Argentinian President (5)
10 Thrash, beat (4)
11 Sweltering (3)
12 Hence (4)
15 Food for animals (6)
16 Light jacket (6)
19 Carve (4)
21 Obtain (3)
22 Handle (4)
26 Loud noise (5)
27 Fishing boat (7)
28 Sincere (7)
29 V-shaped groove (5)

DOWN

1 Swift, quick (5)
2 Take possession of (7)
3 Roman emperor (4)
4 John - - -, film director (6)
5 Part of the neck (4)
6 Mistake (5)
7 Neil - - -, Labour politician (7)
13 Comedian, - - - Hirst (3)
14 Close (3)
15 Complimentary gift (7)
17 Curly lock of hair (7)
18 Group of seven (6)
20 Seat of authority (5)
23 Genesis (5)
24 Richard - - -, film star (4)
25 Downpour (4)

The Biggest Crossword Book In The World

ACROSS

1 Turned from one langauge to another (10)
7 A courgette (8)
8 Check proofs (4)
9 Salver (4)
10 Cockney part of London (4, 3)
12 Scenic (11)
14 Ailment (7)
16 Adam's son (4)
19 Hockey on horseback? (4)
20 New York borough (3, 5)
21 Referring to oneself (10)

DOWN

1 Tease (5)
2 Old, primitive (7)
3 Bathe (4)
4 Stirs (8)
5 Expel (5)
6 Soul singer, - - - Warwick (6)
11 Throbs (8)
12 Bedtime headrest (6)
13 Argument (7)
15 Hangman's knot (5)
17 Child's nurse (5)
18 Capital of Switzerland (4)

The Biggest Crossword Book In The World

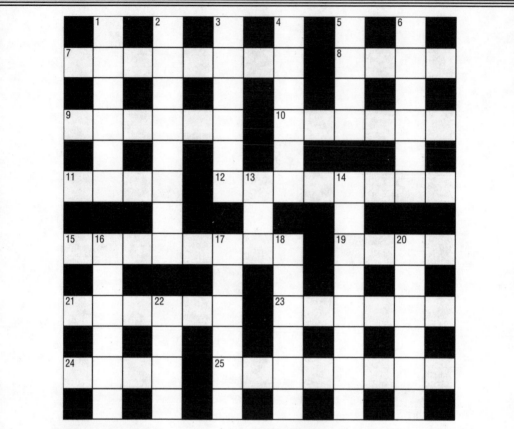

ACROSS

7 Garden plant (8)
8 At what time? (4)
9 Appoint (6)
10 Sickly looking (6)
11 Type of shoe (4)
12 Bought back (8)
15 Group of Scottish islands (8)
19 Fasten (4)
21 Sand and cement mix (6)
23 English county (6)
24 Passport endorsement (4)
25 Farmyard bird (8)

DOWN

1 Container (6)
2 Feign illness (8)
3 Main meal (6)
4 Tickled (6)
5 Absent without leave (inits) (4)
6 Withdraw (6)
13 Small spot on a potato (3)
14 Makes bigger (8)
16 Remarkably strange (6)
17 Straightforward (6)
18 Mislead (6)
20 Dark-red wine (6)
22 Top of a feeding bottle (4)

The Biggest Crossword Book In The World

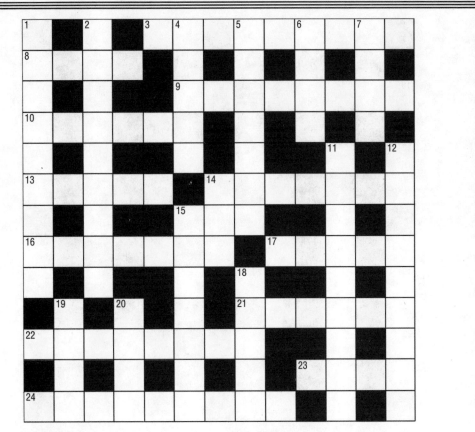

ACROSS

3 Endless (9)
8 Medieval weapon (4)
9 Good-natured
   friendliness (8)
10 Israeli currency unit (6)
13 Sporting fixture (5)
14 Author, - - - Archer (7)
15 In low spirits (3)
16 Not any (7)
17 *A Fish Called - - -*,
   film (5)
21 Small pleasure boat (6)
22 Height (8)
23 Home of the Incas (4)
24 A climax (9)

DOWN

1 Pastime (9)
2 Strange behaviour (9)
4 Dignified, eminent (5)
5 Inflamed (7)
6 Cartoon locomotive,
   - - - the Engine (4)
7 Departure (4)
11 Cuts short (9)
12 Religious building (9)
14 Glass container (3)
15 Shut off (7)
18 Velocity (5)
19 Aspersion (4)
20 Partiality (4)

The Biggest Crossword Book In The World

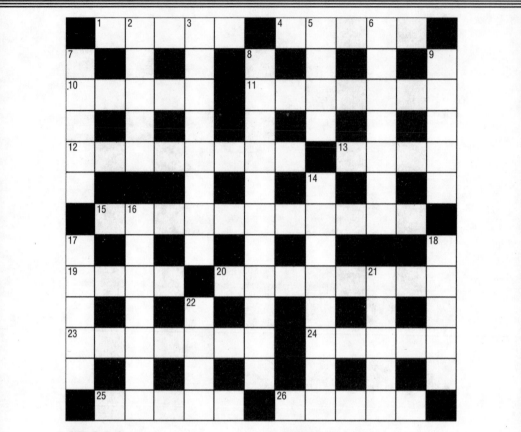

ACROSS

1 Oversentimental (5)
4 Craft (5)
10 Supple and athletic (5)
11 Large stone statue (7)
12 Bestial deed (8)
13 Take a different course (4)
15 *Prime Suspect* star (5, 6)
19 Money-making racket (4)
20 Hinder (8)
23 Distinguished (7)
24 Male bee (5)
25 Cabaret show (5)
26 US state (5)

DOWN

2 Tarka, perhaps (5)
3 Religious speaker (8)
5 Castle tower (4)
6 Free time (7)
7 Fold in material (5)
8 Pollute (11)
9 Penniless (5)
14 Kept from flying (8)
16 Scrutinise (7)
17 Escort (5)
18 Move slowly (5)
21 Stall at a funfair (5)
22 List of dishes available (4)

The Biggest Crossword Book In The World

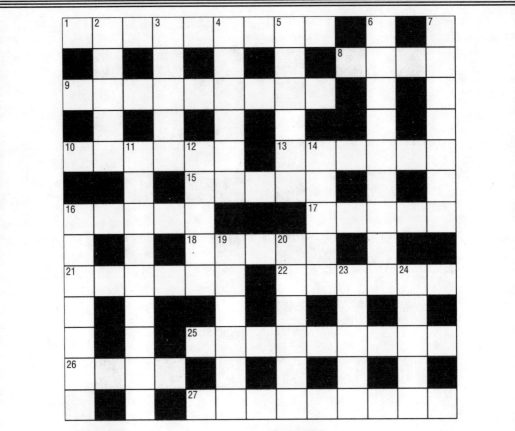

ACROSS

1 Isolate (9)
8 Martial art (4)
9 Hampshire woodland (3, 6)
10 Emphasis (6)
13 One-sided (6)
15 Prime number (5)
16 Actress, - - - Imrie (5)
17 Sorceress (5)
18 Canadian leaf emblem (5)
21 Besides (6)
22 Foreigners? (6)
25 Accompaniment to lamb (4, 5)
26 Skin complaint (4)
27 Breed of dog (9)

DOWN

2 Vote (5)
3 Search and rob (5)
4 Bright and colourful (6)
5 Collection of cells (6)
6 Promise (9)
7 King or Queen (7)
11 Unwilling (9)
12 Walk with heavy footsteps (5)
14 Stairpost (5)
16 English cheese (7)
19 Formal dress (6)
20 More recent (6)
23 Very angry (5)
24 Wall recess (5)

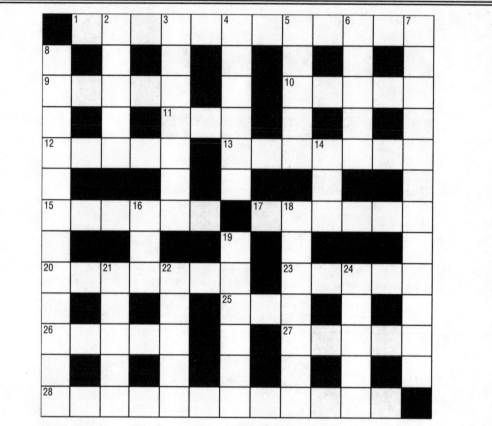

ACROSS

1 Outbreak of rain and lightning (12)
9 Light timber (5)
10 French sculptor (5)
11 Golf ball support (3)
12 Wear (5)
13 Take part in (7)
15 Island home of The Bounty mutineers (6)
17 Child's playground ride (6)
20 Blaze (7)
23 Liable to (5)
25 Buddy (3)
26 Kill by immersion in water (5)
27 Random arrangement (2, 3)
28 Ceased (12)

DOWN

2 Beatles No 1, - - - *Goodbye* (5)
3 Tidiest (7)
4 Hope for (6)
5 Play the guitar (5)
6 Bill - - -, member of The Goodies (5)
7 Adjustable spanner (6-6)
8 Forgetful (6-6)
14 Edgar Allan - - -, American author (3)
16 Winter driving hazard (3)
18 Make clear (7)
19 Tall, cylindrical head covering (3, 3)
21 Dental string (5)
22 Beatles' drummer, - - - Starr (5)
24 Orange-yellow (5)

The Biggest Crossword Book In The World

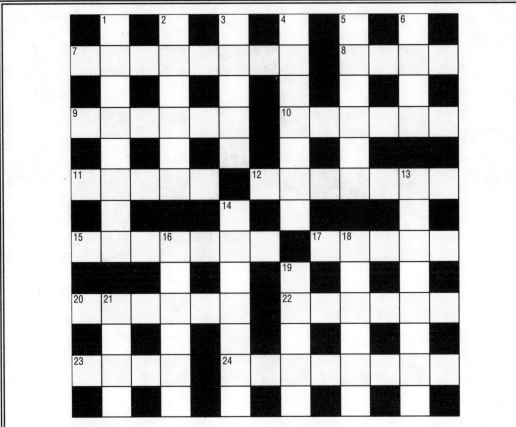

ACROSS

7 Word blindness (8)
8 **Former** German
currency (4)
9 Politician,
- - - Jackson (6)
10 Sober (6)
11 Bruce Lee film,
- - - *the Dragon* (5)
12 Despicable (7)
15 Difficult (7)
17 Commit to memory (5)
20 **Former** monetary unit
of Spain (6)
22 Pester in a
hostile way (6)
23 German Mrs (4)
24 Personal beliefs (8)

DOWN

1 Make-up (8)
2 Passing look (6)
3 British-based charity (5)
4 Highest military rank (7)
5 Blur (6)
6 Coarse sand (4)
13 Rebellion (8)
14 Museum worker (7)
16 Helpful, practical (6)
18 Cream cake (6)
19 Scope (5)
21 Previous name for
Republic of Ireland (4)

The Biggest Crossword Book In The World

ACROSS

1 The Queen Mother's home (8, 5)
7 Fervour (5)
8 Gymnastic performer (7)
9 Father of all Jews (7)
10 Comedian, - - - Wise (5)
11 Children's TV programme (7)
17 Kind of daisy (5)
18 Speak foolishly (7)
20 Crush (7)
21 Poetry (5)
22 Necessary, essential (13)

DOWN

1 Fine brandy (6)
2 Convince (6)
3 Notable period of time (5)
4 Reap and gather in (7)
5 Suave (6)
6 One of two alternatives (6)
8 Excellent (9)
12 Vain, futile (7)
13 Dwarf tree (6)
14 Pay back (6)
15 Chubby-faced angel (6)
16 Mourn (6)
19 Projecting edge of the roof (5)

The Biggest Crossword Book In The World

ACROSS

1 Honey drink (4)
4 Tropical American bird (6)
8 West Indian state (8)
9 Period of time (4)
10 Therefore (5)
11 Longed for (7)
13 Innate skill (6)
15 Small dotted block (6)
17 Study of animals (7)
19 Drinking tube (5)
22 Disconnect, unfasten (4)
23 The lost continent (8)
24 Paddy Ashdown's real first name (6)
25 The Orient (4)

DOWN

2 Rub out (5)
3 Fiasco (7)
4 Orderly (4)
5 Shaky, infirm (8)
6 Dislike strongly (5)
7 Serving dish for soup (6)
12 Become motionless (8)
14 Measure (6)
16 Afternoon performance (7)
18 Unrestrained (5)
20 Wrong (5)
21 Murder (4)

The Biggest Crossword Book In The World

ACROSS
1 Weather forecaster (13)
7 Irritate (7)
8 Smooth woollen cloth (5)
9 Ship's men (4)
10 Deserted, abandoned (8)
12 Believe (6)
14 Breed of dog (6)
16 Compassion, pity (8)
17 Period of fasting (4)
20 Rugged (5)
21 Berkshire town (7)
23 Midlands town (13)

DOWN
1 Route planner (3)
2 Large steak (1-4)
3 Musical instrument (4)
4 Followed orders (6)
5 First letter of a name (7)
6 Cure, remedy (9)
8 Inhabitant of Brittany (6)
9 Wine-bottle opener (9)
11 Gypsy (6)
13 Humorous, funny (7)
15 Place of worship (6)
18 Live (5)
19 Cripple, disable (4)
22 Firearm (3)

The Biggest Crossword Book In The World

ACROSS
1 Merger (11)
9 Small European principality (7)
10 Depth of colour (5)
11 Spiritual teacher (4)
12 Insincere praise (8)
14 Treacle (5)
15 Spanish island (5)
20 Made bigger (8)
22 Jail (4)
24 Colloquial speech (5)
25 Couple (7)
26 Strict (4, 3, 4)

DOWN
2 Hospital worker (7)
3 Naked (4)
4 Almost (6)
5 Chemist's glass (4, 4)
6 Deliver a speech (5)
7 Beg (5)
8 Nairobi's country (5)
13 Angered (8)
16 Ardent (7)
17 Bread ingredient (5)
18 Jam ingredient (6)
19 Narrow side-street (5)
21 South American animal (5)
23 Nick Faldo's sport (4)

The Biggest Crossword Book In The World

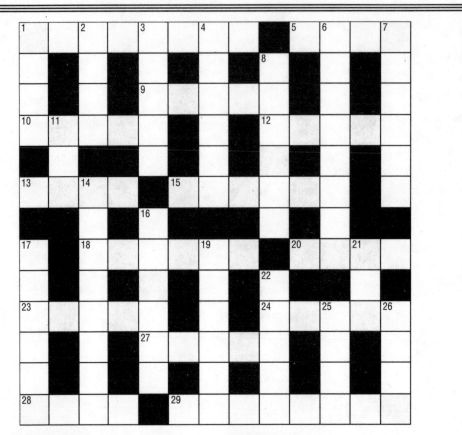

ACROSS

1 Snake-killing animal (8)
5 TV presenter, - - - Wax (4)
9 Extremely large (5)
10 Fangs (5)
12 Not silently (5)
13 Cat's cry (4)
15 The Duke of Edinburgh (6)
18 Celebrated (6)
20 Aquatic bird (4)
23 Politician, - - - Parkinson (5)
24 Goods for sale (5)
27 Prolonged absence from own country (5)
28 Bathroom powder (4)
29 Gifted (8)

DOWN

1 Encounter (4)
2 Hub of a wheel (4)
3 Should (5)
4 Look (for) (6)
6 Disconnect (8)
7 Over there (6)
8 Paper fastener (6)
11 Supplement (3)
14 Ceremonial (8)
16 Symbol (6)
17 Large grasshopper (6)
19 TV presenter, - - - Jonsson (6)
21 Field crop (3)
22 Root vegetable (5)
25 Take a break (4)
26 Seaside grit (4)

The Biggest Crossword Book In The World

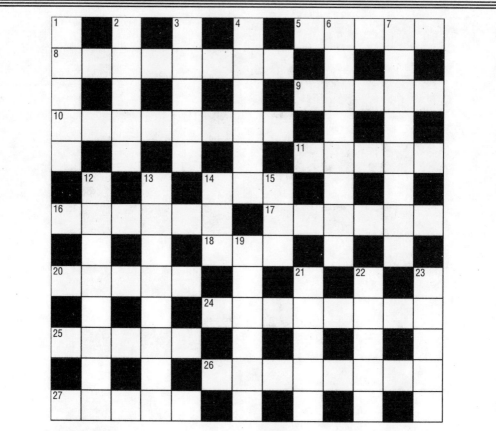

ACROSS
5 Edible nut (5)
8 Fiddled (8)
9 Drinking vessel (5)
10 Generation (3-5)
11 Initiate (5)
14 Actress, - - - Leoni (3)
16 Tower of London
   warders (6)
17 Despicable person (6)
18 Metal container (3)
20 Untreated rubber (5)
24 Pledge (8)
25 Marconi's invention (5)
26 Floor covering (8)
27 Intense excitement (5)

DOWN
1 Carnivorous mammal (5)
2 Rest on bended legs (5)
3 Cheerful (5)
4 Standing (6)
6 Overshadowed (8)
7 Hard to understand (8)
12 American state (8)
13 Stupid person (8)
14 Explosive (1, 1, 1)
15 Beard of barley (3)
19 Sarcastic (6)
21 One of the Three
   Musketeers (5)
22 Hesitate (5)
23 Burglar's tool (5)

The Biggest Crossword Book In The World

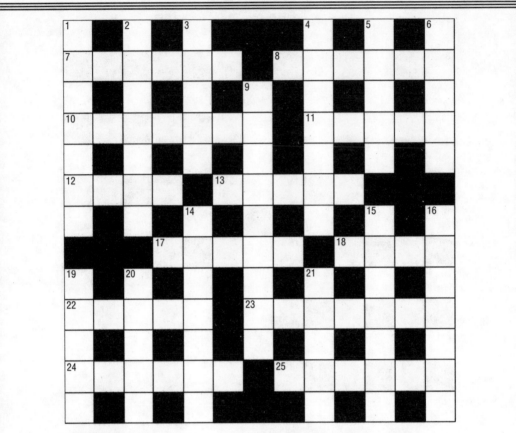

ACROSS

7 Thriller writer, Dame - - - Christie (6)
8 Boarder (6)
10 Strong desire (7)
11 Lively dance (5)
12 Ponder (4)
13 Incorrect (5)
17 Guffaw (5)
18 Stringed toy (2-2)
22 Chunk of cheese (5)
23 Confusion and bustle (7)
24 Rectangle (6)
25 Catchy advertising verse (6)

DOWN

1 Louis Armstrong's nickname (7)
2 Story with a moral (7)
3 Arab chief (5)
4 Group of actors (7)
5 Sprightly (5)
6 Burst, destroy (5)
9 Combined totals (9)
14 Greek eating house (7)
15 Town (7)
16 Weatherworn stone (7)
19 Sudden attack (5)
20 Muddle (5)
21 Mind (5)

The Biggest Crossword Book In The World

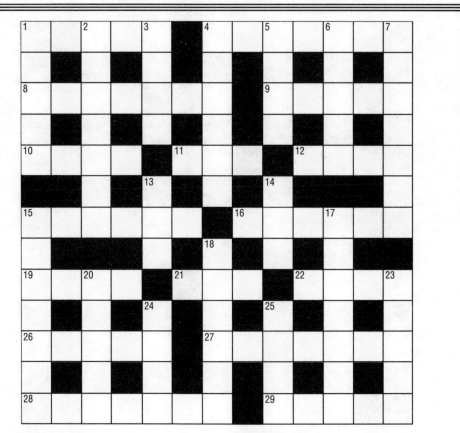

ACROSS

1 Squeeze (5)
4 Extremely innocent (7)
8 Brief account (7)
9 Kingdom (5)
10 Measure of land (4)
11 *Jamaica - - -*, novel (3)
12 US state, east of Indiana (4)
15 Dismal, dull (6)
16 Neglect (6)
19 Frozen flakes (4)
21 Darn (3)
22 Peruse writing (4)
26 Force out of residence (5)
27 Perform surgery (7)
28 Harmed (7)
29 Danger (5)

DOWN

1 Italian food (5)
2 Digit (7)
3 Warmth (4)
4 No matter who (6)
5 Young woman (4)
6 Disinclined (5)
7 Write (7)
13 Teacher's favourite (3)
14 Time gone by (3)
15 Hang from above (7)
17 The great outdoors (4, 3)
18 Musical disc (6)
20 Narcotic (5)
23 Live (5)
24 Male deer (4)
25 Far down (4)

The Biggest Crossword Book In The World

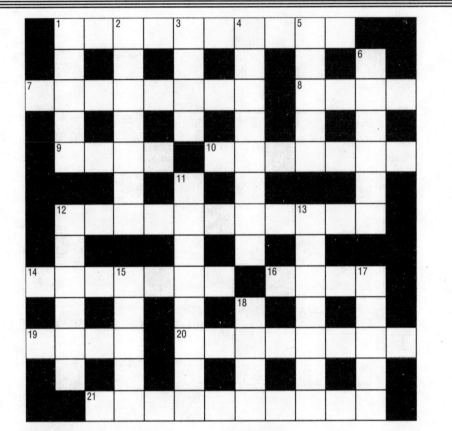

ACROSS

1 Inflammation of the larynx (10)
7 Small parrot (8)
8 Medicinal plant (4)
9 Eternally (4)
10 High-pitched scream (7)
12 Focus the mind (11)
14 High-speed warship (7)
16 Rescue from harm (4)
19 Scottish family (4)
20 Answer (8)
21 Charity fund-raising event (3, 4, 3)

DOWN

1 Sierra - - -, Commonwealth country (5)
2 Principal girl's school (7)
3 Metal fixing pin (4)
4 Signal (8)
5 Senseless (5)
6 William - - -, *Coronation Street* star (6)
11 Throw overboard (8)
12 Cricketer, - - - Ambrose (6)
13 Modified (7)
15 Kind, sort (5)
17 Very dark wood (5)
18 Additional (4)

The Biggest Crossword Book In The World

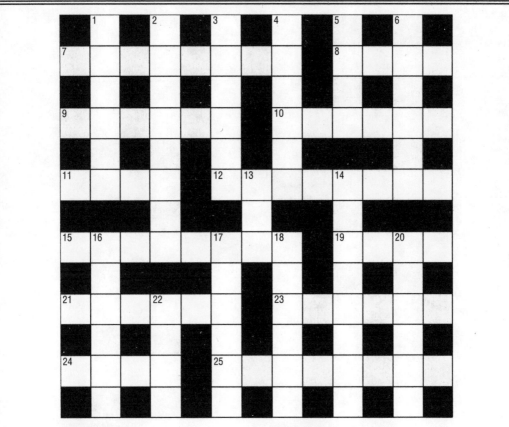

ACROSS

7 Dickens novel,
- - - *Papers* (8)
8 Gassy water (4)
9 Throat (6)
10 Niece's brother (6)
11 Went (4)
12 Devon port (8)
15 Spirit distilled
from potatoes (8)
19 Deficit (4)
21 Guy - - -,
Dambusters leader (6)
23 Singer, - - - Estefan (6)
24 Horse's hair (4)
25 Scrooge's first name (8)

DOWN

1 Shape (6)
2 Outline of
bare essentials (8)
3 Circus tent (3, 3)
4 Extremely thin (6)
5 Please reply (1, 1, 1, 1)
6 Commercial (6)
13 Cut away branches (3)
14 Observer (8)
16 Jacques - - -, French
president (6)
17 Lobster claw (6)
18 Royal seal (6)
20 Splinter (6)
22 Cast off (4)

The Biggest Crossword Book In The World

ACROSS

3 Catherine wheels, eg (9)
8 William - - -, former British PM (4)
9 Medicated lozenge (8)
10 Crafty (6)
13 All (5)
14 Weapons store (7)
15 Evil act (3)
16 Slim (7)
17 Father and son actors, Martin and Charlie (5)
21 Dish of crushed oats, dried fruits and nuts (6)
22 Capital of Finland (8)
23 Large tooth (4)
24 Birmingham railway station (3, 6)

DOWN

1 Prohibition bar (9)
2 Stammered (9)
4 Insinuate (5)
5 Oriental (7)
6 Leave out, skip (4)
7 Type of seaweed (4)
11 Famous celebrity (9)
12 Manchester United star (4, 5)
14 Tune, melody (3)
15 Discussion forum (7)
18 Happy look (5)
19 Small valley (4)
20 Egyptian goddess (4)

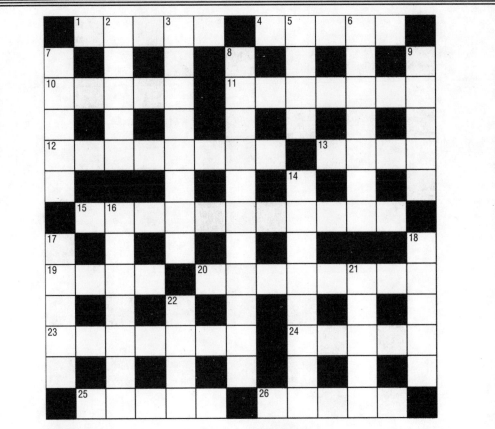

ACROSS

1 Thick solid piece (5)
4 Holy person (5)
10 Conjuring (5)
11 Issue (7)
12 Conan Doyle's detective, - - - Holmes (8)
13 Spiral conductor (4)
15 Softly-spoken American actor (4, 7)
19 Thomas - - -, English composer (4)
20 Postpones (8)
23 Group of organisms (7)
24 Sky colour (5)
25 Aptitude (5)
26 Den (5)

DOWN

2 William - - -, Former Tory Party leader (5)
3 Item of jewellery (8)
5 Keen (4)
6 Capital of Kenya (7)
7 Powerful overhead shot (5)
8 Commercial goods (11)
9 Corner (5)
14 Liqueur made from raw eggs (8)
16 Lamp (7)
17 Rope for catching cattle (5)
18 Off-centre (5)
21 Stage in a competition (5)
22 Data storage medium (4)

The Biggest Crossword Book In The World

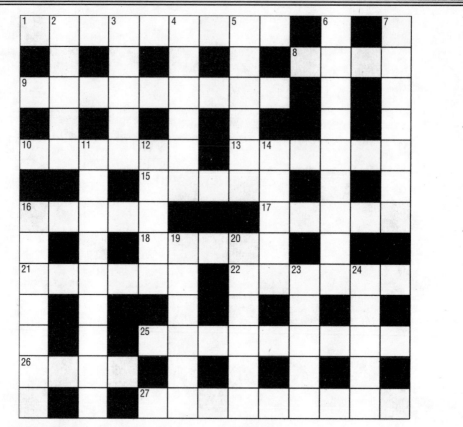

ACROSS

1 Disregarded (9)
8 Large seagoing vessel (4)
9 Devon holiday resort (9)
10 Calm (6)
13 Vibrate (6)
15 Zodiac sign (5)
16 Mature person (5)
17 Jumped (5)
18 Emotionally strained (5)
21 Anne - - -, wife of Henry VIII (6)
22 Insult (6)
25 Janitor (9)
26 Milk pudding (4)
27 Got back (9)

DOWN

2 Avoid (5)
3 Approx. one and three-quarter pints (5)
4 Kitchen appliance (6)
5 Whole (6)
6 Radio band (5, 4)
7 Wealthy (7)
11 Patricia - - -, actress (9)
12 Spruce, dapper (5)
14 Railway union (5)
16 Curtly - - -, cricketer (7)
19 Make very angry (6)
20 South African township (6)
23 Signal light (5)
24 Female relative (5)

The Biggest Crossword Book In The World

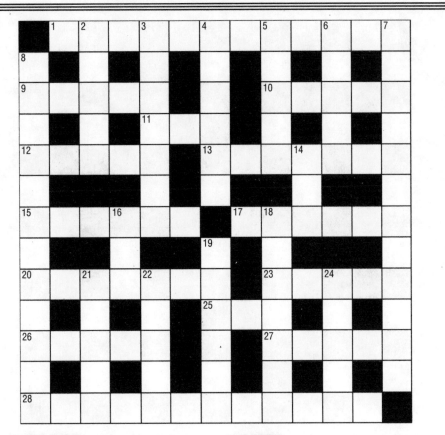

ACROSS
1 Peter - - -, nightclub owner (12)
9 Make invalid (5)
10 Cured pig meat (5)
11 Grief, anguish (3)
12 Johanna - - -, Heidi author (5)
13 Unsteady (7)
15 Small stone (6)
17 Actress, - - - Goldberg (6)
20 Walker (7)
23 Cry of a horse (5)
25 Poultry product (3)
26 Cheerful (5)
27 Engine (5)
28 Everyone (3, 3, 6)

DOWN
2 Sharp (5)
3 Animosity (3-4)
4 Ravenous (6)
5 Fix firmly (5)
6 Financial gain (5)
7 *EastEnders* actress (5, 7)
8 Non-alcoholic drink (12)
14 Double act (3)
16 Baby's protective cloth (3)
18 Word game (7)
19 Extract from a speech (6)
21 Important person (5)
22 Ancient language (5)
24 Lay to rest (5)

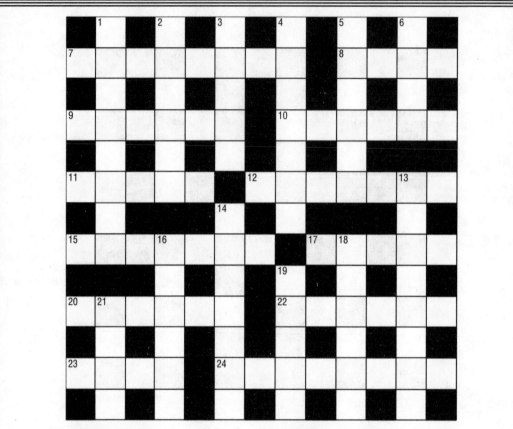

ACROSS

7 Small bits of coloured paper thrown at weddings (8)
8 Gesture (4)
9 Nautical cartoon character (6)
10 Various (6)
11 School subject (5)
12 Dirty, filthy (7)
15 Island off the coast of Italy (7)
17 Office paperwork (5)
20 Body of Roman soldiers (6)
22 Subtle difference (6)
23 Accent (4)
24 Foolishly brave (8)

DOWN

1 America's Centennial state (8)
2 In a new way (6)
3 Male ox (5)
4 Matthew - - -, rower (7)
5 Niggling pain (6)
6 Above (4)
13 Royal lady (8)
14 Landscape (7)
16 Hockey-like game (6)
18 Fatal (6)
19 Rap sharply (5)
21 Comedy actor, - - - Sykes (4)

The Biggest Crossword Book In The World

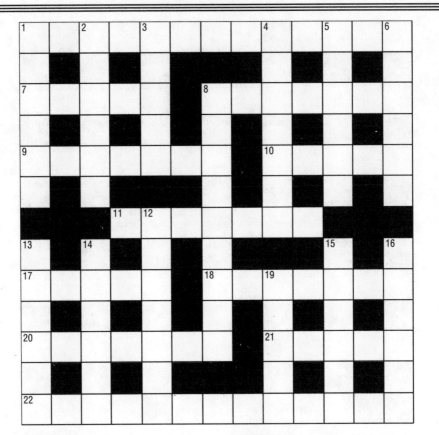

ACROSS

1 Mutineer, rebel (13)
7 Tennis player,
- - - Ivanisevic (5)
8 Small, fragrant flower (7)
9 Convent (7)
10 Soldier's exercise (5)
11 Thicket (7)
17 *Crossroads'* dimwit (5)
18 Throb (7)
20 Amount of wear (7)
21 Grilled bread (5)
22 Infringement,
offence (13)

DOWN

1 Queen's title (6)
2 Italian city (6)
3 Thrust forward (5)
4 Late (7)
5 Capital of Texas (6)
6 Annually (6)
8 Kitchen utensil (6, 3)
12 Branch of science (7)
13 Express disapproval (6)
14 Variety of goat (6)
15 Wild animal hunt (6)
16 Thrashed (6)
19 Water lily (5)

The Biggest Crossword Book In The World

ACROSS

1 Want (4)
4 Young cat (6)
8 Donald - - -, land speed record holder (8)
9 Ex *EastEnders*' actor - - - Kemp (4)
10 Velvety cloth (5)
11 Visibly distressed (7)
13 Very cold (6)
15 Label (6)
17 Islamic holy month (7)
19 Stiff (5)
22 Mexican dish in a folded tortilla (4)
23 European republic (8)
24 Light wind (6)
25 Irritable (4)

DOWN

2 Computer missive (1, 4)
3 Put in the bank (7)
4 Leg joint (4)
5 Permit (8)
6 Wading bird (5)
7 Take to be true without proof (6)
12 Rough walk (8)
14 40th US president (6)
16 Weather conditions (7)
18 Love (5)
20 Cake topping (5)
21 Blackthorn fruit (4)

The Biggest Crossword Book In The World

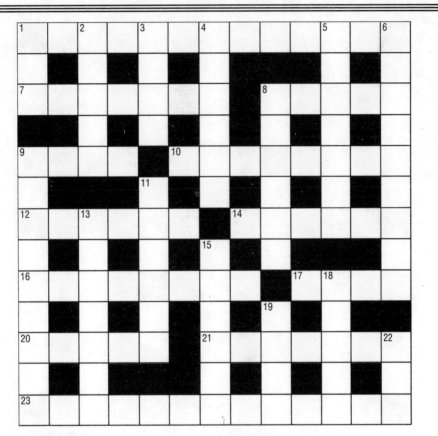

ACROSS

1 Interrogate closely (5-8)
7 Indian language (7)
8 Welsh county (5)
9 Retained (4)
10 Carefree (8)
12 Border of a page (6)
14 Bubble over (6)
16 Superior (2-6)
17 Active and brisk (4)
20 Divide by two (5)
21 Pamphlet (7)
23 Hollywood legend (6, 7)

DOWN

1 Trophy (3)
2 Come clean (3, 2)
3 Oliver's partner (4)
4 Joined together (6)
5 False (7)
6 Discreditable publicity (9)
8 Hand warmers (6)
9 Former name of Cambodia (9)
11 Penetrate (6)
13 Walked for pleasure (7)
15 Fitness (6)
18 Oriental rice dish (5)
19 Twist out of shape (4)
22 Convert (a hide) into leather (3)

The Biggest Crossword Book In The World

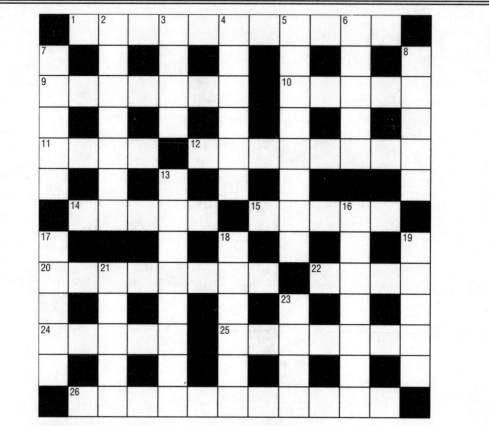

ACROSS

1 Cigarette vendor (11)
9 Italian composer (7)
10 Dizzy (5)
11 Thick string (4)
12 Rebel (8)
14 Visual riddle (5)
15 Matthew - - -,
   TV celebrity (5)
20 Shopkeeper (8)
22 Expenditure (4)
24 Sticky substance
   from a tree (5)
25 S American river (7)
26 Question officially (11)

DOWN

2 See (7)
3 Parched, dry (4)
4 Small exclusive group (6)
5 Flimsy nightie (8)
6 Grasslike plant (5)
7 Person in poor
   condition (5)
8 Wales (5)
13 Vegetable strips (8)
16 Sentry (4, 3)
17 Administrative centre
   of Cornwall (5)
18 Eat greedily (6)
19 Bend low (5)
21 Cathy - - -, actress (5)
23 High-pitched sound (4)

The Biggest Crossword Book In The World

ACROSS

1 Picked (8)
5 Insect larva (4)
9 Wood joint (5)
10 Liquor (5)
12 Hidden store (5)
13 Prune with shears (4)
15 Cheese-making ingredient (6)
18 Occur (6)
20 Scrutinise carefully (4)
23 Mourning song (5)
24 Narrow bay (5)
27 Yugoslavia's currency unit (5)
28 Supernatural tale (4)
29 Uncouth (8)

DOWN

1 Pretentious person (4)
2 Company emblem (4)
3 Object orbiting the sun (5)
4 Property (6)
6 Amorous (8)
7 Jeremy - - -, TV prankster (6)
8 Further back (6)
11 Lubricate (3)
14 Intrinsic (8)
16 Rapid (6)
17 Victory platform (6)
19 Alcoholic drink (6)
21 Gibbon, eg (3)
22 John - - -, snooker player (5)
25 Volcanic discharge (4)
26 Words of a book (4)

The Biggest Crossword Book In The World

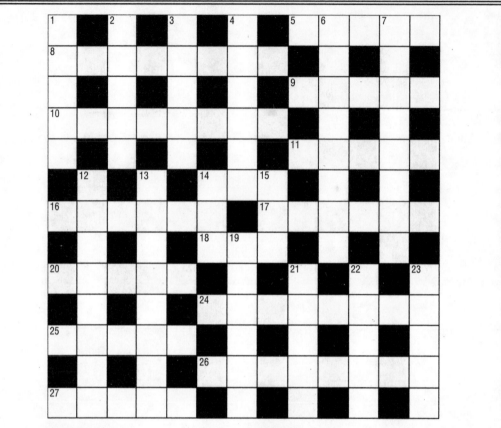

ACROSS

5 Chopped meat (5)
8 District (8)
9 Chew noisily (5)
10 French 'Mr' (8)
11 Little (5)
14 Upper atmosphere (3)
16 Preliminary plan (6)
17 Elaborately presented (6)
18 Local boozer (3)
20 Suds, bubbles (5)
24 Placed apart (8)
25 Mountain song (5)
26 Shrub with
    large flowers (8)
27 Hoard, collect (5)

DOWN

1 Go up (5)
2 Scarcely sufficient (5)
3 Allege (5)
4 Hit (6)
6 Heartless (8)
7 Entire (8)
12 Inherited property (8)
13 Indifferent (8)
14 Highland
    politicians (1, 1, 1)
15 Lout (slang) (3)
19 Depose (6)
21 Smooth in manner (5)
22 Stop (a motor) (5)
23 Perfectly suited (5)

The Biggest Crossword Book In The World

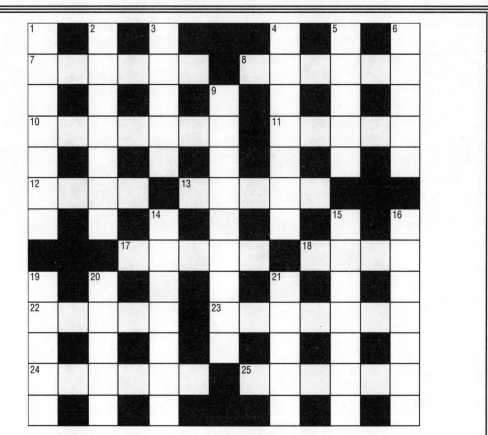

ACROSS

7 Hamper (6)
8 Delay (6)
10 Mechanical piano (7)
11 Kofi - - -, UN chief (5)
12 Give out (4)
13 Unit of gas (5)
17 Extensive view (5)
18 Bell-shaped fruit (4)
22 Mountainous Asian country (5)
23 Coarsely reviling (7)
24 Wild American cat (6)
25 Muslim country ruler (6)

DOWN

1 Cleaver (7)
2 Live, dwell (7)
3 English county (5)
4 Strange in appearance (7)
5 Great pain (5)
6 Practical joke (5)
9 New York borough (9)
14 Party pooper (7)
15 Swerve (7)
16 French city (7)
19 Block of cast metal (5)
20 Tip over (5)
21 Wheat used to make pasta (5)

The Biggest Crossword Book In The World

ACROSS

1 Motion picture (5)
4 Without making a noise (7)
8 Look down on (7)
9 Waterway (5)
10 Tibetan monster (4)
11 Location of the Royal Botanic Gardens (3)
12 Tidings (4)
15 Railway station worker (6)
16 Season of the year (6)
19 Engine oil-well (4)
21 No matter which (3)
22 Breathe (4)
26 Pester (5)
27 Formal speech (7)
28 Raise, lift up (7)
29 Original (5)

DOWN

1 Dirty, soiled (5)
2 Caller (7)
3 Author, - - - Blyton (4)
4 Canada's largest province (6)
5 Paul - - -, England footballer (4)
6 Metric weight (5)
7 **Ex** Russian President (7)
13 King's title (3)
14 Jamaican spirit (3)
15 Extract from a book (7)
17 Make use of (7)
18 Money received (6)
20 Gambling resort, - - - Carlo (5)
23 Intuition (5)
24 Indian bird (4)
25 Blunder (4)

The Biggest Crossword Book In The World

ACROSS

1 Irregular (10)
7 Form a mental picture (8)
8 Implore (4)
9 Wicked (4)
10 The Big Apple (3, 4)
12 Unfortunate (11)
14 Hereditary title (7)
16 Ballad (4)
19 Badger's home (4)
20 American lorry driver (8)
21 One who studies
 the stars (10)

DOWN

1 Snow leopard (5)
2 Upper limit (7)
3 Illicit gains (4)
4 Dish of eggs,
 beaten and fried (8)
5 Put to practical use (5)
6 Hugh - - -,
 comedy actor (6)
11 Missing soldier (8)
12 Bookworm (6)
13 Flower bud (7)
15 Scott's companion (5)
17 Germaine - - -,
 feminist (5)
18 Give notice (4)

The Biggest Crossword Book In The World

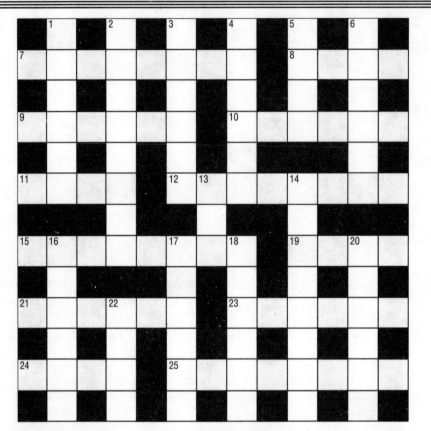

ACROSS

7 Queue of traffic (8)
8 Firm, steady (4)
9 Church district (6)
10 Danger (6)
11 Constituency (4)
12 Circular coastal fort (8)
15 Golfing accessory (8)
19 Type, kind (4)
21 German composer (6)
23 Fabric sample (6)
24 Method (4)
25 Well-trained (8)

DOWN

1 Harm (6)
2 Covered arcade (8)
3 Confusion (6)
4 Jayne Torville, eg (6)
5 A distance away (4)
6 Attack (6)
13 Every (3)
14 Extremely happy (8)
16 Reflect (6)
17 Portuguese capital (6)
18 Reply (6)
20 Fresh (6)
22 Part of a shoe (4)

The Biggest Crossword Book In The World

ACROSS

3 December 26th (6, 3)
8 Sporting fixture (4)
9 Receives from ancestors (8)
10 Trafalgar hero (6)
13 Fertile desert spot (5)
14 Spanish holiday island (7)
15 Baby's bed (3)
16 British soldier (7)
17 Maximum allowance (5)
21 Country house (6)
22 Statuette (8)
23 Sussex river (4)
24 Make a copy of (9)

DOWN

1 Battle in 1415 (9)
2 Lake District town (9)
4 Comment (5)
5 Restrain, hinder (7)
6 Disease microbe (4)
7 Choir voice (4)
11 Sea walk (9)
12 Gunpowder ingredient (9)
14 Test for motor vehicles (1,1,1,)
15 Relating to the heart (7)
18 Business representative (5)
19 Scottish region (4)
20 Throw (4)

ACROSS

1 Beating of the heart (5)
4 Pixie-like, delicate (5)
10 Frighten (5)
11 Linked (7)
12 BBC current affairs programme (8)
13 Ponder (4)
15 Father of actor Emilio Estevez (7, 5)
19 Book of the Bible (4)
20 Behaviour (8)
23 Souvenir (7)
24 Lift up (5)
25 Thief's cache (5)
26 Large crow (5)

DOWN

2 Reversal of political policy (1-4)
3 Wet thoroughly (8)
5 Send to sleep (4)
6 Enter without invitation (7)
7 Skilled (5)
8 Hunch (11)
9 Venomous snake (5)
14 British singer (5, 3)
16 Effort (7)
17 Fragment of bread (5)
18 Chop off (5)
21 Stand together (5)
22 Responsibility (4)

The Biggest Crossword Book In The World

ACROSS

1 Former ruler of Tibet (5, 4)
8 Powdery dirt (4)
9 Reproduce (9)
10 Condition (6)
13 Exuberant (6)
15 Islamic country (5)
16 First Premier of the Soviet Union (5)
17 Scottish town (5)
18 Prisoner's excuse (5)
21 Emotional shock (6)
22 Approach and speak to (6)
25 Edible nut (9)
26 Possibility of danger (4)
27 Forever (9)

DOWN

2 Entertain (5)
3 Share out (5)
4 Chinese fruit with juicy pulp (6)
5 Courage (6)
6 Notre Dame resident? (9)
7 Horror writer, - - - King (7)
11 Tease (9)
12 Desmond - - -, TV presenter (5)
14 Caper (5)
16 Sweepstake (7)
19 Lasso (6)
20 Beat repeatedly (6)
23 Bedtime drink? (5)
24 Static, unmoving (5)

The Biggest Crossword Book In The World

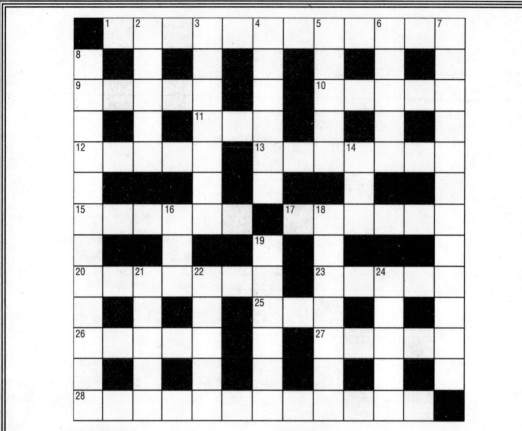

ACROSS

1 Form of transport (5, 3, 4)
9 Fray (5)
10 Peace Prize founder (5)
11 Filled pastry case (3)
12 Accurate (5)
13 Soon (7)
15 Enhance (6)
17 Indian pasty (6)
20 Capital of Maine (7)
23 Seventh sign of the zodiac (5)
25 Jerry's adversary (3)
26 Bring upon oneself (5)
27 Madonna film (5)
28 Worldwide traveller (12)

DOWN

2 Oldest Japanese city (5)
3 Disbeliever (7)
4 Take into custody (6)
5 Wild Australian dog (5)
6 Russ - - -, British comedian (5)
7 *Kojak* star (5,7)
8 Getting faster (12)
14 Edge of a wheel (3)
16 Debtor's note (1, 1, 1)
18 Illness (7)
19 Somewhat (6)
21 Small lizard (5)
22 Sudden increase (5)
24 Groom's partner (5)

The Biggest Crossword Book In The World

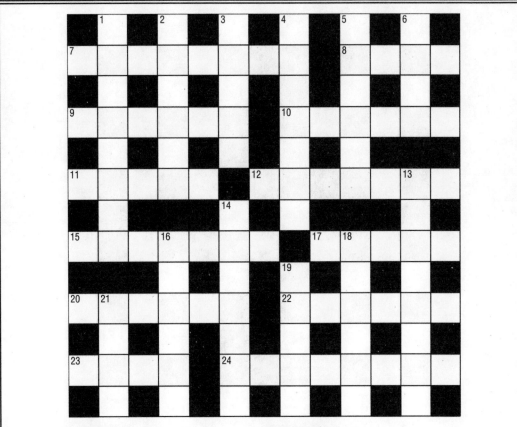

ACROSS

7 New Year's Eve (8)
8 Visage (4)
9 Uproar (6)
10 Person who shoots
with a bow and arrow (6)
11 Tree producing
red berries (5)
12 Police building (7)
15 Findings of a jury (7)
17 Ancient Mexican? (5)
20 Summer house (6)
22 Assortment (6)
23 Steering place
on a ship (4)
24 American lift (8)

DOWN

1 Alone (8)
2 Enid Blyton character,
- - - Jane (6)
3 Garden ornament (5)
4 Succession of leaders (7)
5 Remnant (6)
6 Highest point (4)
13 Telephone exchange
worker (8)
14 Mod's transport (7)
16 Envisaged in sleep (6)
18 Meander (6)
19 Excessive desire (5)
21 Assist (4)

The Biggest Crossword Book In The World

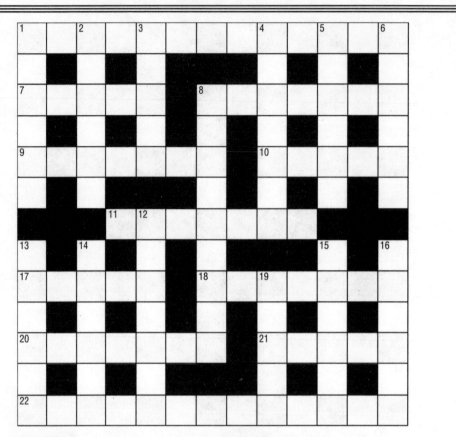

ACROSS

1 Brummie comedian (6,7)
7 Touch lightly (5)
8 Small house for pigeons (7)
9 Multi-socket plug (7)
10 Oil-producing fruit (5)
11 Cutting (humour) (7)
17 Gloomier (5)
18 Exterior (7)
20 Ornamental hedge-clipping (7)
21 Clean with a brush (5)
22 Spiral fairground ride (6-7)

DOWN

1 Picture cut into odd shaped pieces (6)
2 Mariner (6)
3 Upright (5)
4 Meat-filled pasta envelopes (7)
5 Exotic flower (6)
6 Chuckle (6)
8 Large bedroom (9)
12 Normal (7)
13 On-off button (6)
14 Drive forward (6)
15 Ward off (6)
16 Hot condiment (6)
19 Savour (5)

The Biggest Crossword Book In The World

ACROSS

1 Unit of power (4)
4 Apprehended (6)
8 Grappled (8)
9 Cash register (4)
10 Embed (5)
11 Bow and arrow sport (7)
13 Hungarian language (6)
15 Dwell (6)
17 German state (7)
19 Greasy (5)
22 Donated (4)
23 Come between (8)
24 Pay attention (6)
25 Measuring device (4)

DOWN

2 Protective garment (5)
3 Region of Italy (7)
4 Male foal (4)
5 Style of bowling (8)
6 Temporary obstacle (5)
7 Founder of the
English nation (6)
12 Annoy, pester (8)
14 Yasser - - -,
PLO chairman (6)
16 Tool for gripping bolts (7)
18 Quick-thinking (5)
20 Final amount (5)
21 Type of beer (4)

The Biggest Crossword Book In The World

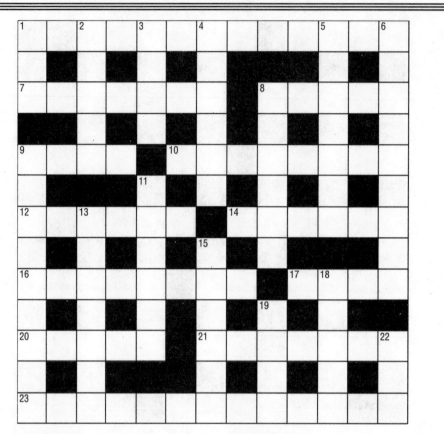

ACROSS

1 Military flyers (5, 3, 5)
7 Punishment (7)
8 Town famous for its china (5)
9 Metal pin which screws into a nut (4)
10 Incorrect description (8)
12 Capital of Taiwan (6)
14 An ideal society (6)
16 Sudden occurrence (8)
17 At that time (4)
20 Rough (5)
21 African language (7)
23 Public protest (13)

DOWN

1 Knock firmly (3)
2 Barbra Streisand film (5)
3 Animal of the cat family (4)
4 National airline of Spain (6)
5 Pickled herring fillet (7)
6 Amuse (9)
8 Contribute (6)
9 Engaged (9)
11 Fireside (6)
13 Intervening period (7)
15 Breed of hound (6)
18 Hollywood madam, - - - Fleiss (5)
19 US space centre (4)
22 James Bond creator, - - - Fleming (3)

The Biggest Crossword Book In The World

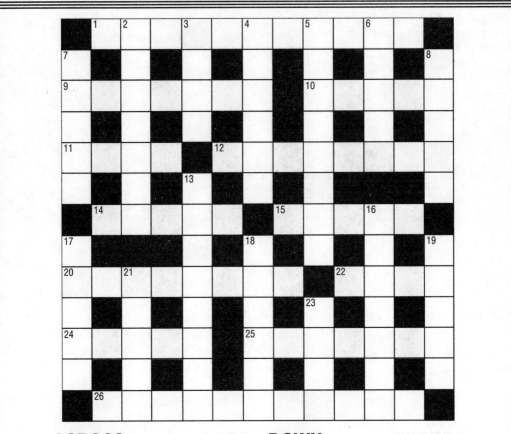

ACROSS

1 Henry VIII's third wife (4,7)
9 Lacking taste (7)
10 Welcome (5)
11 Aristocrat (4)
12 Monty Python star (4,4)
14 Confess (5)
15 Small hut (5)
20 Aardvark, eg (8)
22 Common (4)
24 Irish county (5)
25 Imaginary circle around the earth (7)
26 Outcome (5, 6)

DOWN

2 Made certain (7)
3 Catch sight of (4)
4 Tolerate, live through (6)
5 Conjurer (8)
6 Overthrow (5)
7 Frogman (5)
8 Unreasonably high (5)
13 Dress with a bib top (8)
16 Utterly stupid (7)
17 Stop for a time (5)
18 Go back (6)
19 Tom's adversary (5)
21 Robber (5)
23 Deep chasm (4)

The Biggest Crossword Book In The World

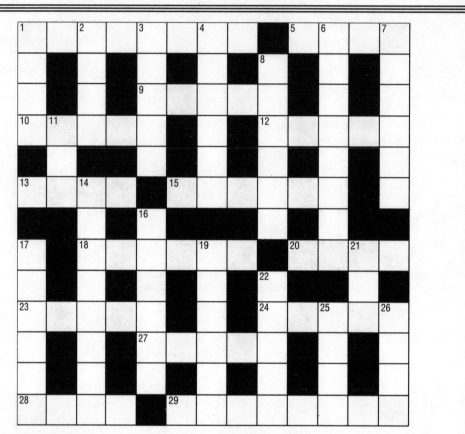

ACROSS

1 Response (8)
5 Traded (4)
9 Dig into (5)
10 Greek bread (5)
12 Demise (5)
13 Shelter for cows (4)
15 Perplex, bewilder (6)
18 Skin drawing (6)
20 Object (4)
23 Actor's confidential speech to the audience (5)
24 Dairy product (5)
27 Of the ears (5)
28 Merriment (4)
29 Intuition (8)

DOWN

1 Play wildly (4)
2 Horizontal mine entrance (4)
3 The present age (5)
4 Do a favour for (6)
6 Decorative object (8)
7 Be uncertain (6)
8 Average (6)
11 Climbing plant (3)
14 Win back (8)
16 Brook (6)
17 Beverage sachet (3, 3)
19 King of the fairies (6)
21 Phase of history (3)
22 Brilliant display (5)
25 Eve's garden (4)
26 Animal flesh (4)

The Biggest Crossword Book In The World

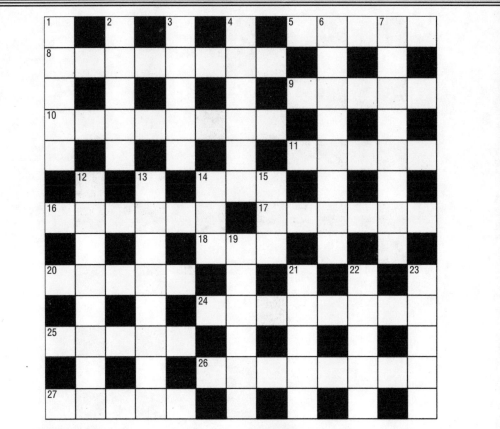

ACROSS

5 Ancient Italian (5)
8 Calming drug (8)
9 Soft and flexible (5)
10 American film star (2, 6)
11 Promotional description (5)
14 Not many (3)
16 Colour (6)
17 Horn (6)
18 Uninteresting (3)
20 Lessen (5)
24 Teeth? (8)
25 Feathery (5)
26 Type of celery (8)
27 Uncultivated land (5)

DOWN

1 Nile dam (5)
2 Foster permanently (5)
3 Shares in a business (5)
4 Suburban street (6)
6 Ignore (8)
7 One of the Channel Islands (8)
12 Wood preservative (8)
13 Worldwide computer network (8)
14 Supplied with food (3)
15 For what reason? (3)
19 Shouted (6)
21 Pale with shock (5)
22 Sorcerer of Aladdin's lamp (5)
23 Children's charity (5)

The Biggest Crossword Book In The World

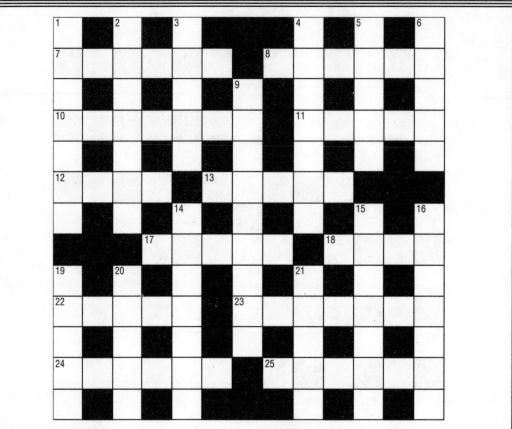

ACROSS
7 Obstruct (6)
8 Spanish fleet (6)
10 Undercurrent (3-4)
11 English diary writer (5)
12 Look of lust (4)
13 Sea snail (5)
17 Recording device (5)
18 Soap bubbles (4)
22 Robbery (5)
23 Unpredictable (7)
24 Russian capital (6)
25 America's 50th state (6)

DOWN
1 Germ-free (7)
2 Bartered (7)
3 Exhaust (5)
4 Wrestle (7)
5 Insects with black and yellow stripes (5)
6 Movement (5)
9 Birthplace of Jesus (9)
14 Demolish (7)
15 Cleaning aid (7)
16 Telepathic (7)
19 Part of a cricket wicket (5)
20 Bring to an end (5)
21 Vision (5)

The Biggest Crossword Book In The World

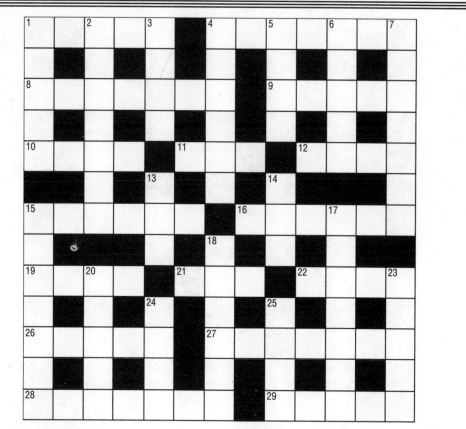

ACROSS

1 Food accompaniment (5)
4 Important (7)
8 Greek wine (7)
9 On top of (5)
10 Simple (4)
11 Turkish hat (3)
12 *Born Free* lioness (4)
15 Walk unsteadily (6)
16 Time-honoured (3-3)
19 Decorative band (4)
21 Negative vote (3)
22 Sequence of events in a novel (4)
26 Lacking skill (5)
27 Thorn (7)
28 Chivalrous (7)
29 Egon - - -, restaurant critic (5)

DOWN

1 Rugby players' huddle (5)
2 Spoke (7)
3 Impressive, grand (4)
4 Earth, eg (6)
5 Calf meat (4)
6 Ogre (5)
7 Down wind (7)
13 Shade tree (3)
14 Heavy goods vehicle (1, 1, 1)
15 Experimenting (7)
17 Waterproof fabric (7)
18 Floor covering (6)
20 Baby's wrap (5)
23 Extremely small (5)
24 Highest volcano in Europe (4)
25 Landing stage (4)

The Biggest Crossword Book In The World

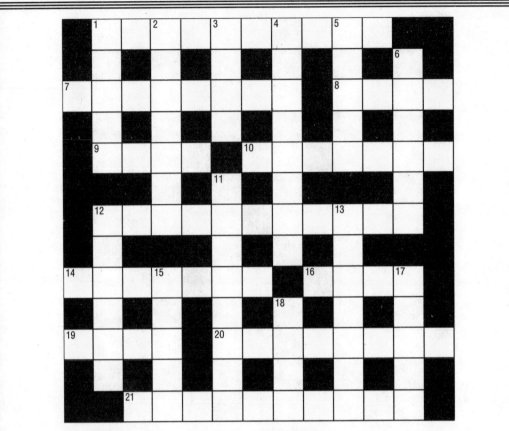

ACROSS

1 Enlarge beyond normal expectations (10)
7 Gambling game using playing cards (8)
8 Robin - - -, politician (4)
9 Dull and monotonous (4)
10 Imitator (4-3)
12 Experience (11)
14 Male relative (7)
16 Sneak a look (4)
19 Roster (4)
20 Ultimate, final (8)
21 Inferior (6-4)

DOWN

1 African antelope (5)
2 Praise publicly (7)
3 Bloodthirsty (4)
4 Reasonable (8)
5 In poor taste (5)
6 Legal worker (6)
11 Other self (5, 3)
12 Litter of pigs (6)
13 Inactivity (7)
15 Leg-puller (5)
17 Chapter (5)
18 Give nourishment to (4)

The Biggest Crossword Book In The World

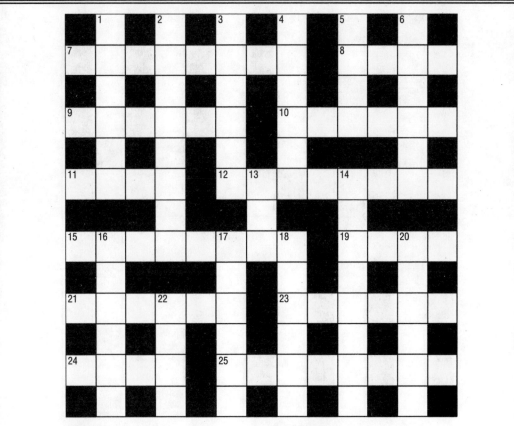

ACROSS

7 Appendage (8)
8 Timber (4)
9 Undergarment (6)
10 Four times twenty (6)
11 Promote (4)
12 Increase in number (8)
15 Joined together again (8)
19 Abandon, desert (4)
21 Not fixed to the same position (6)
23 Leisurely saunter (6)
24 Wreck (4)
25 Chinese dog (4-4)

DOWN

1 Utter foolishness (6)
2 Physicist famous for his theory of relativity (8)
3 Casualty (6)
4 Ill, sick (6)
5 Drink from a bottle (4)
6 Fatal (6)
13 Utilise (3)
14 Secondary (8)
16 Old Testament book (6)
17 Deep ditch (6)
18 Tyrant, dictator (6)
20 Ripe (6)
22 Hebridian island (4)

The Biggest Crossword Book In The World

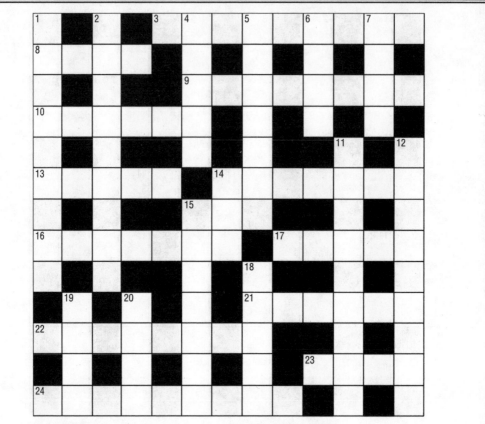

ACROSS

3 English county (9)
8 Neat, slim (4)
9 Horrified (8)
10 Fit (6)
13 Of the moon (5)
14 Sheriff's officer (7)
15 Slash (3)
16 Scottish civil engineer (7)
17 Adhesive mixture (5)
21 Reddish-brown
   hair colour (6)
22 Japanese ritual
   suicide (8)
23 Capital of the Algarve (4)
24 Urgent information
   bulletin (9)

DOWN

1 Firmness (9)
2 Forcefully (9)
4 Reflection (5)
5 Final layer of paint (7)
6 Gripped (4)
7 Actress, - - - Perlman (4)
11 Insignificant person! (9)
12 Part of the day (9)
14 Growth on a tree that
   develops into a leaf (3)
15 Vital (7)
18 One side of a coin? (5)
19 Manufacture (4)
20 Low-voiced singer (4)

The Biggest Crossword Book In The World

ACROSS

1 Pleated frilling (5)
4 *Buster* actress,
- - - Walters (5)
10 Private teacher (5)
11 Heavyweight boxer,
- - - Holyfield (7)
12 Country featured in
Gullivar's Travels (8)
13 Large bundle
of hay (4)
15 Lady cop (11)
19 Fruit flesh (4)
20 Burger and chips,
eg (4, 4)
23 Obtain (7)
24 Blockade (5)
25 Less than (5)
26 Complete trust (5)

DOWN

2 To such time as (5)
3 Ghastly (8)
5 America's Beehive
state (4)
6 Harrison Ford film,
- - - *Jones* (7)
7 Fashion (5)
8 Recovered from
illness (11)
9 Wept, sobbed (5)
14 Italian
noblewoman (8)
16 Slanting (7)
17 Javelin (5)
18 Goodbye (5)
21 In the open (5)
22 Bona - - -, genuine (4)

The Biggest Crossword Book In The World

ACROSS

1 Explosive mixture (9)
8 Be aware of (4)
9 Dairy vehicle (4, 5)
10 Revolve (6)
13 German POW camp (6)
15 Request food at restaurant (5)
16 Well done! (5)
17 Part of a target (5)
18 Palpitate (5)
21 Noel Coward comedy, - - - *Spirit* (6)
22 Go back on (a promise) (6)
25 Raincoat (9)
26 Support bar (4)
27 Alpine plant (9)

DOWN

2 Togetherness (5)
3 Good, genuine (5)
4 Jockey, - - - Swinburn (6)
5 Pass by (of time) (6)
6 Cheek, backchat (9)
7 Strut (7)
11 Level-headed (9)
12 Mouth peg (5)
14 Set of people (5)
16 All-in-one outfit for a young child (7)
19 Person who announces important news (6)
20 George - - -, author (6)
23 Gentle poke with the elbow (5)
24 Species (5)

The Biggest Crossword Book In The World

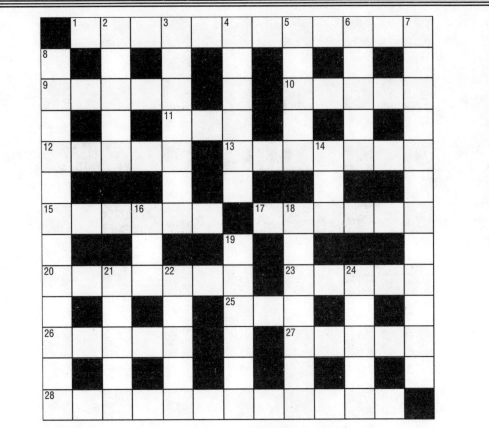

ACROSS
1 British singer (5, 7)
9 Animal charity (inits) (5)
10 Ben - - -, mountain (5)
11 Cheat, swindle (3)
12 One of the
   Queen's dogs (5)
13 Cricket position (4-3)
15 Male parent (6)
17 Walk like a duck (6)
20 Alfred Hitchcock film (7)
23 Precocious young
   woman (5)
25 Psychic, - - - Geller (3)
26 *The Winding
   Stair* poet (5)
27 French river port (5)
28 Voluntary fast (6, 6)

DOWN
2 Pariah (5)
3 Easily broken (7)
4 Slight wave (6)
5 Priest (5)
6 Iron forge block (5)
7 Conflict of opinions (12)
8 British entertainer (5, 7)
14 Object of worship (3)
16 Shade (3)
18 Beau (7)
19 Sign of the zodiac (6)
21 Muscular strength (5)
22 Hindu social class (5)
24 Inebriated (5)

The Biggest Crossword Book In The World

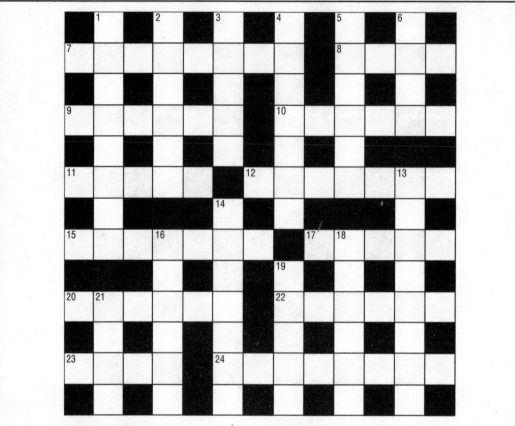

ACROSS

7 The American government (5, 3)
8 Cry out (4)
9 Sea-robber (6)
10 A group of acrobats (6)
11 Rot (5)
12 Former soldier (7)
15 Imperial (7)
17 Tree (5)
20 Cold symptom (6)
22 Fiery, passionate (6)
23 Japanese wrestling (4)
24 Concluded (8)

DOWN

1 Event, occurrence (8)
2 Peruvian llama (6)
3 The trembling poplar (5)
4 Suffocate (7)
5 Metal used for plating (6)
6 Exchange (4)
13 Collection of documents (8)
14 Quick music (7)
16 Small earthquake (6)
18 Small pincered insect (6)
19 Method of cooking (5)
21 Common sense (4)

The Biggest Crossword Book In The World

ACROSS

1 Amazed (13)
7 Take away without permission (5)
8 Clothing (7)
9 Intense delight (7)
10 Yearn for (5)
11 Very bad (7)
17 Swimming stroke (5)
18 Capital of Cyprus (7)
20 Type of biscuit (4, 3)
21 Girl's name (5)
22 **Former Bond girl and** *The Upper Hand* actress (5,8)

DOWN

1 Fringed tuft (6)
2 Troubled (6)
3 TV cook, - - - Smith (5)
4 Characteristic (7)
5 Bedlam (6)
6 Assassinated (6)
8 Former name for Ethiopia (9)
12 Pistol holder (7)
13 Burn slightly (6)
14 Lively dance (6)
15 Home of a Hindu holy man (6)
16 Inn (6)
19 Professional comedian (5)

The Biggest Crossword Book In The World

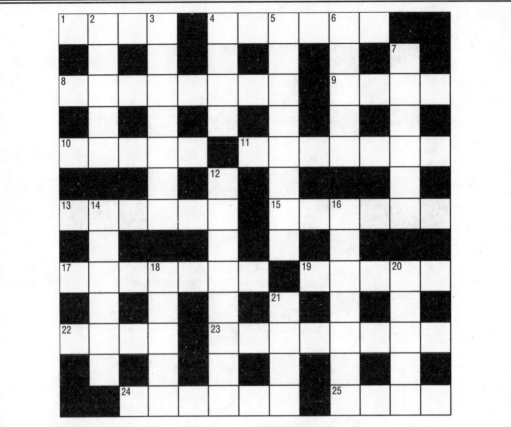

ACROSS
1 Helper (4)
4 Motor racing competition (2, 4)
8 The 'Mad Monk' of Russia (8)
9 Mild mannered (4)
10 Romantic British poet (5)
11 Muslim face veil (7)
13 Period before Christmas (6)
15 Yorkshire moor (6)
17 Lee - - -, golfer (7)
19 Gradient (5)
22 Cooker (4)
23 Seat of the Dutch government (3, 5)
24 Solemn promise (6)
25 Island where Napoleon was first exiled to (4)

DOWN
2 Rome's country (5)
3 Investigate (7)
4 Old stringed instrument (4)
5 Small orange (8)
6 Legendary maiden (5)
7 Heed (6)
12 London's third international airport (8)
14 Deduce (6)
16 Irish county (7)
18 Type of plastic (5)
20 Exactly (5)
21 Hereditary factor (4)

The Biggest Crossword Book In The World

ACROSS

1 American singer (6, 7)
7 Go before (7)
8 Earlier, previous (5)
9 Applaud (4)
10 Cure (8)
12 Get free of (6)
14 *Jungle Book* character (6)
16 Haphazardly (8)
17 Shortly (4)
20 Scottish lord (5)
21 Nestle (7)
23 Tricky phrase (6, 7)

DOWN

1 Opening (3)
2 Greek letter (5)
3 Thought (4)
4 Prime number (6)
5 Drawback (7)
6 Inhabitant of Oslo? (9)
8 Venom (6)
9 American automobile manufacturer (9)
11 Support (6)
13 Entrust to carrier (7)
15 Cupboard (6)
18 Period of darkness (5)
19 Japanese volcano (4)
22 Hearing organ (3)

The Biggest Crossword Book In The World

ACROSS

1 Heir to the throne (5, 6)
9 Astrologer, - - - Grant (7)
10 Young eel (5)
11 Ballerina's skirt (4)
12 Surprises suddenly (8)
14 Uncanny (5)
15 Venomous snake (5)
20 Sufficient (8)
22 Rhythmical song (4)
24 Set down in a letter (5)
25 Fruitful (7)
26 Items made with baked clay (11)

DOWN

2 Ribbon (7)
3 Cheese-making fluid (4)
4 Spanish ball game (6)
5 Cold sweet (3-5)
6 Polite (5)
7 Loyalty, fidelity (5)
8 Copper and zinc alloy (5)
13 Quarrel (8)
16 Obstruction (7)
17 Islamic religious ruling (5)
18 Smother (6)
19 Tossing pole (5)
21 Heather (5)
23 Raffle, lottery (4)

The Biggest Crossword Book In The World

ACROSS

1 Narrow sledge (8)
5 Summit (4)
9 Strong string (5)
10 Onion-like vegetables (5)
12 African mammal? (5)
13 Relieve (4)
15 Former Labour PM (6)
18 Adequate (6)
20 Coax away from (4)
23 Two pints (5)
24 Ornamental edging (5)
27 Legal (5)
28 Top of a building (4)
29 British poet (8)

DOWN

1 Hard work (4)
2 French cheese (4)
3 Greedy (5)
4 In the middle of (6)
6 Telescope part (8)
7 Balkan republic (6)
8 Consider (6)
11 Actress, - - - Gabor (3)
14 Summary of a play (8)
16 Bump (6)
17 Alcoholic drink (6)
19 Tactless (6)
21 Trouble (3)
22 Repeatedly (5)
25 Wading bird (4)
26 Incline (4)

The Biggest Crossword Book In The World

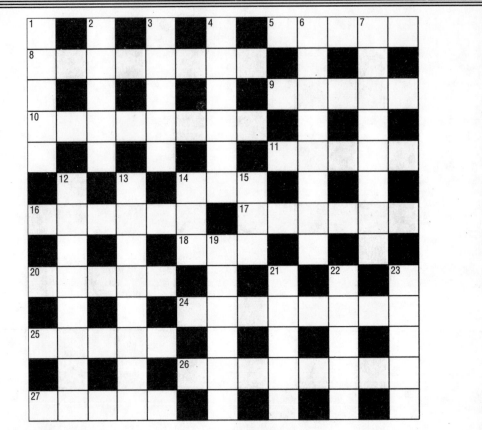

ACROSS

5 Spectre (5)
8 Native of Vienna? (8)
9 Synthetic fibre (5)
10 Orchestral music (8)
11 Change position (5)
14 Charge (3)
16 Bone in the lower leg (6)
17 Apologise profusely (6)
18 A couple (3)
20 Turning machine (5)
24 Hired killer (8)
25 Stubble remover (5)
26 Computer programme (8)
27 Oyster's gem (5)

DOWN

1 Stone-worker (5)
2 Something worth having (5)
3 Clear soup (5)
4 *Peter Pan* author (6)
6 British airport (8)
7 Without punishment (4-4)
12 Minister's house (8)
13 Busy traffic period (4, 4)
14 Chubby (3)
15 Self image (3)
19 Sagacity (6)
21 Commonwealth member (5)
22 Playwright, - - - Wilde (5)
23 Attack (5)

The Biggest Crossword Book In The World

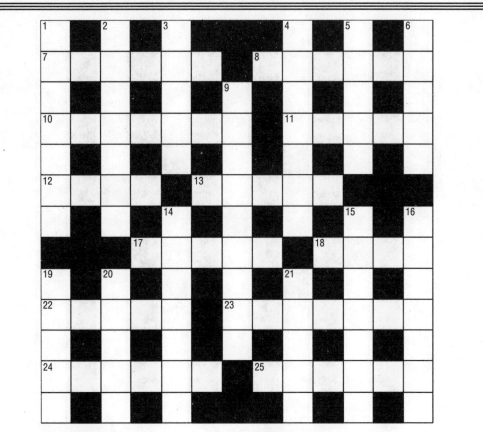

ACROSS

7 Connect (6)
8 Rouse from sleep (6)
10 Hidden danger (7)
11 Enormous (5)
12 Gymnastic exercise (4)
13 Unpleasant (5)
17 Woman whose husband has died (5)
18 Spool (4)
22 Dark-coloured (5)
23 Type of poison (7)
24 Persons composing a tribe or nation (6)
25 Project (6)

DOWN

1 Ornamental staff (7)
2 Pare away (7)
3 Sound of a frog (5)
4 Glorious - - -, start of grouse shooting (7)
5 Item of clothing (5)
6 South American mountains (5)
9 Suddenly (3, 2, 4)
14 Penny farthing, eg (7)
15 Deduced (7)
16 States without proof (7)
19 Make fit (5)
20 Football club, - - - Villa (5)
21 Trap (5)

The Biggest Crossword Book In The World

ACROSS

1 Popular style (5)
4 Salty fish (7)
8 Tart (7)
9 Washed out (3, 2)
10 Not common (4)
11 Rug (3)
12 Short gaiter (4)
15 English town,
- - - Keynes (6)
16 Sheen (6)
19 Bring up (4)
21 In a natural state (3)
22 Bond (4)
26 Alliance (5)
27 Simon - - -, *Coronation Street* actor (7)
28 Self-centred person (7)
29 Have a swim (5)

DOWN

1 Venomous snake (5)
2 Army bigwig (7)
3 Foil (4)
4 Lost (6)
5 Charlie - - -, fictional detective (4)
6 Lowest deck of a ship (5)
7 China's longest river (7)
13 Spinning toy (3)
14 Have food (3)
15 Tent used for social occasions (7)
17 Passage, crossing (7)
18 Useful tool (6)
20 Spanish friend? (5)
23 Slight tint (5)
24 Strongly against (4)
25 Action word (4)

The Biggest Crossword Book In The World

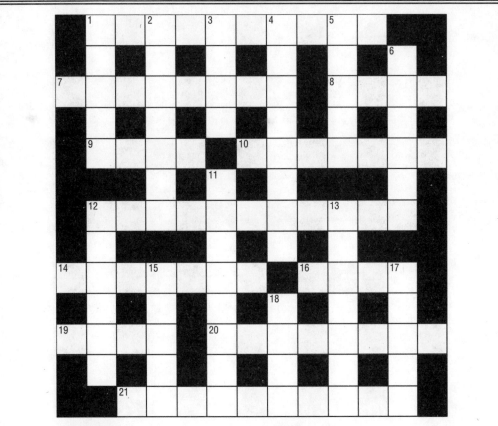

ACROSS

1 Possible (2, 3, 5)
7 Kitchen gadget (3-5)
8 A Saudi? (4)
9 Three-squared (4)
10 Bubble in a pipe (7)
12 Classic children's story (5,6)
14 Graceful animal (7)
16 In poor taste (4)
19 Make with wool (4)
20 The original English clown (8)
21 Former BBC war reporter and Independent MP (6,4)

DOWN

1 Large musical instrument (5)
2 Oberon's wife (7)
3 US television award (4)
4 Passenger plane (8)
5 Speech pattern (5)
6 Rallying call (3, 3)
11 Roof window (8)
12 Muscular (6)
13 Unsuspecting (7)
15 Surplus (5)
17 Cuban dictator, - - - Castro (5)
18 Jungle cat (4)

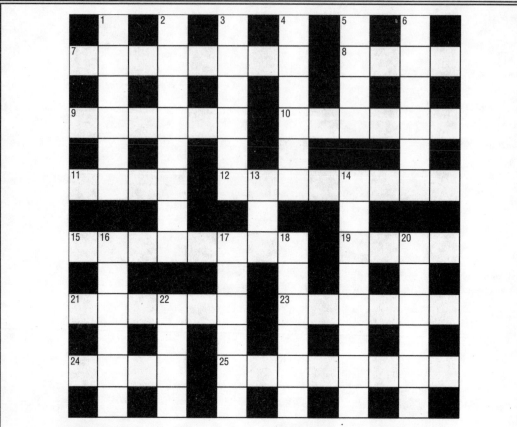

ACROSS

7 Child's game (8)
8 Bunch of hair (4)
9 Mad (6)
10 Impressionist painter (6)
11 Trial record (4)
12 Excited (8)
15 Volume (8)
19 Mass of floating ice (4)
21 Rain cloud (6)
23 Soothsayer (6)
24 Magnetic metal (4)
25 Worked out (8)

DOWN

1 Meeting for spirit contact (6)
2 American state (8)
3 Inattentive (6)
4 Frightening movie (6)
5 Astonish (4)
6 Bureau (6)
13 Bowler, eg (3)
14 Popular breed of dog (8)
16 Place where bees are kept (6)
17 Take out a policy (6)
18 Tower of London guard (6)
20 Turned over (6)
22 Written promise (4)

The Biggest Crossword Book In The World

ACROSS

3 Width (9)
8 Fix, repair (4)
9 Land-locked Asian country (8)
10 Busy, energetic (6)
13 Fireplace (5)
14 Under (7)
15 Teacher's title (3)
16 Jotting block (7)
17 Sucrose (5)
21 Common (6)
22 Guilty (8)
23 Advanced betting stake (4)
24 Avalanche (4-5)

DOWN

1 Easily irritated (9)
2 Bring about (9)
4 Naseem - - -, British boxer (5)
5 Overcome (7)
6 Type of gas (4)
7 Dirt (4)
11 Walkway from a ship (9)
12 Part played by an actor (9)
14 Make an offer at auction (3)
15 Timber yard (7)
18 Use up completely (5)
19 Urban development (4)
20 Pack away (4)

The Biggest Crossword Book In The World

ACROSS

1 Judge's hammer (5)
4 Rabbit's cage (5)
10 Quaintly amusing (5)
11 Intellectual person (7)
12 Official record (8)
13 Suspend (4)
15 Laundry container (5, 6)
19 Paper quantity (4)
20 Cripple (8)
23 Of the hip (7)
24 In front (5)
25 Toy bear (5)
26 Weak and feeble (5)

DOWN

2 Beside the length (5)
3 Enrolled (8)
5 Strong impulse (4)
6 Burn to ashes (7)
7 Regard with respect (5)
8 Likeness (11)
9 Saying, maxim (5)
14 Mischievous adventure (8)
16 Picture in the mind (7)
17 Repulsively fat (5)
18 Martial art using sticks (5)
21 Return on investment (5)
22 Decorative fastener (4)

The Biggest Crossword Book In The World

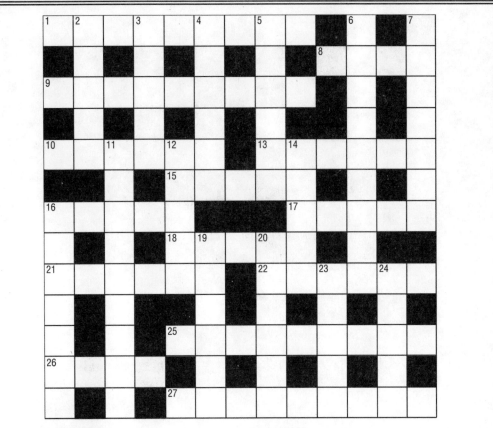

ACROSS

1 Circus performer (4, 5)
8 Salary (4)
9 Female boss (9)
10 Untidy writing (6)
13 Fit to be eaten (6)
15 Prepared (5)
16 Diving apparatus (5)
17 Side (5)
18 Tiny amount (5)
21 Indian religious teacher (6)
22 Stefan - - -, former Wimbledon winner (6)
25 Very unhappy (9)
26 Dribble (4)
27 Top floor flat (9)

DOWN

2 Sci-fi author, - - - Asimov (5)
3 John Major's wife (5)
4 Suitable for crops (6)
5 Go beyond (6)
6 Car part (9)
7 Frenzied (7)
11 Circular journey (5, 4)
12 Anger, fury (5)
14 Welsh county (5)
16 Financial aid (7)
19 Deep narrow gorge (6)
20 Mortar (6)
23 Celebration, party (5)
24 Governs (5)

The Biggest Crossword Book In The World

ACROSS
1 Pedigree animal (12)
9 Of people (5)
10 Automated machine (5)
11 Indian state (3)
12 Movie camera (5)
13 Secret procedure (7)
15 Belgian ferry port (6)
17 Twin-speaker sound (6)
20 Prisoner (7)
23 Tom - - -, former Dr Who (5)
25 Traditional cooker (3)
26 Headquarters of the MCC (5)
27 Catapult (5)
28 Expert marksman (12)

DOWN
2 Moist, damp (5)
3 Former name for Yangon (7)
4 Anxiety (6)
5 Large crowd (5)
6 Revolt (5)
7 Alcohol-induced bravery (5, 7)
8 English mountain range (7, 5)
14 Overwhelming respect (3)
16 Newt (3)
18 Pepper sauce (7)
19 Shortage (6)
21 Middle-Eastern country (5)
22 Greek fable writer (5)
24 Cutting-blade (5)

The Biggest Crossword Book In The World

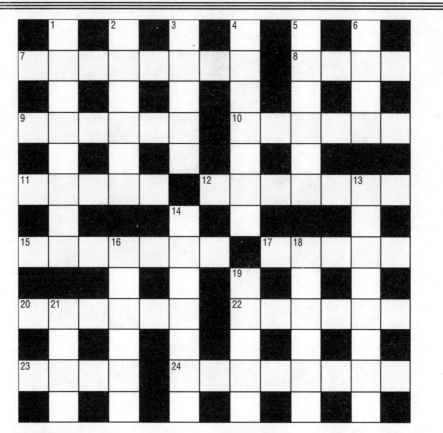

ACROSS

7 *Fanny by - - -,*
TV serial (8)
8 Squirrel's nest (4)
9 Japanese martial art (6)
10 Annoy (6)
11 State of rest (5)
12 Member of a
legislative body (7)
15 Bedding plant (7)
17 Corroded (5)
20 Aimless chatter (6)
22 Pale coloured (6)
23 Become smudged (4)
24 Social escort (8)

DOWN

1 Novelist, - - - Steel (8)
2 Flatfish (6)
3 Eskimo dwelling (5)
4 Plug, bung (7)
5 Black Sea port (6)
6 In this place (4)
13 Exact (2, 3, 3)
14 Gag (7)
16 Strong protest (6)
18 Heavy overcoat (6)
19 Spread out (5)
21 Large marble (4)

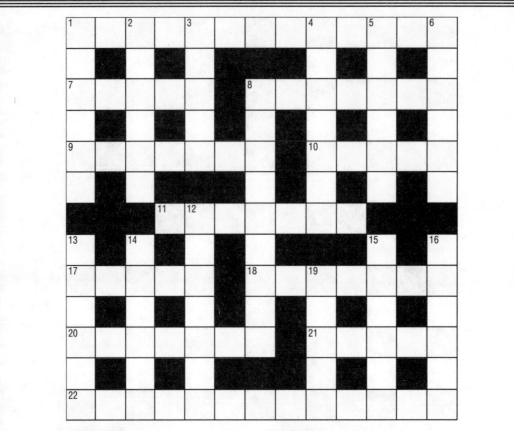

ACROSS

1 Beatles No 1 (4, 3, 2, 4)
7 Opponent (5)
8 Straight course (7)
9 Church stand (7)
10 Cunning (5)
11 Noel - - -,
House Party host (7)
17 Type of beer (5)
18 Accounts examiner (7)
20 Upgrade (7)
21 Group of eight (5)
22 Eddie Murphy film (7, 6)

DOWN

1 Upper area in
a theatre (6)
2 Beginner (6)
3 Beautiful girl (5)
4 Came into view (7)
5 Source (6)
6 Lace hole (6)
8 Have a pleasant
trip! (3, 6)
12 Frankie - - -, jockey (7)
13 Help (6)
14 Fairground game (6)
15 Motionless (6)
16 Free of charge (6)
19 Drivel (5)

The Biggest Crossword Book In The World

ACROSS

1 Chew (4)
4 Bathed (6)
8 Survey (8)
9 Nutritious bean (4)
10 Evidence (5)
11 The Netherlands (7)
13 Clergyman in charge of a congregation (6)
15 Actor's trade union (6)
17 Robert - - -, disgraced businessman (7)
19 Publish (5)
22 Scorch, char (4)
23 Legitimate target (4, 4)
24 Item of crockery (6)
25 Motion of the sea (4)

DOWN

2 Not at any time (5)
3 Exhausted (4, 3)
4 Charity for the blind (1, 1, 1, 1)
5 Recent arrival (8)
6 Artist's stand (5)
7 Young swan (6)
12 Productive (8)
14 Counting frame (6)
16 Vertical (7)
18 Flinch (5)
20 Wanderer (5)
21 Without firmness (4)

The Biggest Crossword Book In The World

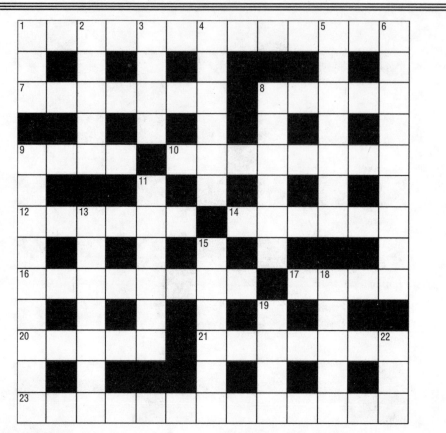

ACROSS

1 Upright, vertical (13)
7 Pope (7)
8 Tiger - - -, US golfer (5)
9 Movie (4)
10 Capital of Chile (8)
12 Vacation, holiday (6)
14 Not often (6)
16 Thrown out (8)
17 Nell - - -, mistress of
   Charles II (4)
20 Knack (5)
21 Fish (7)
23 The King of Skiffle (6, 7)

DOWN

1 Young seal (3)
2 Of the kidneys (5)
3 Viking, - - - the Red (4)
4 Overcome (6)
5 Spotted cat (7)
6 Inland county of
   Northern Ireland (9)
8 Wilt (6)
9 Absent-minded (9)
11 Stablehand (6)
13 Army or navy rank (7)
15 System (6)
18 Twist (5)
19 Smile (4)
22 Aromatic spirit (3)

The Biggest Crossword Book In The World

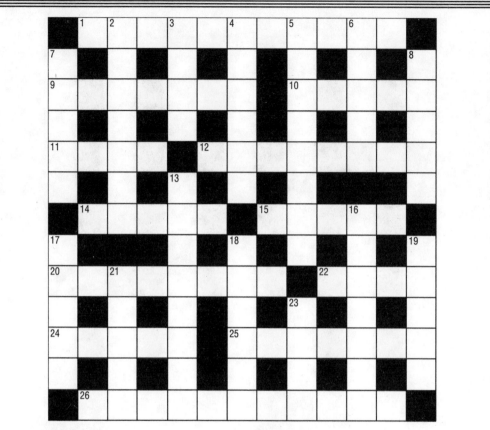

ACROSS

1 British singer (3, 8)
9 Biggest (7)
10 Spacious (5)
11 Support (4)
12 Pleasant fantasy (8)
14 Retail outlet (5)
15 Former Mayor of Carmel,
- - - Eastwood (5)
20 Rigorous exam (4, 4)
22 Long coat (4)
24 Nobleman (5)
25 Inscription on
a tombstone (7)
26 Unusual,
extraordinary (11)

DOWN

2 Heathrow, eg (7)
3 Make beer (4)
4 Batman's city (6)
5 Large terrier (8)
6 Call to mind (5)
7 Dozed (5)
8 Small person (5)
13 Simulation (8)
16 River flowing between
Canada and the USA (7)
17 Jewish religious
minister (5)
18 Climb (6)
19 Closely fitting (5)
21 Home of Rangers
Football club (5)
23 Floor covering (4)

The Biggest Crossword Book In The World

ACROSS

1 Forgiving (8)
5 Solid nourishment (4)
9 Incriminate (5)
10 Curt, blunt (5)
12 Corn (5)
13 Grizzly, eg (4)
15 Sterile (6)
18 Pale yellow (6)
20 Thin piece of wood (4)
23 Supply (5)
24 Fire raising (5)
27 Afterwards (5)
28 New Testament book (4)
29 Small kitchen (8)

DOWN

1 Brewing ingredient (4)
2 Bellow (4)
3 Surmise (5)
4 African country ruled by Idi Amin in the 1970s (6)
6 Not compulsory (8)
7 Remove, cancel (6)
8 Comment (6)
11 Lamb's mother (3)
14 Prosperous (8)
16 Taste (6)
17 Everest guide (6)
19 Sensual (6)
21 Commotion (3)
22 Song (5)
25 Rational (4)
26 Dark blue colour (4)

The Biggest Crossword Book In The World

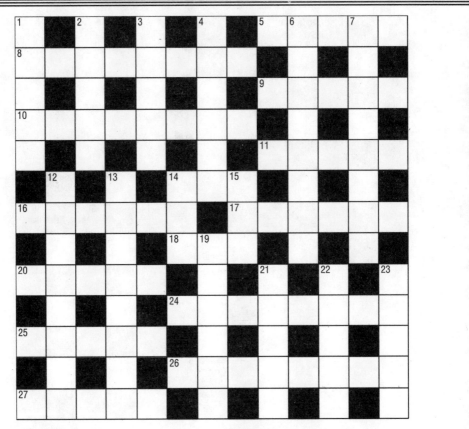

ACROSS

5 Difficult question (5)
8 Max - - -, British singer (8)
9 Leg bone (5)
10 Mended (8)
11 Flax (5)
14 Foolish person (3)
16 Social outcast (6)
17 Desert language? (6)
18 However (3)
20 Cereal (5)
24 Pessimistic (8)
25 Truck (5)
26 Hand-held firework (8)
27 Monster (5)

DOWN

1 End prematurely (5)
2 Open (5)
3 Rugby player, - - - Hastings (5)
4 Ballroom dance in fast time (6)
6 Earliest (8)
7 Outbreak of disease (8)
12 Dressing gown (8)
13 Leonardo - - -, *Titanic* actor (8)
14 Bashful (3)
15 Gentle tap (3)
19 Free from liability (6)
21 Egyptian capital (5)
22 Trivial (5)
23 Lenny - - - comedian (5)

The Biggest Crossword Book In The World

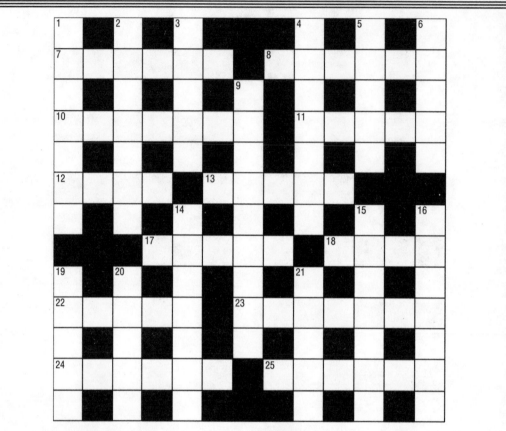

ACROSS

7 *Tom - - -*, Mark Twain novel (6)
8 Tall tree (6)
10 Playhouse (7)
11 The Devil (5)
12 Cain's brother (4)
13 Shaggy-haired oxen (5)
17 Variety of pansy (5)
18 Harsh, dry cough (4)
22 Hand warmer (5)
23 Chris - - -, radio and TV star (7)
24 Line on a weather map (6)
25 French mime artist, - - - Marceau (6)

DOWN

1 Smoker's receptacle (7)
2 Add sugar (7)
3 Pasta sauce (5)
4 Ulrika - - -, TV presenter (7)
5 Polish currency (5)
6 Crash (a vehicle) (5)
9 Make laws (9)
14 Tolerant (7)
15 Unfilled job (7)
16 Bowling pin (7)
19 Once more (5)
20 Benefactor (5)
21 Chinese mafia (5)

The Biggest Crossword Book In The World

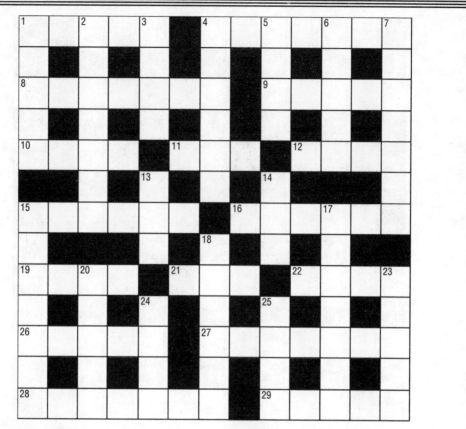

ACROSS
1 Confiscate (5)
4 Attack with vigour (7)
8 Supervise (7)
9 Boxing-match (5)
10 Carry (4)
11 Jewel (3)
12 Tied servant (4)
15 Catastrophic (6)
16 Mr Hyde's doctor? (6)
19 Midday (4)
21 Court (3)
22 German river (4)
26 Horrify (5)
27 Reading method
for the blind (7)
28 Classify (7)
29 Very wet (5)

DOWN
1 Animal's nose (5)
2 Refreshing drink (4, 3)
3 Irish Gaelic (4)
4 Beer maker (6)
5 Hand warmer (4)
6 Dispute (5)
7 Obedient (7)
13 Relatives (3)
14 New, modern (3)
15 African country (7)
17 Christmas cake (4, 3)
18 Move unsteadily (6)
20 Smell (5)
23 Foe (5)
24 Similar, like (4)
25 R and B musician,
- - - Domino (4)

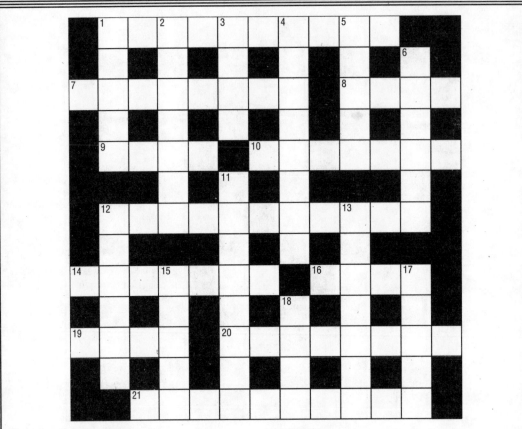

ACROSS

1 Fire-lighter (10)
7 Star-shaped figure (8)
8 English county (4)
9 Eastern ruler (4)
10 Suffer (7)
12 London's traditional home of the press (5, 6)
14 Porridge ingredient (7)
16 Ram down (concrete) (4)
19 Following (4)
20 Electrical connection (8)
21 South Coast headland (6, 4)

DOWN

1 Fragment (5)
2 Become aware (7)
3 Swampy ground (4)
4 Suggest as a candidate (8)
5 Joint between foot and leg (5)
6 Chesspiece (6)
11 Second largest ocean (8)
12 Dreaded (6)
13 Indirect (7)
15 Thirty-nine inches (5)
17 Tartan cloth (5)
18 Debauch (4)

The Biggest Crossword Book In The World

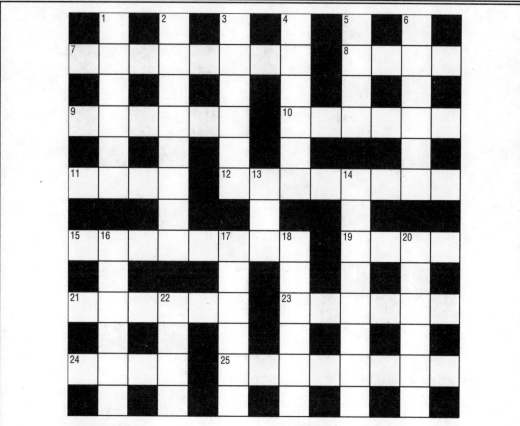

ACROSS

7 Report (8)
8 Depression (4)
9 All over the world (6)
10 Foul tasting (6)
11 Fish-eating eagle (4)
12 Booze free! (3-5)
15 Refused to attend (8)
19 Banner (4)
21 Australian 'bear' (6)
23 Behaviour (6)
24 Elliptical (4)
25 Move towards
the same point (8)

DOWN

1 Part of a shirt (6)
2 Small exercise weight (8)
3 Fanatic (6)
4 Die of hunger (6)
5 Prayer ending (4)
6 Tennis player,
- - - Seles (6)
13 Devon river (3)
14 Lawbreaker (8)
16 Adapt over a
long period (6)
17 Catch sight of (6)
18 Insistent request (6)
20 Take retaliation (6)
22 Male ox (4)

The Biggest Crossword Book In The World

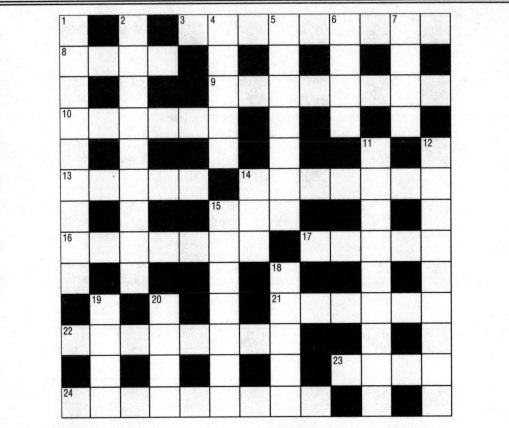

ACROSS

3 Irish county (9)
8 Comply (4)
9 Outrageous (8)
10 Writing desk (6)
13 Wedge placed
under a wheel (5)
14 Firmness (7)
15 Purring animal (3)
16 Stress (7)
17 Hospital worker (5)
21 Extension (6)
22 Fixed, unchanging (8)
23 French military cap (4)
24 Children's story (5, 4)

DOWN

1 BBC drama series (5, 4)
2 Large dog (9)
4 Subject of discussion (5)
5 Clairvoyant (7)
6 Garden tool (4)
7 Skating area (4)
11 Bob Mortimer's
partner (3, 6)
12 Dorset resort (4, 5)
14 Judo grade (3)
15 Get in touch (7)
18 Glenn Close film,
- - - *Attraction* (5)
19 Actress, - - - Bryan (4)
20 Lenin's state (1, 1, 1, 1)

The Biggest Crossword Book In The World

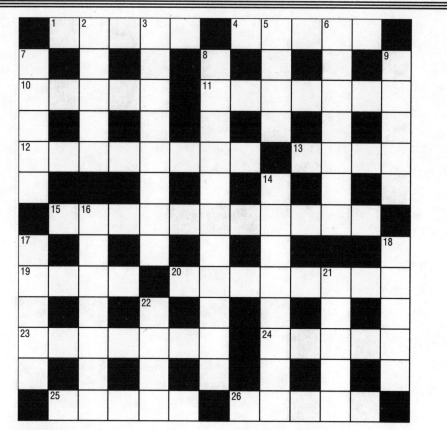

ACROSS

1 Watch over, protect (5)
4 Sound judgement (5)
10 Doctor (5)
11 Farthest from
the centre (7)
12 Tale (8)
13 Betray (4)
15 Freemason chief (5, 6)
19 Doubtful? (4)
20 Without limits (8)
23 Open porch (7)
24 Pleasant smell (5)
25 Compensate (5)
26 *Out of Africa* actress,
- - - Streep (5)

DOWN

2 Needless (5)
3 Going backwards (8)
5 Horse feed (4)
6 Put on a list (7)
7 Smudge (5)
8 Emotional (11)
9 Bed aboard a ship (5)
14 Calculate roughly (8)
16 Soccer official (7)
17 Adele - - -,
Emmerdale actress (5)
18 Go over the
main points (5)
21 *Ebony And* - - -,
song (5)
22 Ballerina, - - - Pavlova (4)

The Biggest Crossword Book In The World

ACROSS

1 Borough (9)
8 Al - - -, Former US Vice President (4)
9 Barbra - - -, Hollywood star (9)
10 Improved (6)
13 Comfortable (2, 4)
15 Robbed (5)
16 Dividend (5)
17 Not religious (5)
18 Humiliate (5)
21 Soft, gentle breeze (6)
22 Drawing instrument (6)
25 Made bigger (9)
26 Marsh plant (4)
27 Limits (9)

DOWN

2 Release (5)
3 Inactive (5)
4 Place inside (6)
5 Book published once a year (6)
6 Sentimental (9)
7 Cowboy film (7)
11 Kitchen gadget (3, 6)
12 Written piece (5)
14 Conical tent (5)
16 Bird of prey (7)
19 Third-placed contestant's medal (6)
20 Strong alcoholic drink (6)
23 Military shop (5)
24 Incompetent (5)

The Biggest Crossword Book In The World

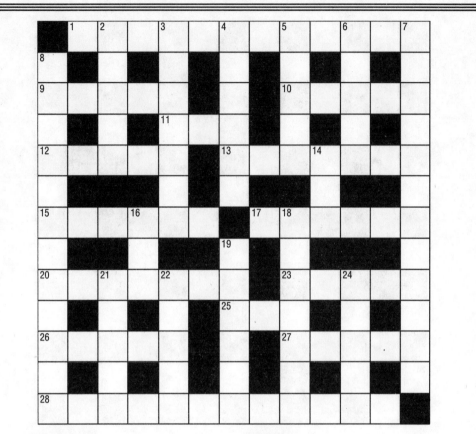

ACROSS

1 *Love Hurts* star (3,9)
9 Cousin's father (5)
10 Lobster pot (5)
11 Arithmetic problem (3)
12 Support, prop (5)
13 Leave in the lurch (7)
15 Napping (6)
17 Cross out (6)
20 *The - - -,*
Shakespeare play (7)
23 Footwear (5)
25 Not at home (3)
26 Assumed name (5)
27 Month of the year (5)
28 Businessman (12)

DOWN

2 Happen (5)
3 Grapple (7)
4 Barry - - -,
TV,s film critic (6)
5 Pilgrim city (5)
6 Massage (5)
7 Constantly (12)
8 Prove (12)
14 Convent lady (3)
16 The sixth sense? (1, 1, 1)
18 Choose to refrain (7)
19 Bram - - -,
Dracula author (6)
21 Damp (5)
22 Come after (5)
24 Greek island (5)

The Biggest Crossword Book In The World

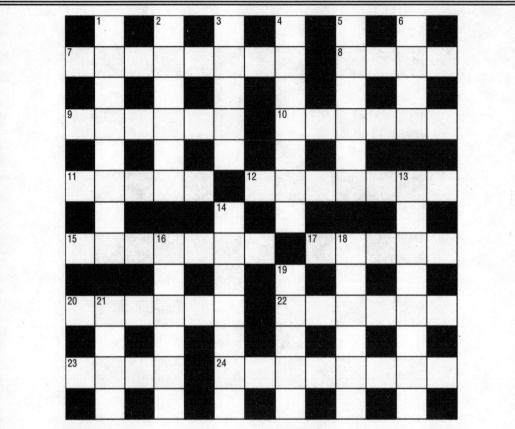

ACROSS
7 Alex - - -,
soccer manager (8)
8 Went by horse (4)
9 Clyde's
partner-in-crime (6)
10 Excite (6)
11 Asian country (5)
12 Wild pig (4, 3)
15 Coarse fabric (7)
17 Actions (5)
20 Flag (6)
22 Overlook (6)
23 Yorkshire valley (4)
24 Infinite time (8)

DOWN
1 Soft drink (8)
2 Topics for discussion (6)
3 Showy flower (5)
4 As a substitute (7)
5 Wood decay (3-3)
6 Object of worship (4)
13 Remnants (8)
14 Blacksmith (7)
16 Poem of 14 lines (6)
18 Disgraceful (6)
19 Proposal (5)
21 At a distance (4)

The Biggest Crossword Book In The World

ACROSS
1 Global (13)
7 Cold, chilly (5)
8 Successful show (7)
9 Express disapproval (7)
10 Stringed instrument (5)
11 Reduce in quantity (7)
17 Course (5)
18 Give power to (7)
20 Take cover (7)
21 Purpose (5)
22 *Mrs Doubtfire* star (5,8)

DOWN
1 Collision force (6)
2 Capital of Albania (6)
3 Verse (5)
4 Forbidden (7)
5 Form of pasta (6)
6 Cream (6)
8 Golden bloom (9)
12 Merseyside football team (7)
13 Art rubber (6)
14 Impressive (6)
15 Yacht harbour (6)
16 Social position (6)
19 Ward off (5)

The Biggest Crossword Book In The World

ACROSS

1 Grow dim (4)
4 Equipment (6)
8 Outdoor meal (8)
9 Repulsive person? (4)
10 Longest river in France (5)
11 West Indian state (7)
13 *The Blue - - -*, Brooke Shields film (6)
15 Messy (6)
17 Take prisoner (7)
19 Caption (5)
22 Reminder (4)
23 Girth (8)
24 Scanty (6)
25 Office furniture (4)

DOWN

2 Memorable American battle (5)
3 Trade stoppage (7)
4 Dressmaking fold (4)
5 In good spirits (8)
6 British airport (5)
7 Unbiased (6)
12 Trespasser (8)
14 Astonished (6)
16 Final part (4, 3)
18 Cavalry unit (5)
20 English city (5)
21 Unladen weight of a vehicle (4)

The Biggest Crossword Book In The World

ACROSS

1 Kevin Costner film (5, 2, 6)
7 Disease also known as lockjaw (7)
8 John - - -, actor (5)
9 Condiment (4)
10 Mediator (8)
12 Steven - - -, film star (6)
14 Means of exit (6)
16 Voting age (8)
17 Scoff (4)
20 Walk slowly (5)
21 Calamity (7)
23 Parking regulator (7, 6)

DOWN

1 Seizure (3)
2 Applaud (5)
3 Dip in liquid (4)
4 Dashboard (6)
5 Extremely bad (7)
6 Onlooker (9)
8 Tusked seal (6)
9 Whoopi Goldberg film (6, 3)
11 Cloak (6)
13 Branch of mathematics (7)
15 Rushed, busy (6)
18 Correct (5)
19 Computer facts (4)
22 Oriental currency (3)

The Biggest Crossword Book In The World

ACROSS

1 *Coronation Street* actress (7,4)
9 Rower (7)
10 Part of the arm (5)
11 Put down noisily (4)
12 Plastic case containing reel of tape (8)
14 Permit (5)
15 Winter sportsman (5)
20 Shaken (8)
22 Optimal (4)
24 Caribbean country (5)
25 Sign of recognition (7)
26 Road-building machine (11)

DOWN

2 Overseas letters (3, 4)
3 Explosive device (4)
4 Hire payment (6)
5 Souvenir, reminder (8)
6 Planet's circular path (5)
7 Search for underground water (5)
8 Heavy cloth (5)
13 Bob Hoskins film (4, 4)
16 Kill (7)
17 Masculine? (5)
18 Subdivision (6)
19 Alternative (5)
21 Fool (5)
23 Jack's girl! (4)

The Biggest Crossword Book In The World

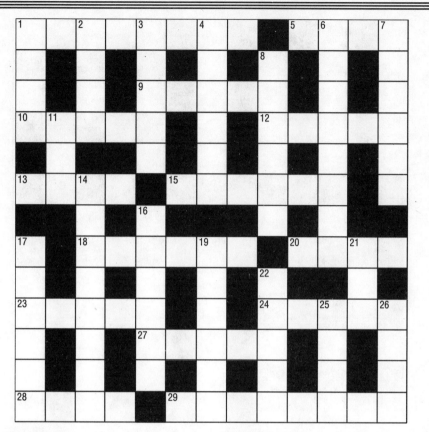

ACROSS

1 Apache Indian chief (8)
5 Warning device on a car (4)
9 Small bird (5)
10 Turn away (5)
12 Without preparation (2-3)
13 Greyish-brown colour (4)
15 Minister (6)
18 Qualified practitioner (6)
20 Prophet (4)
23 Blazing (5)
24 Carpenter's tool (5)
27 Cherub (5)
28 Network (4)
29 Deer-like animal (8)

DOWN

1 Swimming display (4)
2 Isle of Wight town (4)
3 Speedy (5)
4 Very tiny (6)
6 Riches, wealth (8)
7 Agile (6)
8 Roofing material (6)
11 By way of (3)
14 Film, *Four - - - and a Funeral* (8)
16 Piercing shriek (6)
17 Former English cricket captain, - - - Gooch (6)
19 Atmospheric gas (6)
21 Sooner than (3)
22 Healing ointment (5)
25 Dole cheque (4)
26 Go by horse (4)

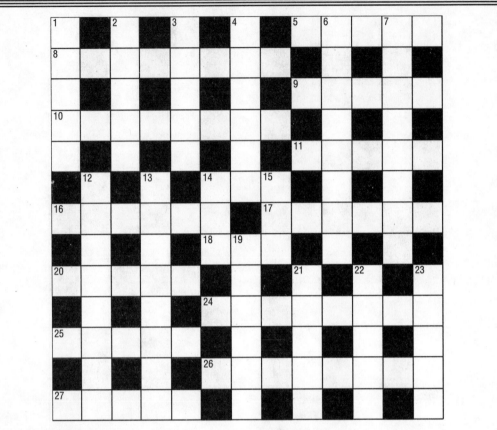

ACROSS

5 Spanish warrior (2, 3)
8 Anne - - -, Shakespeare's wife (8)
9 Plant with sword-like leaves (5)
10 A west country speciality (5, 3)
11 Object (5)
14 Public vehicle (3)
16 Inform (6)
17 Like better (6)
18 Greek letter (3)
20 Turkish meat dish (5)
24 Oxygen increasing exercises (8)
25 American restaurant (5)
26 Obstruction (8)
27 Scrape, abrade (5)

DOWN

1 Rough hut (5)
2 Danielle - - -, novelist (5)
3 Singer, - - - Wynette (5)
4 French cake (6)
6 Sound of chuckling (8)
7 Furious (8)
12 Guest-house owner (8)
13 Band of tissue joining bones (8)
14 Extra cricket run (3)
15 Medicinal spring (3)
19 Threefold (6)
21 Freshwater fish (5)
22 Last game in a competition (5)
23 David - - -, singer (5)

The Biggest Crossword Book In The World

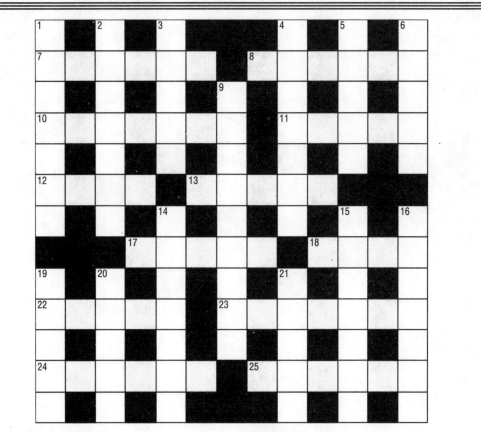

ACROSS

7 One from New Delhi? (6)
8 Farm implement (6)
10 Catherine - - -, author (7)
11 Ponder (5)
12 Breaking waves (4)
13 In the midst of (5)
17 Egg-beater (5)
18 Present (4)
22 Amount of time (5)
23 Spectators standing area (7)
24 Not transparent (6)
25 A shoal of whales (6)

DOWN

1 Exchange opinions about (7)
2 Postpone temporarily (7)
3 Error, slip (5)
4 Obvious (7)
5 Spring flower (5)
6 Capital of Bangladesh (5)
9 Bad blood (9)
14 Firearm (7)
15 Bull teaser (7)
16 Shakespeare tragedy (7)
19 Famous racecourse (5)
20 Winston Churchill's trademark (5)
21 Solve (a code) (5)

The Biggest Crossword Book In The World

ACROSS

1 Cuttlefish ink (5)
4 First book of the Bible (7)
8 Gap, hole (7)
9 Grinding tooth (5)
10 Jump (4)
11 Cunning (3)
12 Titled gentleman (4)
15 Foul smell (6)
16 Detachment of guards (6)
19 Western defence organisation (4)
21 Cry of a cat (3)
22 Ear part (4)
26 Extensive (5)
27 Strew (7)
28 Old-fashioned living room (7)
29 Compassion (5)

DOWN

1 Backless seat (5)
2 Get ready (7)
3 Sour-tasting (4)
4 Fancy-man (6)
5 Anaesthetise (4)
6 Volley of applause (5)
7 Filled pastry dish (7)
13 Extremely cold (3)
14 State of conflict (3)
15 Ultraviolet light (3, 4)
17 Domestic cock (7)
18 Riddle (6)
20 Hard drinker (5)
23 Before time (5)
24 Nevada's divorce town (4)
25 Tranquil (4)

The Biggest Crossword Book In The World

ACROSS
1 Vanishes (10)
7 Likely to change (8)
8 Indication (4)
9 Fibres that stand up
   from the weave (4)
10 Red pepper (7)
12 Always on the go (11)
14 Storage box (7)
16 Funny story (4)
19 Harness (4)
20 Green petrol (8)
21 Salad garnish (10)

DOWN
1 Wilt (5)
2 Edible shellfish (7)
3 Formal, proper (4)
4 Style (8)
5 Happen again (5)
6 Drug user (6)
11 Animal (8)
12 Racing car (3, 3)
13 Third stage of man (4, 3)
15 Classical music show (5)
17 Balanced odds (5)
18 Cricketer, - - - Stewart (4)

The Biggest Crossword Book In The World

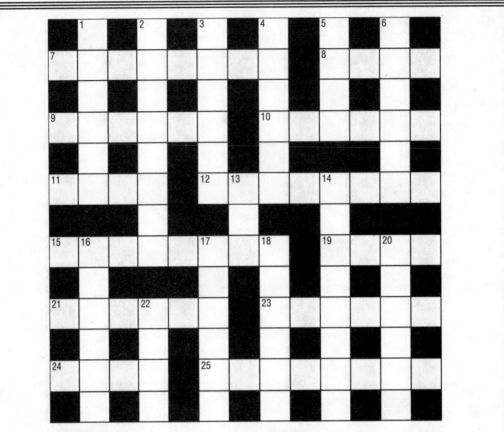

ACROSS
7 Displays (8)
8 Certain (4)
9 Sentimental song (6)
10 Selected (6)
11 Layer of mineral (4)
12 Lengthen (8)
15 Agent (8)
19 Strike with a whip (4)
21 Spring up (6)
23 Near-sighted (6)
24 Labour (4)
25 Legendary knight (8)

DOWN
1 Breathe out (6)
2 Cruelty (8)
3 Intermediate (6)
4 Of the mind (6)
5 Capital of Norway (4)
6 Very keen (6)
13 Auction item (3)
14 Bolted (8)
16 Use (6)
17 King of the Huns (6)
18 Sir - - - Hillary, mountaineer (6)
20 Mariner (6)
22 Epsom horse race (4)

The Biggest Crossword Book In The World

ACROSS

3 Metric distance (9)
8 Flank (4)
9 False impression (8)
10 Indoor row of shops (6)
13 Game of chance (5)
14 Colonist (7)
15 Piece of turf (3)
16 Welsh mountain (7)
17 Resin (5)
21 Delicate plant (6)
22 Charles - - -, French statesman (2, 6)
23 Vitality (4)
24 TV's match-making show (5, 4)

DOWN

1 Set up (9)
2 Training (9)
4 Table of contents (5)
5 Bound by contract (7)
6 Effortless (4)
7 Space in a house (4)
11 Compulsive drinker (9)
12 Dispute (4, 5)
14 Male child (3)
15 **11 Down** might be this! (7)
18 Small fish (5)
19 Exchange for money (4)
20 Unlikely tale (4)

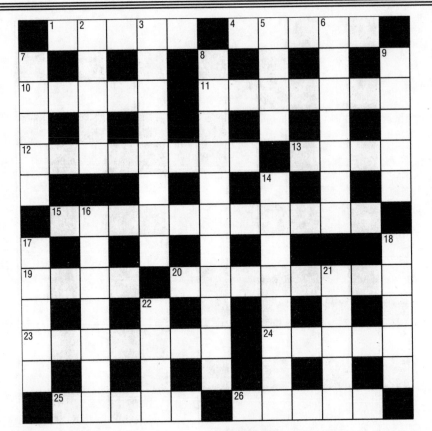

ACROSS

1 Thong (5)
4 Say something! (5)
10 Lady golfer, - - - Davies (5)
11 Reason to visit the doctor? (7)
12 Suffocation (8)
13 River mud (4)
15 Solitary (11)
19 Heated (4)
20 Particular (8)
23 Exemplary work of art (7)
24 Bring (pressure) to bear (5)
25 Listened to (5)
26 Condition (5)

DOWN

2 Pulsate strongly (5)
3 Examined (8)
5 Fragment (4)
6 Sale (7)
7 Gather information (5)
8 Ex *Coronation Street* actress (6, 5)
9 John - - -, English poet (5)
14 Next to (8)
16 Recount (7)
17 Two times (5)
18 Severe (5)
21 Pay for (5)
22 Russian emperor (4)

The Biggest Crossword Book In The World

ACROSS

1 Emily Bronte novel,
- - - *Heights* (9)
8 Drag (4)
9 Alight (9)
10 Secondary channel (6)
13 Agree to (6)
15 String of coral islands (5)
16 Small hill (5)
17 Arctic duck (5)
18 Highest grade in an
examination (5)
21 Fair-haired (6)
22 Instinctive (6)
25 Domineering (9)
26 Excessively
sentimental (4)
27 Adaptable (9)

DOWN

2 Incorporate (5)
3 Laughing animal (5)
4 Strong and sturdy (6)
5 Average (6)
6 Yield, submit (9)
7 State of disorder (7)
11 Lengthened (9)
12 Cold meal (5)
14 Free from dirt (5)
16 Jewish settlement (7)
19 Clergyman (6)
20 Break, opening (6)
23 Break into pieces (5)
24 Of the same value (5)

The Biggest Crossword Book In The World

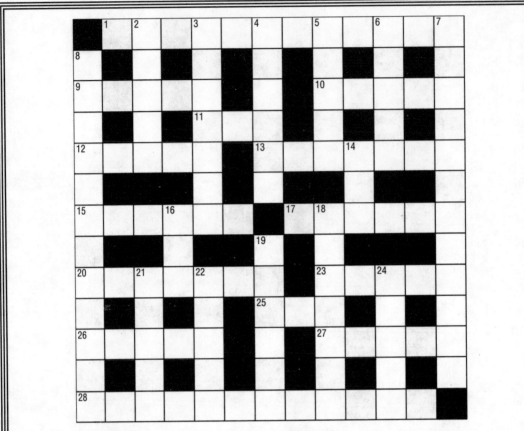

ACROSS

1 *EastEnders* actor (4, 8)
9 From Dublin? (5)
10 Search (5)
11 Tot up (3)
12 Secret appointment (5)
13 Native of Newcastle? (7)
15 Gloomy (6)
17 Tropical woody grass (6)
20 Arctic whale (7)
23 Savoury dish (5)
25 Fury (3)
26 Asian republic (5)
27 Proportion (5)
28 Shakespeare's London
  playhouse (5, 7)

DOWN

2 *Princess - - -*, Judith
  Krantz novel (5)
3 Hindu sage (7)
4 Tense (2, 4)
5 Musical party (5)
6 Shun (5)
7 Spanish tourist
  resort (12)
8 Patrick Swayze film (5, 7)
14 Batter (3)
16 Cut down (3)
18 Canadian province (7)
19 Base beneath
  a statue (6)
21 Cowboy display (5)
22 Throw (5)
24 Following (5)

The Biggest Crossword Book In The World

ACROSS

7 John Wayne's Oscar-winning film (4, 4)
8 Avoid (4)
9 Throat wash (6)
10 Boxlike container in a chest (6)
11 Cloth for drying (5)
12 Comprise (7)
15 Rising actress (7)
17 The son of Isaac (5)
20 German composer (6)
22 Look in a casual manner (6)
23 Horse's iron footplate (4)
24 University term (8)

DOWN

1 Escape from prison (5, 3)
2 West Indian music (6)
3 Unkind (5)
4 Pupil (7)
5 Lebanon's neighbour (6)
6 Untainted (4)
13 Thick slice of bread? (8)
14 Closest (7)
16 Athletic bean? (6)
18 Stimulate (6)
19 Hydrogen weapon (1-4)
21 Feel pain (4)

The Biggest Crossword Book In The World

ACROSS

1 Ordinary, normal (13)
7 Uncertainty (5)
8 Road surfacing
material (7)
9 Coached (7)
10 Published insult (5)
11 Adhesive label (7)
17 Frighten (5)
18 Fred - - -,
cricket legend (7)
20 Residue (7)
21 Poker hand (5)
22 Tough-guy
actor (6,7)

DOWN

1 Modernise (6)
2 Regard as the same (6)
3 Provide food (5)
4 Sudden urge (7)
5 Close to hand (6)
6 Small (6)
8 Formally gives
up position (9)
12 Spring catch in a lock (7)
13 Roman emperor (6)
14 Capital of Croatia (6)
15 Attack from a
concealed position (6)
16 Song of loyalty (6)
19 Out of condition (5)

The Biggest Crossword Book In The World

ACROSS

1 Wander (4)
4 TV personality,
- - - Turner (6)
8 From Montreal? (8)
9 Group of aligned
nations (4)
10 Popular pub game (5)
11 Pitiless struggle (3, 4)
13 Solicitor (6)
15 Mental exertion (6)
17 Short chopper (7)
19 Theatrical performance
for children (5)
22 Sleeveless cloak (4)
23 Total business sales (8)
24 Garden plant (6)
25 Rebel (4)

DOWN

2 City in Nebraska (5)
3 Precisely (7)
4 The largest continent (4)
5 Village in north
Cornwall (8)
6 Glowing coal (5)
7 Association football (6)
12 Eastern (8)
14 Buoyant (6)
16 Taste (7)
18 Sphere of combat (5)
20 Lock of hair (5)
21 Type of whale (4)

The Biggest Crossword Book In The World

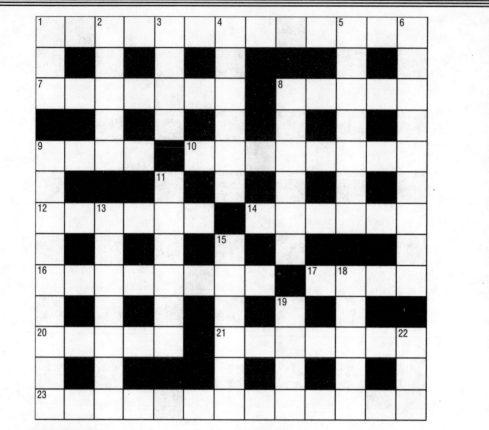

ACROSS

1 Illegal (7, 3, 3)
7 Short excerpt (7)
8 Separately (5)
9 Askew (4)
10 Answer (8)
12 Swaddle (6)
14 Agricultural implement (6)
16 Suggestion (8)
17 Rain heavily (4)
20 Boy's name (5)
21 Child's toy (4, 3)
23 A literary scholar (1, 3, 2, 7)

DOWN

1 Era (3)
2 Become different (5)
3 Tidy (4)
4 Tie up with rope (6)
5 Novice (7)
6 Scottish pop quartet (3, 3, 3)
8 Seem (6)
9 The smallest continent (9)
11 From what place (6)
13 Pungent alkaline gas (7)
15 Carnivorous mammal (6)
18 Large bird (5)
19 Cause pain (4)
22 Welfare body (1,1,1)

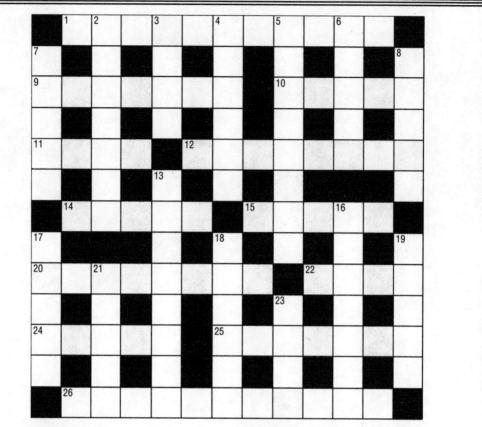

ACROSS

- **1** Organise, arrange (11)
- **9** Backache (7)
- **10** Breath through the nose (5)
- **11** Trolley bus (4)
- **12** Feud, quarrel (8)
- **14** Brimless cap (5)
- **15** Below (5)
- **20** Scold, rebuke (8)
- **22** Exist (4)
- **24** Location (5)
- **25** Household chore (7)
- **26** Gets faster (11)

DOWN

- **2** Rush about angrily (7)
- **3** Practical joke (4)
- **4** Before (6)
- **5** Inhabitant (8)
- **6** Screw of tobacco (5)
- **7** Teacher of Aristotle (5)
- **8** Entrails (5)
- **13** Aircraft fuel (8)
- **16** Large building (7)
- **17** Fearless (5)
- **18** Writer (6)
- **19** Mix, fuse (5)
- **21** Hysteria (5)
- **23** Old Roman garment (4)

The Biggest Crossword Book In The World

ACROSS

1 Oven-cooked Indian food (8)
5 Handle (4)
9 Correct (5)
10 Hawaiian greeting (5)
12 Loft (5)
13 Average level of achievement (4)
15 Shopkeeper (6)
18 Judith - - -, American novelist (6)
20 Red Sea port (4)
23 Créme de la créme (5)
24 Clan leader (5)
27 Interval (5)
28 Roar (4)
29 Postponed (8)

DOWN

1 Bye-bye! (2-2)
2 Roman emperor (4)
3 American talk show host, - - - Winfrey (5)
4 Hardship (6)
6 Brought up, raised (8)
7 Radio transmitter (6)
8 Carbohydrate (6)
11 Sign of the zodiac (3)
14 Earn vast amounts of money! (4, 2, 2)
16 Fondle (6)
17 Zoo worker (6)
19 Fierce verbal attack (6)
21 Adam's partner (3)
22 Picture (5)
25 Composer, - - - Novello (4)
26 Detect (4)

The Biggest Crossword Book In The World

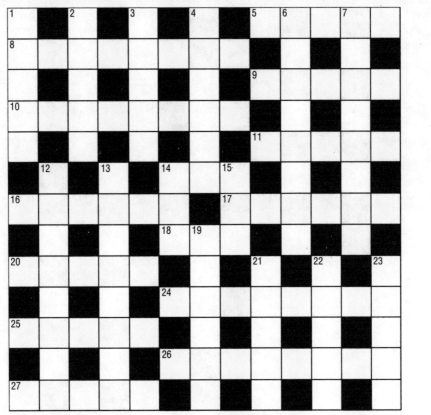

ACROSS
5 In solitude (5)
8 On the outside (8)
9 Camber (5)
10 West Indian island (8)
11 Short, simple song (5)
14 The Briny (3)
16 Scanty (6)
17 Gardener's tool (6)
18 Drawn match (3)
20 Calvin - - -, American fashion designer (5)
24 Indian city (8)
25 Tennis player, - - - Becker (5)
26 Section (8)
27 Trite (5)

DOWN
1 Large and bulky (5)
2 Earthenware mug (5)
3 Trailing part of a wedding dress (5)
4 Japanese martial art (6)
6 Sweet on a stick (8)
7 Odd number (8)
12 Affluent (4-2-2)
13 Engine starter system (8)
14 Collection, group (3)
15 Had some food (3)
19 Sloping typeface (6)
21 Pungent (5)
22 Leave bare (5)
23 Temporary loss of consciousness (5)

The Biggest Crossword Book In The World

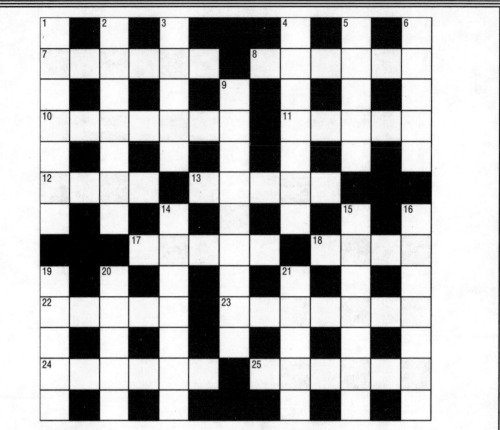

ACROSS

7 Car lock-up (6)
8 Open-topped
   container (6)
10 Long (7)
11 Actress, - - - Imrie (5)
12 Politically
    Conservative (4)
13 Plain and dull (5)
17 Lady (5)
18 Increase (4)
22 This planet (5)
23 Disease (7)
24 Part of the eye (6)
25 Continent (6)

DOWN

1 Dexterity (7)
2 Farm building (7)
3 Semiprecious stone (5)
4 Accomplish purpose (7)
5 Talent (5)
6 Book of maps (5)
9 Love of fires (9)
14 Nil (7)
15 Cheese dish (7)
16 Rare (7)
19 Long for (5)
20 Talk foolishly (5)
21 Beachy Head, eg (5)

The Biggest Crossword Book In The World

ACROSS

1 Irish county (5)
4 Free time (7)
8 Fit of temper (7)
9 Break out (5)
10 Divine (4)
11 Flower plot (3)
12 Fly like a sparrow (4)
15 Traditional Lancashire dish (6)
16 Emotionally aroused (6)
19 Pipe (4)
21 Genetic fingerprints (1, 1, 1)
22 Fleshy stonefruit (4)
26 Run away to marry (5)
27 Fuss (7)
28 Contributor (7)
29 Source (5)

DOWN

1 Two-masted sailing vessel (5)
2 Curly lock of hair (7)
3 Enclosed ground adjoining a building (4)
4 Joanna - - -, actress (6)
5 Large mountain goat (4)
6 Normal (5)
7 Warrant (7)
13 Dove's call (3)
14 Tide movement (3)
15 Impetuous person (7)
17 Finished (3, 4)
18 Hidden gunman (6)
20 Colour (5)
23 Flooded land (5)
24 Pressed woollen fabric (4)
25 Chunk of cake (4)

The Biggest Crossword Book In The World

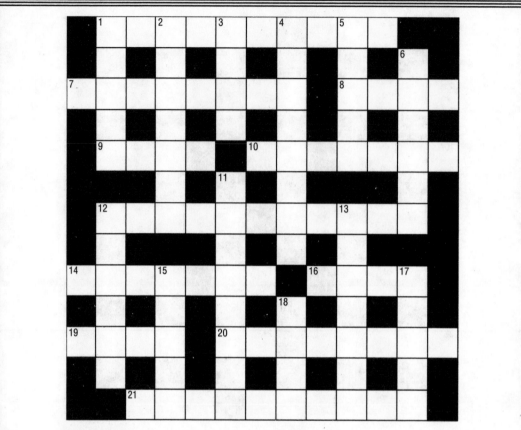

ACROSS
1 Hampshire city (10)
7 Kim - - -, film star (8)
8 Tablet (4)
9 Reverberate (4)
10 General plan (7)
12 Pattern of zig-zag lines (11)
14 Pantomime character (3, 4)
16 Joke (4)
19 Open-topped container (4)
20 Callously (8)
21 *War and Peace* author (3, 7)

DOWN
1 Moby Dick, eg (5)
2 Not one or the other (7)
3 Far up (4)
4 Beg (8)
5 Drive out (5)
6 Descend sharply (6)
11 Gradually (3, 2, 3)
12 Not solid (6)
13 Ham it up! (7)
15 Swelling (5)
17 Keep count (5)
18 Fight of honour (4)

The Biggest Crossword Book In The World

ACROSS

7 Hurry up! (4, 4)
8 Army base (4)
9 Indian PM,
  - - - Gandhi (6)
10 Main meal of the day (6)
11 Slender-bodied
  pond creature (4)
12 Blend of tea (4, 4)
15 Unlucky number (8)
19 Lofty (4)
21 Spicy Italian sausage (6)
23 Pale from illness (6)
24 Ale (4)
25 Copied (8)

DOWN

1 Alteration (6)
2 Tiny fragment
  of wood (8)
3 Expression (6)
4 Eight-legged
  arachnid (6)
5 Religious portrait (4)
6 Hinder (6)
13 Chopping tool (3)
14 Free oneself (3-5)
16 Supreme bliss (6)
17 Remedy (6)
18 Small piece of cloth (6)
20 Tarry (6)
22 Feeling (4)

The Biggest Crossword Book In The World

ACROSS

3 London theatre (9)
8 Literary composition (4)
9 Liable to happen soon (8)
10 Martin - - -, comedy actor (6)
13 Navigation aid (5)
14 Wife's partner (7)
15 Female parent (3)
16 Brass instrument (7)
17 Bike (5)
21 Beginning (6)
22 Volcano which destroyed Pompeii (8)
23 Serpent's sound (4)
24 Kent city (9)

DOWN

1 Unrecognised place (9)
2 Riddle (9)
4 Crop up (5)
5 Large amount of money (4, 3)
6 Declare untrue (4)
7 Arm bone (4)
11 Mockingly ironic (9)
12 Draw attention to (9)
14 Shed (3)
15 Autobiographical record (7)
18 Sheriff's men (5)
19 Reject (4)
20 Sell (drugs) illegally (4)

The Biggest Crossword Book In The World

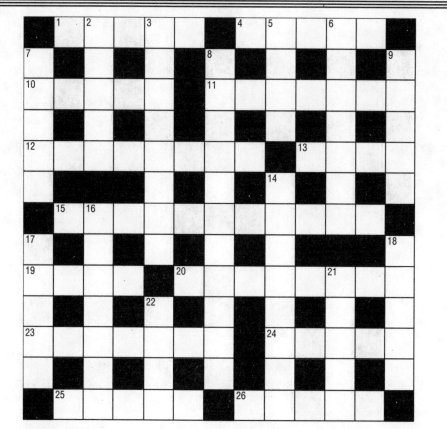

ACROSS
 1 Shabby (5)
 4 Bog (5)
10 Seance board (5)
11 Make void (7)
12 Australian capital (8)
13 German Mrs (4)
15 Reflect (11)
19 Blueprint (4)
20 Inscribed (8)
23 Matching jumper and cardigan (7)
24 Aquatic mammal (5)
25 Haughty expression (5)
26 Sacred song (5)

DOWN
 2 Straighten up (5)
 3 Grotesque imitation (8)
 5 Brick barrier (4)
 6 Simenon's famous French detective (7)
 7 Indentation (5)
 8 Charge with a crime (11)
 9 Treacle (5)
14 Brilliant (8)
16 Applause (7)
17 Rush (5)
18 Decorate (5)
21 Essential (5)
22 Land encircled by water (4)

The Biggest Crossword Book In The World

ACROSS

1 Inflamation of the joints (9)
8 Loud shout (4)
9 Christmas show (9)
10 Holiday accomodation (6)
13 Chatter idly (6)
15 Make merry (5)
16 American state (5)
17 Unoccupied (5)
18 Clothing (5)
21 Sofa, couch (6)
22 Abduct (6)
25 Large lorry (3-6)
26 Bridle strap (4)
27 Dutch portrait painter (9)

DOWN

2 Arrive at (5)
3 The Ritz, eg (5)
4 Prisoner (6)
5 Protected against disease (6)
6 Nappy fastener (6, 3)
7 Old (7)
11 Daughter of Tsar Nicholas II (9)
12 Gradually wear away (5)
14 Jean - - -, racing driver (5)
16 Animate (7)
19 Sleep (6)
20 US space station (6)
23 Singer, - - - Ross (5)
24 Correct (5)

459

The Biggest Crossword Book In The World

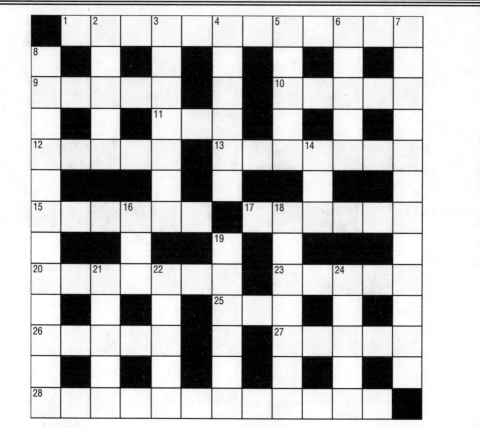

ACROSS
1 Government employee (5, 7)
9 Be ready for (5)
10 Italian explorer, - - - Polo (5)
11 Hurricane centre (3)
12 Bertie - - -, Irish PM (5)
13 Fleshy fruit (7)
15 Rag-and-bone man (6)
17 Beethoven's first name (6)
20 Autumn month (7)
23 Scratch (5)
25 Diligent insect (3)
26 Monk's outfit (5)
27 Traffic-light colour (5)
28 TV presenter (5, 7)

DOWN
2 Angry (5)
3 Extreme (7)
4 Shriek (6)
5 Ladies' man (5)
6 Artery (5)
7 Street (12)
8 Disastrous (12)
14 Not a gentleman! (3)
16 As well as (3)
18 Arrogant person (7)
19 Baby's bed (6)
21 Small drum (5)
22 Conductor's wand (5)
24 Of a city (5)

The Biggest Crossword Book In The World

ACROSS
7 Custom (8)
8 Singer, - - - Grant (4)
9 Frieze (6)
10 Small tower (6)
11 Gate catch (5)
12 Provoked (7)
15 Unbeliever (7)
17 Region of China (5)
20 Stereotyped phrase (6)
22 Saturate (6)
23 Even number (4)
24 Marine creature (3, 5)

DOWN
1 Conceited (8)
2 Sharp-tasting (6)
3 Thread (5)
4 London football club (4, 3)
5 Capital of Iran (6)
6 Rim (4)
13 Wield (8)
14 Discredit (7)
16 Accompany (6)
18 Compartment in a refrigerator (6)
19 Novelist, - - - Wallace (5)
21 Booty (4)

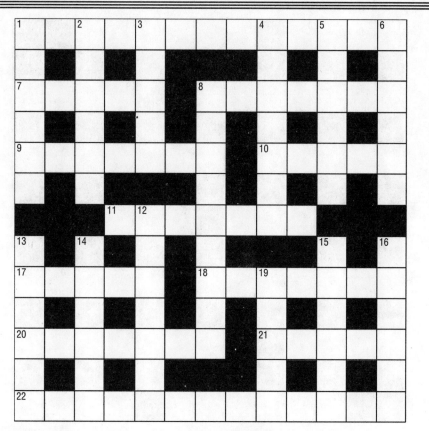

ACROSS

1 Comedy actress (4, 9)
7 Hard toil (5)
8 Worry greatly (7)
9 Expand (7)
10 Exclusive press story (5)
11 Store boss (7)
17 Meat jelly (5)
18 Debonair (7)
20 Fast sailing ship (7)
21 Charles - - -, actor (5)
22 Green? (13)

DOWN

1 Mick - - -, singer (6)
2 Almost (6)
3 Adam's ale (5)
4 Stock Exchange index (7)
5 Magazine chief (6)
6 French ferry port (6)
8 Jean - - -, *Corrie's* Hilda Ogden (9)
12 New alcoholic drink (7)
13 Chinese exercise (3, 3)
14 Nymph, fairy (6)
15 Alfresco meal (6)
16 Consented (6)
19 Move furtively (5)

ACROSS

1 Large hawk (4)
4 Make an intense effort (6)
8 Rockets (8)
9 Top, peak (4)
10 Tag (5)
11 Fireproof dish (7)
13 Oscar-winning film about an American general (6)
15 Bring into being (6)
17 Stimulated (7)
19 Fermenting agent (5)
22 Lean (4)
23 Ninepins (8)
24 Spanish dictator (6)
25 Resist strongly (4)

DOWN

2 Spanish holiday island (5)
3 Simplest (7)
4 Fodder store (4)
5 Carry out investigation (8)
6 Foolish (5)
7 Abstain from (6)
12 Gillian - - -, *The X-Files* star (8)
14 Frightened (6)
16 Chosen by vote (7)
18 Say (5)
20 Ledge (5)
21 Ballpoint pen (4)

The Biggest Crossword Book In The World

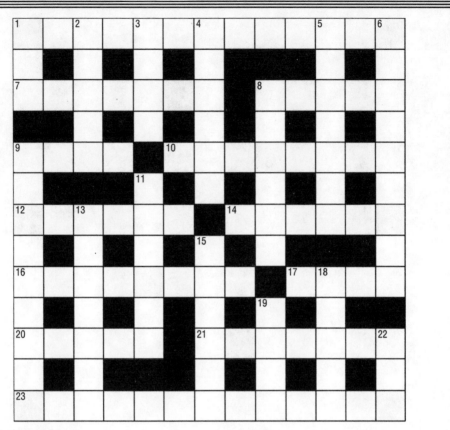

ACROSS

1 PM's road of residence (7, 6)
7 Prickly plant (7)
8 Active (5)
9 Garden hut (4)
10 Muscular (8)
12 Cricket dismissal (3, 3)
14 Ice cream topped with fruit etc. (6)
16 Usually (8)
17 Replica (4)
20 Sierra - - -, African country (5)
21 From Milan or Rome? (7)
23 *Rain Man* actor (6,7)

DOWN

1 Precise point (3)
2 Cue ball colour (5)
3 Jot (4)
4 Ethnic area (6)
5 Expelled from a property (7)
6 Disloyalty (9)
8 Shop stewards call? (3-3)
9 Throttled (9)
11 Junior clergyman (6)
13 Agitated (7)
15 Sledge (6)
18 Drug from a poppy (5)
19 Fraction (4)
22 Grandmother (3)

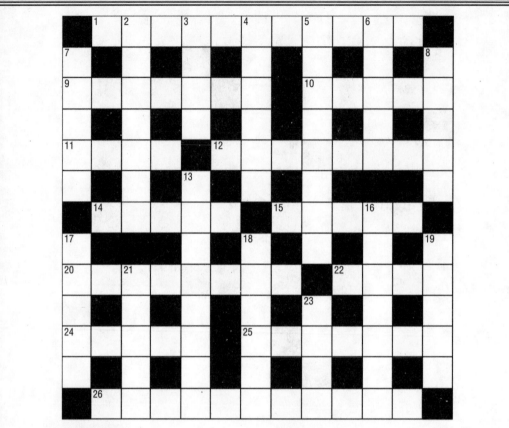

ACROSS

1 Low body temperature (11)
9 Old pal's get-together (7)
10 A small wood (5)
11 Emblem (4)
12 Charlotte Bronte novel (4, 4)
14 Trademark (5)
15 Wander (5)
20 Increased in size (8)
22 Set foot (4)
24 Press, TV, etc. (5)
25 Seedless raisin (7)
26 Go downhill (11)

DOWN

2 Not as old (7)
3 American state (4)
4 Tim - - -, British tennis player (6)
5 Renovate (8)
6 Suggest (5)
7 Rubbish (5)
8 Scuffle (5)
13 Overwhelm (8)
16 Entice (7)
17 Crowbar (5)
18 Powered water scooter(3-3)
19 Scatter in fine drops (5)
21 Army clergyman (5)
23 Speak as if drunk (4)

The Biggest Crossword Book In The World

ACROSS

1 In the open air (8)
5 On the loose (4)
9 Storage box (5)
10 Musical phrase (5)
12 Small earrings (5)
13 First man in the Bible (4)
15 Spanish lady (6)
18 Putrid (6)
20 Remainder (4)
23 Hymn, - - - with Me (5)
24 Principle (5)
27 Interlace (5)
28 Calendar fixture (4)
29 Incline, rise (8)

DOWN

1 Stand next to (4)
2 Person's lot (4)
3 Be outstandingly good (5)
4 Part of a contract (6)
6 Adjust (8)
7 Rubbed out (6)
8 School period (6)
11 Concealed (3)
14 Impermeable (8)
16 Scattered (6)
17 Calm (6)
19 Finger-shaped cake (6)
21 Former *Crimewatch UK* presenter, - - - Cook (3)
22 Horse (5)
25 Back of the neck (4)
26 Sound of a horn (4)

The Biggest Crossword Book In The World

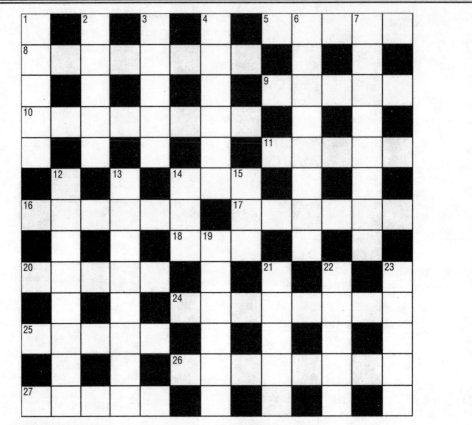

ACROSS

5 Make ashamed (5)
8 Surprised (8)
9 Simple fellow? (5)
10 Nocturnal burrowing
mammal (8)
11 Herb used in cooking (5)
14 *You - - -*, TV show (3)
16 Manage, control (6)
17 Quantity (6)
18 Berate, henpeck (3)
20 Bric-a-brac item (5)
24 At whatever time (8)
25 Subside (5)
26 Improved (8)
27 Bring (5)

DOWN

1 Blend of tea (5)
2 Stone monument (5)
3 Cooker (5)
4 Proclamation (6)
6 Sussex town (8)
7 Irish castle (8)
12 Having great worth (8)
13 European sea (8)
14 Mountain peak (3)
15 Label (3)
19 Capital of Greece (6)
21 Soldier from
down under (5)
22 Oust (5)
23 Naive person (5)

The Biggest Crossword Book In The World

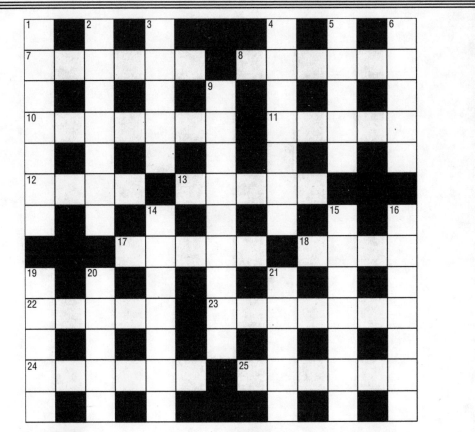

ACROSS

7 Hot water spring (6)
8 Urge to eat (6)
10 Result (7)
11 Goat's cry (5)
12 Greyish-yellow (4)
13 Biblical betrayer (5)
17 Modify slightly (5)
18 Infant (4)
22 Generally recognised (5)
23 Vigorous campaign (7)
24 Fashionable (6)
25 Method of voting secretly (6)

DOWN

1 Sent to Coventry (7)
2 Inexplicable event (7)
3 Criminal (5)
4 Small pulling vessel (7)
5 Think alike (5)
6 Vicious person (5)
9 Sulkiness (9)
14 Welsh county (7)
15 Competent (7)
16 Tammy - - -, Country singer (7)
19 Glide over ice (5)
20 Tall building (5)
21 Native of Havana (5)

The Biggest Crossword Book In The World

ACROSS

1 Young soldier (5)
4 Fairness (7)
8 Italian composer (7)
9 Church structure (5)
10 Defy (4)
11 Scottish river (3)
12 Chief (4)
15 Zodiac sign (6)
16 Money holder (6)
19 Bird charity
21 Ancient (3)
22 Sculpture of a head (4)
26 Outspoken (5)
27 Steve - - -, jockey (7)
28 Improve (7)
29 Layer of rock (5)

DOWN

1 Roman love-god (5)
2 Propriety (7)
3 Slender (4)
4 Carpenter (6)
5 Stock market speculator (4)
6 Bury (5)
7 Hearing distance (7)
13 Dynamite (1, 1, 1)
14 Metal food container (3)
15 Tall mammal (7)
17 Chuckled (7)
18 Gardener's frame (6)
20 Steal (game) (5)
23 Taut (5)
24 Body's outer layer (4)
25 Twist of hair (4)

The Biggest Crossword Book In The World

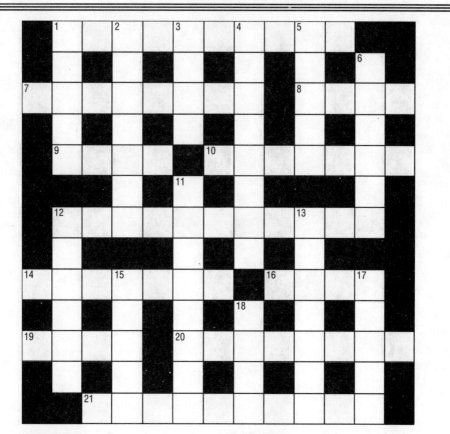

ACROSS

1 Californian city (3, 7)
7 Tagged (8)
8 Relating to the mouth (4)
9 In the thick of (4)
10 Area of fruit trees (7)
12 *Platoon* actor (6, 5)
14 Large bird (7)
16 Remove (4)
19 Old wound mark (4)
20 Merry-go-round (8)
21 Determined, dogged (10)

DOWN

1 South American beast (5)
2 Volunteer police officer (7)
3 Royal mistress, - - - Gwyn (4)
4 Ill-fated BBC soap opera (8)
5 Age (5)
6 Stephen King novel (6)
11 Ignores (8)
12 Miserable creature (6)
13 Distinctive part (7)
15 Deep ravine (5)
17 Throw out, expel (5)
18 God of love (4)

The Biggest Crossword Book In The World

ACROSS

7 Adherent (8)
8 Simply (4)
9 Over there (6)
10 Excited (6)
11 Strong wind (4)
12 Made bigger (8)
15 Explorers (8)
19 Court shoe (4)
21 Large sandy expanse (6)
23 American fashion
   designer, - - - Klein (6)
24 Eager, excited (4)
25 Scrooge's first name (8)

DOWN

1 Long straight cigar (6)
2 Short thick club (8)
3 Change direction
   abruptly (6)
4 Trying experience (6)
5 Meditation method (4)
6 Claim, accuse (6)
13 And not (3)
14 Disgusted (8)
16 Glacial period (3, 3)
17 High regard (6)
18 Closely guarded piece
   of information (6)
20 First (voyage) (6)
22 Therefore (4)

The Biggest Crossword Book In The World

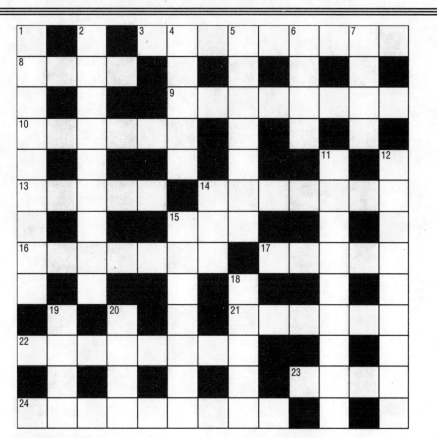

ACROSS

3 Final words of Julius
Caesar (2, 2, 5)
8 Family ancestry chart (4)
9 Trousers (8)
10 Purpose for a course
of action (6)
13 Hard-wearing fabric (5)
14 Brother or sister (7)
15 Friend (3)
16 Jailer (7)
17 Ransack (5)
21 Northern Ireland
county (6)
22 Contagious (8)
23 Principal (4)
24 Fatigue (9)

DOWN

1 Tax on legal
documents (5, 4)
2 A hundredth
anniversary (9)
4 Underground root (5)
5 Implement, tool (7)
6 Boulder (4)
7 Dinosaur (1-3)
11 An eye for
an eye? (3, 3, 3)
12 Harmony (9)
14 Announce (3)
15 Old-age payment (7)
18 Salary (5)
19 Minicab (4)
20 Darts throwing line (4)

The Biggest Crossword Book In The World

ACROSS

1 Mother-of-pearl (5)
4 Hickory nut (5)
10 Film comic, - - - Allen (5)
11 Put on guard (7)
12 Breed of small pony (8)
13 Invoice (4)
15 Disguised (11)
19 Increase (4)
20 Attained (8)
23 Amount of wear (7)
24 Lawful (5)
25 Train driver's union (5)
26 Threaded fastener (5)

DOWN

2 Ascended (5)
3 Queen's enclosure at the theatre (5, 3)
5 Water jug (4)
6 With legs apart (7)
7 Fashionable, smart (5)
8 Impressive, superb (11)
9 Fully grown (5)
14 American car (8)
16 Loving (7)
17 Lesser white heron (5)
18 Make rotten (5)
21 Ill-defined (5)
22 King's title (4)

The Biggest Crossword Book In The World

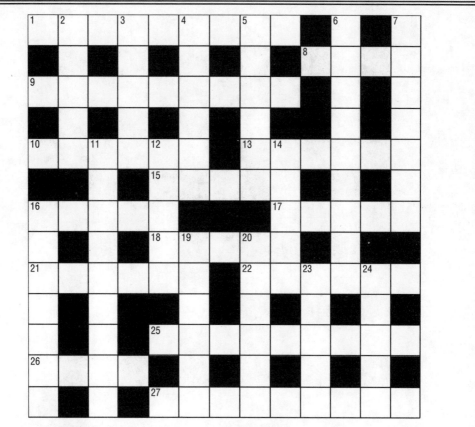

ACROSS

1 Food made from cacao beans (9)
8 Group of workmen (4)
9 Blizzard in the desert? (9)
10 Stick (to) (6)
13 Sew (6)
15 Give a speech (5)
16 Divided country (5)
17 Power line support (5)
18 Johanna - - -, *Heidi* author (5)
21 International agreement (6)
22 Actor, - - - Fox (6)
25 Record of events in date order (9)
26 Waxed cheese (4)
27 Knit closely (9)

DOWN

2 Stash (5)
3 Scrounge (5)
4 Rubbish, refuse (6)
5 Lunge (6)
6 Long thin cigar (9)
7 Muslim leader (3, 4)
11 Fooling around (9)
12 Cook in the oven (5)
14 Lukewarm (5)
16 Food preparation room (7)
19 Nonpoisonous snake (6)
20 Take away (6)
23 Revolve, spin (5)
24 Keepsake (5)

The Biggest Crossword Book In The World

ACROSS
1 Abandoned (12)
9 Gatekeeper's home (5)
10 Sudden thrust forward (5)
11 Disallow (3)
12 Premium Bond computer (5)
13 Curved sword (7)
15 Complain (6)
17 Young cat (6)
20 Joan of Arc's city (7)
23 Neck of mutton (5)
25 Policeman (3)
26 Dark coffee (5)
27 Bequeath (5)
28 Praise (12)

DOWN
2 Peter - - -, snooker player (5)
3 Crisp lettuce (7)
4 Satisfy (a thirst) (6)
5 Bay (5)
6 Red hair colour (5)
7 Bathrobe (8,4)
8 American rock band (9, 3)
14 Ignited (3)
16 Born as (3)
18 Examine carefully (7)
19 Move up (6)
21 Doctor's deputy (5)
22 Astonish (5)
24 Wireless (5)

The Biggest Crossword Book In The World

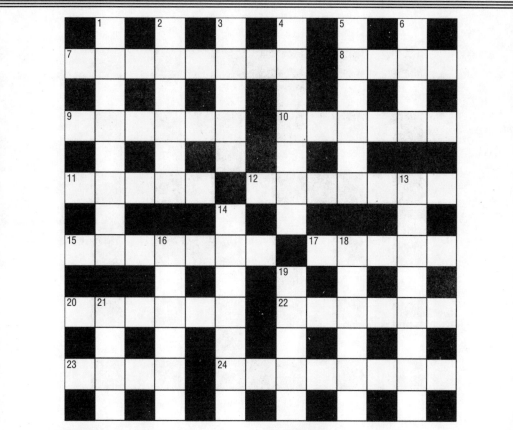

ACROSS

7 Spanish 'Miss' (8)
8 Sixty minutes (4)
9 Leave empty (6)
10 Sanctuary (6)
11 Destruction (5)
12 Go beyond (7)
15 Given up work (7)
17 Soft and creamy sweet (5)
20 Opening manoeuvre (6)
22 Jester's costume (6)
23 Lion's den (4)
24 Financial records (8)

DOWN

1 US state, capital Dover (8)
2 Edible tuber (6)
3 Collier (5)
4 Large flatfish (7)
5 The Duke of Edinburgh (6)
6 Take a new direction (4)
13 Parts of a circle (8)
14 Not on either side (7)
16 Implanted by nature (6)
18 False (6)
19 Slap, blow (5)
21 Seaweed gelatine (4)

The Biggest Crossword Book In The World

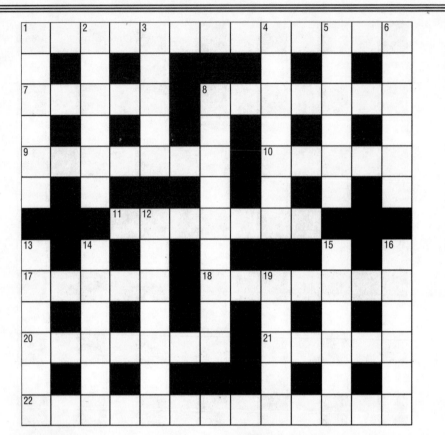

ACROSS

1 Typist's computer (4, 9)
7 Safari animal (5)
8 Before noon (7)
9 Venezuelan river (7)
10 Spherical map of the world (5)
11 Thrust forward (7)
17 Helicopter engine (5)
18 Sing-along entertainment (7)
20 Towed vehicle (7)
21 Cowboy's noose (5)
22 Liable to cause an argument (13)

DOWN

1 Andy - - -, pop artist (6)
2 Partially dried grape (6)
3 Snapshot (5)
4 Infuriated (7)
5 Beau (6)
6 Tattered (6)
8 James Bond film (9)
12 Housebreaker (7)
13 Region around North Pole (6)
14 Reach (6)
15 Art of growing dwarf trees (6)
16 Spring back (6)
19 Leader (5)

The Biggest Crossword Book In The World

ACROSS

1 Undying spirit (4)
4 Sausage in a roll (3, 3)
8 Unseen driving hazard (5, 3)
9 Beer ingredient (4)
10 Poacher's trap (5)
11 Comes into view (7)
13 Expose (6)
15 Public disturbance (6)
17 Network of trains (7)
19 Former Argentinian President (5)
22 Talk indiscreetly (4)
23 Rebellion (8)
24 Protection (6)
25 Swiss mountain range (4)

DOWN

2 Man-made fibre (5)
3 John - - -, author (2, 5)
4 Successor (4)
5 Actor (8)
6 Yellow-orange colour (5)
7 Ancient Greek city (6)
12 Enjoyment (8)
14 Empower, facilitate (6)
16 Small, fragrant flower (7)
18 African republic (5)
20 Confess (3, 2)
21 Land force (4)

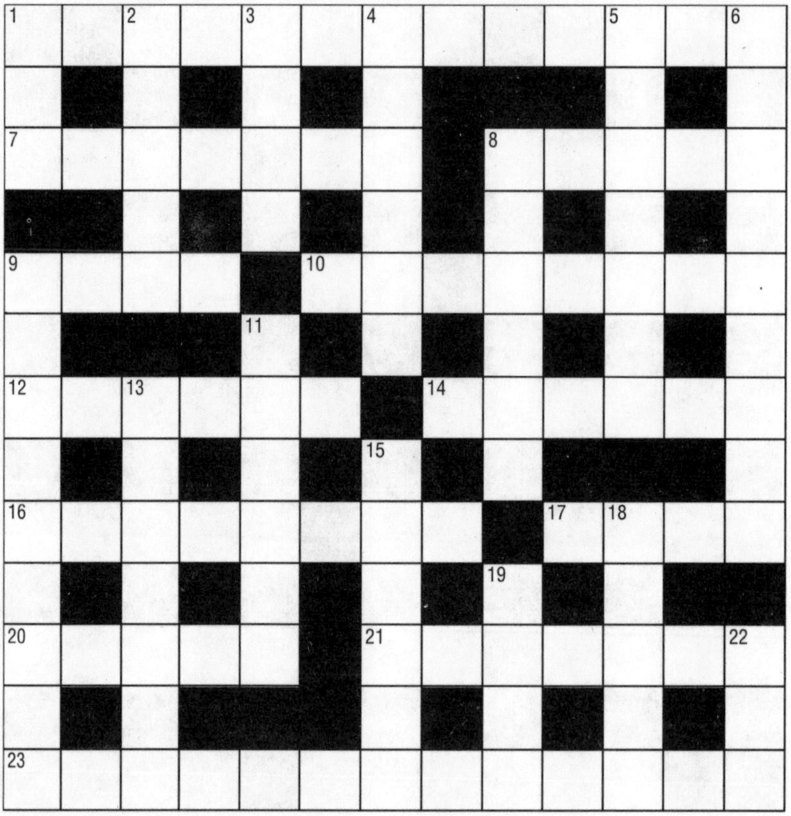

ACROSS

1 Joan of Arc (4, 2, 7)
7 Feign (7)
8 Make up for deficiencies (5)
9 Indonesian island (4)
10 Argued (8)
12 Type of trumpet (6)
14 Fashion designer, - - - Rhodes (6)
16 Sign of the zodiac (8)
17 Require (4)
20 Perform, play out (5)
21 Greedy (7)
23 Rosemarie Ford's husband (6, 7)

DOWN

1 Chart (3)
2 Just right (5)
3 Unlock (4)
4 Appoint (6)
5 Fostered permanently (7)
6 Fixed (9)
8 Be attractive (6)
9 Pirate (9)
11 Feel sorrow (6)
13 Plant with edible stalks (7)
15 Shellfish (6)
18 Out of order (5)
19 TV gardener, - - - Titchmarsh (4)
22 Grass fed to cattle (3)

The Biggest Crossword Book In The World

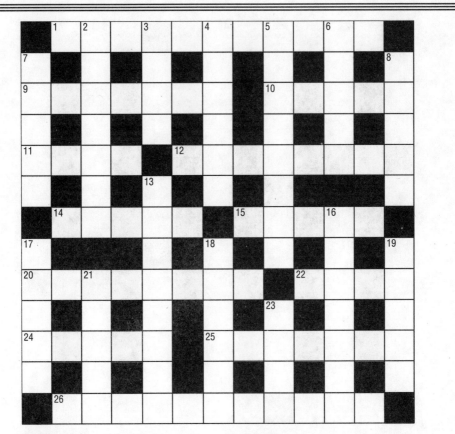

ACROSS

1 Kids TV programme (11)
9 Proceed from
a source (7)
10 Domestic gas unit (5)
11 Twist (4)
12 Column support (8)
14 Accounting entry (5)
15 Holy person (5)
20 Procured (8)
22 Ship's company (4)
24 Expel from
one's country (5)
25 Huntsman's cry (5-2)
26 Cockney pop
duo (4, 3, 4)

DOWN

2 Look at closely (7)
3 Dash, flair (4)
4 Variable (6)
5 Incidentally (2, 3, 3)
6 Choose by voting (5)
7 Garden barrier (5)
8 Aroma (5)
13 Hard (8)
16 Rudolf - - -,
ballet dancer (7)
17 Tom - - -,
Welsh singer (5)
18 Setting agent in
ripe fruit (6)
19 Pounce (5)
21 Upper leg (5)
23 Slipped (4)

The Biggest Crossword Book In The World

ACROSS
1 Asian country (8)
5 Feeble person (4)
9 Kent ferry port (5)
10 Charlie - - -, comedian (5)
12 Circus performer (5)
13 Unsightly (4)
15 Dress (6)
18 Appearance (6)
20 Poke (4)
23 Actor and director, - - - Welles (5)
24 Lump in a tree (5)
27 Cover with glass (5)
28 Horde (4)
29 Garden vegetable (8)

DOWN
1 Servant (4)
2 Roman goddess of the moon (4)
3 Mountain song (5)
4 Lay out for profit (6)
6 Rude, disrespectful (8)
7 Spring, swoop (6)
8 Unkempt child (6)
11 Manipulate (3)
14 *Dangerous* - - -, 1988 Glenn Close film (8)
16 Habitual scrounger (6)
17 Variety of whisky (6)
19 Ironed fold (6)
21 Scottish town (3)
22 Spy (5)
25 Bullets, etc. (4)
26 Advanced (4)

The Biggest Crossword Book In The World

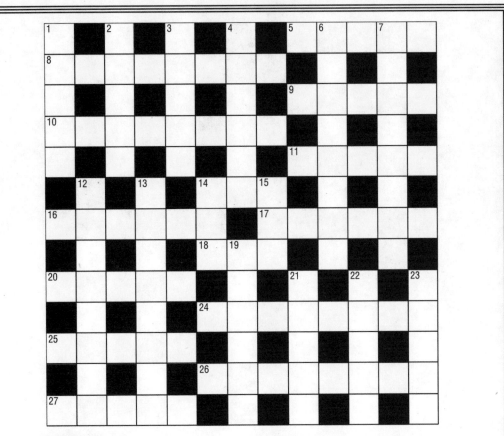

ACROSS
5 Defect (5)
8 Bugle call (8)
9 Intended (5)
10 Rebellious person (8)
11 Employ delaying
tactics (5)
14 Vigour (3)
16 Duchess of York? (6)
17 Against (6)
18 Fabled bird (3)
20 Slightly mad (5)
24 Member of the public (8)
25 Plundered goods (5)
26 Order (8)
27 Provide
entertainment (5)

DOWN
1 Violation of law (5)
2 Lloyd-Webber musical (5)
3 Actress, - - - Keaton (5)
4 Swindle (6)
6 Hole (8)
7 Flooring material (8)
12 Large wine bottle (8)
13 Stirs (8)
14 For every (3)
15 Synthetic plastic
material (1, 1, 1)
19 The East (6)
21 Width (5)
22 Bug (5)
23 Enter into an
alliance (5)

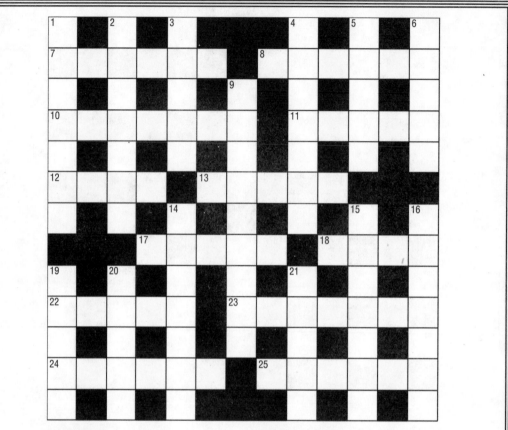

ACROSS

7 Bank employee (6)
8 Occur (6)
10 Former English county (7)
11 Toadstools etc. (5)
12 Region (4)
13 Jazz musician, - - - Armstrong (5)
17 In which place? (5)
18 Unravel (4)
22 Cylindrical (5)
23 Instalment (7)
24 Type of firework (6)
25 Fine, soft paper (6)

DOWN

1 Everlasting (7)
2 Nervous agitation (7)
3 Wild, uncultivated (5)
4 Foolish person (7)
5 Backbone (5)
6 Garden mollusc (5)
9 Deferred (9)
14 Shake, tremble (7)
15 Ratify (7)
16 Everlasting (7)
19 Cornish town (5)
20 Midday meal (5)
21 Finger or toe (5)

The Biggest Crossword Book In The World

ACROSS

1 Hanger-on (5)
4 Disturb (7)
8 Black and
  white horse (7)
9 Portly (5)
10 Liquid loss (4)
11 Groove (3)
12 Words (4)
15 Entire (6)
16 Comfortable
   surroundings (6)
19 Scalp growth (4)
21 Comedian,
   - - - Dennis (3)
22 Cover (4)
26 Musical instrument (5)
27 Rushing stream (7)
28 Completely (7)
29 Sew loosely (5)

DOWN

1 Collar part (5)
2 Graceful (7)
3 Warmth (4)
4 Zeal (6)
5 Simple game (1-3)
6 Ill-treat violently (5)
7 Ability to understand (7)
13 Perform (3)
14 Hint to an actor (3)
15 Restrain, hinder (7)
17 Dud (7)
18 Aristocracy (6)
20 Metal bar (5)
23 Metric unit of capacity (5)
24 Touch (4)
25 Seize (4)

The Biggest Crossword Book In The World

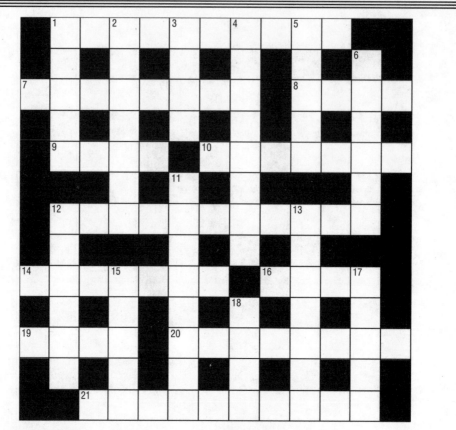

ACROSS

1 Olympic sport (3, 7)
7 Australian egg-laying aquatic mammal (8)
8 Portal (4)
9 Fifty-two weeks (4)
10 Soldier (7)
12 Shakespeare play (2, 3, 4, 2)
14 Art of paper-folding (7)
16 Attire (4)
19 Rotate quickly (4)
20 Severe scolding (8)
21 Container (10)

DOWN

1 Embed (5)
2 Tidal mouth of a large river (7)
3 Retained (4)
4 Australian state (8)
5 Lowest point (5)
6 Withdraw gracefully (3, 3)
11 Go under water (8)
12 Blunt and rude (6)
13 Not rigid (7)
15 Kind, sort (5)
17 Bout of eating and drinking (5)
18 Way of walking (4)

The Biggest Crossword Book In The World

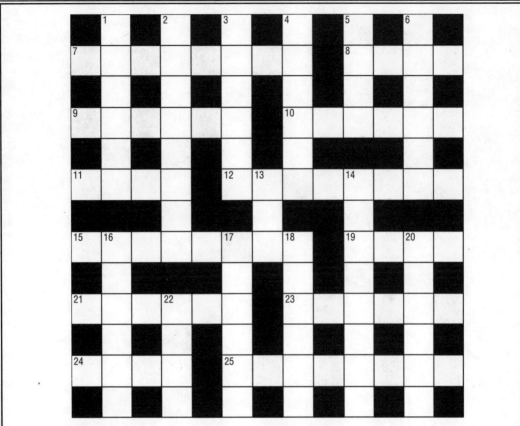

ACROSS
7 American team game (8)
8 Coffin frame (4)
9 Unoccupied (6)
10 Cross and irritable (6)
11 Sign of tiredness (4)
12 Immediately (8)
15 Coloured
   handkerchief (8)
19 Admit openly (4)
21 Capital of Turkey (6)
23 Nearer (6)
24 Earnest request (4)
25 Contemplate mentally (8)

DOWN
1 Spanish tourist resort (6)
2 Hindered (8)
3 Portable computer (6)
4 Extremely drunk! (6)
5 Encourage
   a wrongdoing (4)
6 Danny Glover film,
   - - - *Weapon* (6)
13 Dashed (3)
14 Friendly (8)
16 Golfer, - - - Palmer (6)
17 Subtle difference
   in colour (6)
18 Style of pronunciation (6)
20 Team's first batsman (6)
22 Cry of woe (4)

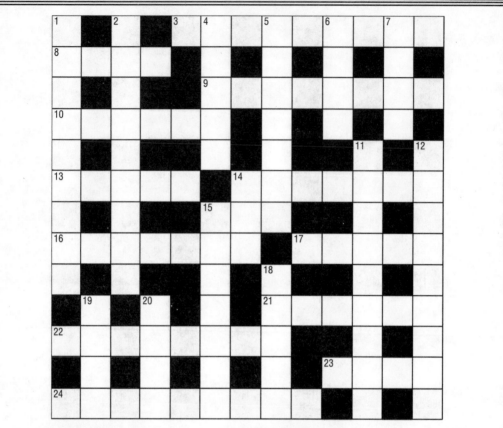

ACROSS

3 Type of biscuit (9)
8 Office chief (4)
9 US city (3, 5)
10 William - - -, *Coronation Street* star (6)
13 Cut wildly (5)
14 Sir Edmund - - -, Everest climber (7)
15 Poignant (3)
16 Asian country (7)
17 Dexterous (5)
21 Stinging plant (6)
22 Mark exactly (8)
23 Sea-rescue group (4)
24 Potassium nitrate (9)

DOWN

1 Forward, pushy (9)
2 Snowballed (9)
4 Tenpin bowling lane (5)
5 Unpalatable (7)
6 Again (4)
7 Telephone part (4)
11 Patron saint of lovers (9)
12 Artificial (9)
14 Cured pork (3)
15 Small fish (7)
18 Come in (5)
19 Prima donna (4)
20 Notice (4)

The Biggest Crossword Book In The World

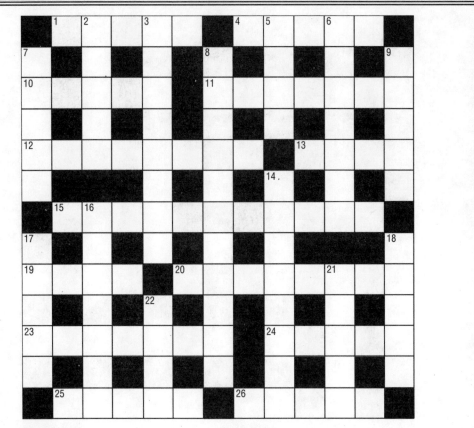

ACROSS

1 Theatrical performance (5)
4 Belly button! (5)
10 Begin (5)
11 Substitute (7)
12 Tiny planet (8)
13 Put by (4)
15 Unlucky (11)
19 Sporting record (4)
20 Deduct (4, 4)
23 Mimic (7)
24 Sign of the zodiac (5)
25 Cry of encouragement (5)
26 Quay (5)

DOWN

2 Precise (5)
3 Underlying (motives) (8)
5 Arched recess (4)
6 Amelia - - -, US aviator (7)
7 Nile dam (5)
8 Tantalising puzzle (5-6)
9 Cut (links) (5)
14 Juvenile (5-3)
16 Norfolk city (7)
17 Attach (5)
18 Romany (5)
21 Card game (5)
22 Stare (4)

The Biggest Crossword Book In The World

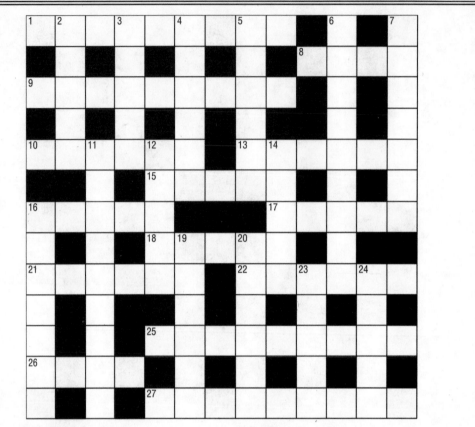

ACROSS
1 Plainclothes policeman (9)
8 Playthings (4)
9 Efficient, practical (9)
10 Academic award (6)
13 Enhance (6)
15 Statement of faith (5)
16 Death bell (5)
17 Measure for pub drinks (5)
18 Very deep pit (5)
21 Spin (6)
22 Cornflakes, eg (6)
25 White metallic element (9)
26 Typeface (4)
27 Arm of the Mediterranean (6, 3)

DOWN
2 Eagle's nest (5)
3 Enigma Variations composer (5)
4 Merchant (6)
5 Expressed (an opinion) (6)
6 Panel, board (9)
7 Telepathic (7)
11 Large breed of dog (5, 4)
12 Dazzling effect (5)
14 Loop with running knot (5)
16 Boris - - -, horror film actor (7)
19 At an earlier time (6)
20 Rub (6)
23 Sticky sap (5)
24 Bright blue (5)

The Biggest Crossword Book In The World

ACROSS
1 Far-fetched (12)
9 Sixteenth of a pound (5)
10 Traded (5)
11 Brazil's chief port (3)
12 Perhaps (5)
13 German prison (7)
15 Detective (6)
17 Honolulu's state (6)
20 Yacht race meeting (7)
23 Denim trousers (5)
25 African antelope (3)
26 Scottish town (5)
27 Rice dish (5)
28 Shop selling
   unusual foods (12)

DOWN
2 Female goat (5)
3 Highest mountain (7)
4 Enforce (6)
5 Alcoholic drink (5)
6 Tasteless (5)
7 Ardent, avid (12)
8 Sympathised (12)
14 At this moment (3)
16 Land of
   the Free? (1, 1, 1)
18 Modifies (7)
19 Meatball (6)
21 Throaty snarl (5)
22 Soldier's jacket (5)
24 Church's main
   walkway (5)

The Biggest Crossword Book In The World

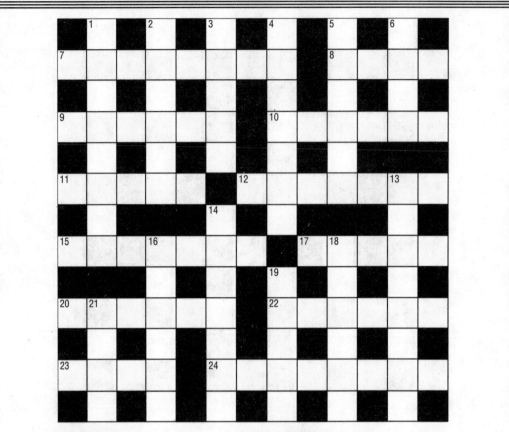

ACROSS

7 Make less complicated (8)
8 Abominable snowman (4)
9 Traditional myth (6)
10 Thriller writer, Dame - - - Christie (6)
11 Oversentimental (5)
12 Odd number (7)
15 Merit (7)
17 Snake poison (5)
20 Partial (6)
22 Tempt (6)
23 Naked (4)
24 Russian policy of openness (8)

DOWN

1 Annoying (8)
2 Maintenance (6)
3 Father and daughter singers Kim and Marty (5)
4 Monumental structure (7)
5 Despot (6)
6 Cut with acid (4)
13 Drive out (evil spirits) (8)
14 Ordinary (7)
16 Smooth hard coating (6)
18 Scope (6)
19 Tree (5)
21 Naming word (4)

The Biggest Crossword Book In The World

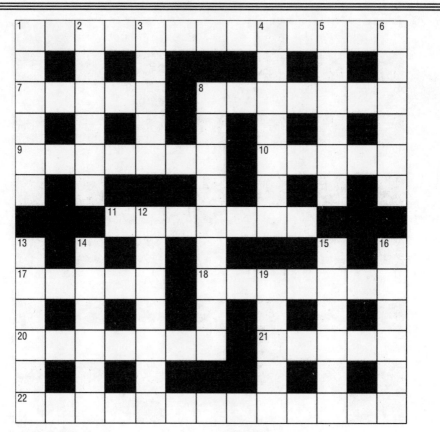

ACROSS
1 Rain, snow etc (13)
7 Ancient Mexican? (5)
8 Tailored individually (7)
9 Tympanic membrane (7)
10 Innocent (5)
11 Kitchen appliance (7)
17 Person owned
by another (5)
18 Pattern (7)
20 Large bag (7)
21 Foster permanently (5)
22 Understandable (13)

DOWN
1 Heavenly body (6)
2 Get by threat (6)
3 Become subject to (5)
4 Defect (7)
5 Sarcastic (6)
6 Required (6)
8 Unwelcome surprise (9)
12 Carry on business (7)
13 Respiratory disorder (6)
14 Horse's fast pace (6)
15 Calm self-possession (6)
16 Boil (6)
19 Accumulate (5)

The Biggest Crossword Book In The World

ACROSS

1 Facial feature (4)
4 Military policeman (6)
8 Bought back (8)
9 Partly open (4)
10 Barbra Streisand film (5)
11 High-pitched scream (7)
13 In any order (6)
15 Marine reptile (6)
17 Break apart (7)
19 Funny (5)
22 English county (4)
23 Card game (8)
24 Santa's cave (6)
25 Caution (4)

DOWN

2 Variety of daisy (5)
3 Built (7)
4 Piece of steak (4)
5 Devote (8)
6 In the know (5)
7 Rogue (6)
12 Tacit, not overtly stated (8)
14 Turn up (6)
16 Arc in the sky (7)
18 Country house (5)
20 Fierce big cat (5)
21 Outdoor swimming complex (4)

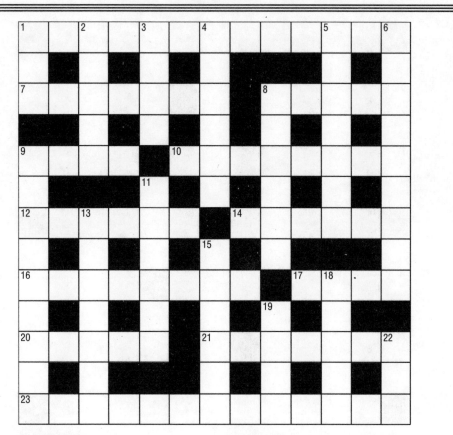

ACROSS
1 Edward VIII's lover (6, 7)
7 Entrance (7)
8 Apportion (5)
9 Shade of colour (4)
10 Commence (8)
12 Scandinavian country (6)
14 Virgin goddess
   of wisdom (6)
16 Supermarket counter (8)
17 Clever (4)
20 Evident (5)
21 Impair (one's
   reputation) (7)
23 Old person (6, 7)

DOWN
1 Hairpiece (3)
2 Classical language (5)
3 US state, capital
   Des Moines (4)
4 Phrase (6)
5 Rescue (7)
6 Paris cathedral (5, 4)
8 Shrewd (6)
9 Stubborn (9)
11 Short coat (6)
13 Girl's public school (7)
15 Rural (6)
18 Sudden attack (5)
19 Very dry
   (champagne) (4)
22 Female bird (3)

The Biggest Crossword Book In The World

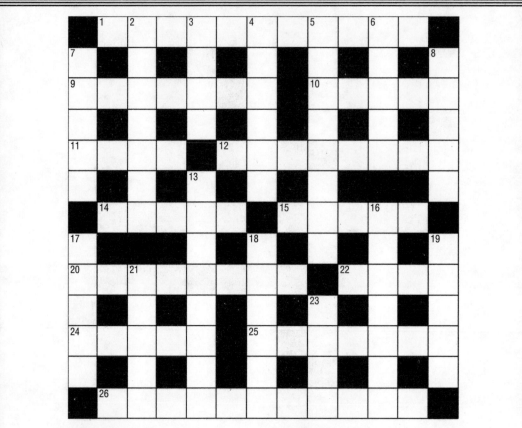

ACROSS

1 On the surface (5,6)
9 Multisocket plug (7)
10 Spooky (5)
11 Portuguese port (4)
12 Secretive (8)
14 Self-evident truth (5)
15 Delegate (5)
20 Covered by clouds (8)
22 Female relative (4)
24 Shelve (5)
25 Timeless (7)
26 Items needed for cooking (11)

DOWN

2 Queen of The Netherlands (7)
3 Take part in an election (4)
4 Stocking support (6)
5 Compliant (8)
6 Daring (5)
7 Social blunder (5)
8 Brawny (5)
13 Wizard (8)
16 Wealthy (7)
17 Unattractive (5)
18 Lee Harvey - - -, alleged assassin (6)
19 Put away (5)
21 Pixie-like (5)
23 Simple (4)

The Biggest Crossword Book In The World

ACROSS

1 Increment (8)
5 Mess (4)
9 The same (5)
10 Fraction (5)
12 John - - -, snooker player (5)
13 Definite winner (4)
15 Mingled (6)
18 Dash-like punctuation mark (6)
20 Equipment (4)
23 Harsh sound (5)
24 Prize for merit (5)
27 Insane (5)
28 Stalk (4)
29 Sign of crying (8)

DOWN

1 Mine entrance (4)
2 Actress, - - - Moore (4)
3 Hot alcoholic drink (5)
4 Not sharp-pointed (6)
6 Village featured in *The Archers* (8)
7 English king (6)
8 Flavoursome herb (6)
11 Weed (3)
14 Practise (8)
16 Talk given to an audience (6)
17 Head of a nunnery (6)
19 Incite (6)
21 Atmosphere (3)
22 Chief councillor (5)
25 Sussex river (4)
26 Profound (4)

The Biggest Crossword Book In The World

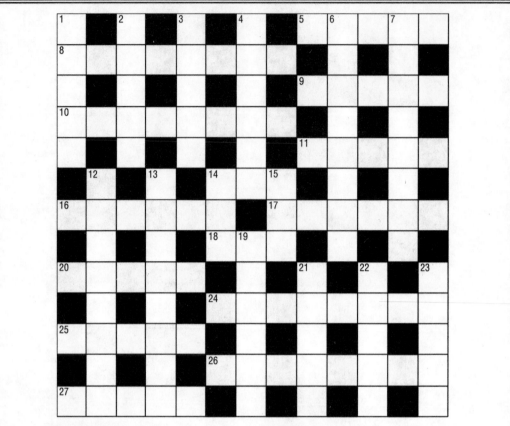

ACROSS

5 Rough road (5)
8 Plan in secret (8)
9 Keanu Reeves film (5)
10 Valuable (8)
11 Nothing, zero (5)
14 Beverage (3)
16 Place where television programmes are filmed (6)
17 Eddie - - -, Grand Prix driver (6)
18 Bundle of banknotes (3)
20 Precipitation (5)
24 Henry VIII's flagship (4, 4)
25 Well-grounded (5)
26 Alienate (8)
27 Scatter (5)

DOWN

1 Opportunity (5)
2 Internal (5)
3 Damage, ruin (5)
4 Game bird (6)
6 Temporary relief (8)
7 Curved terrace of houses (8)
12 Strong (8)
13 Paste (8)
14 Pull along behind (3)
15 Provide assistance (3)
19 Andre - - -, tennis player (6)
21 Wales (5)
22 Beautiful (5)
23 Prise (5)

The Biggest Crossword Book In The World

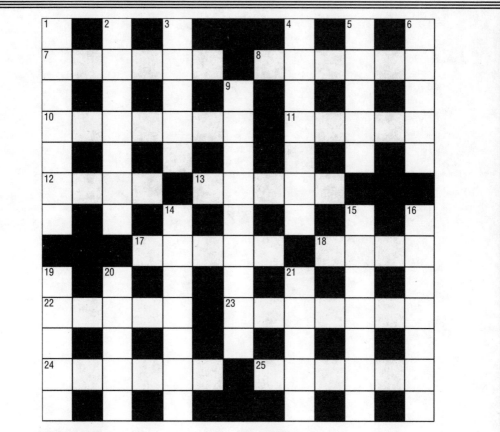

ACROSS

7 Brawling (6)
8 Stray from a path (6)
10 Exterior face (7)
11 Cite (5)
12 Roald - - -, author (4)
13 Add on (5)
17 Hereditary characteristics (5)
18 Reputation (4)
22 Depression (5)
23 Maintenance of goods (7)
24 Equality (6)
25 Turned into (6)

DOWN

1 Rule over (7)
2 Of darkish complexion (7)
3 Kofi - - -, United Nations chief (5)
4 Hard varnish (7)
5 Improvised (2, 3)
6 Narrow inlet (5)
9 Celebratory meal (9)
14 White ant (7)
15 Conjugal (7)
16 Wiped out, erased (7)
19 African republic (5)
20 Legal meeting place (5)
21 Remorse (5)

The Biggest Crossword Book In The World

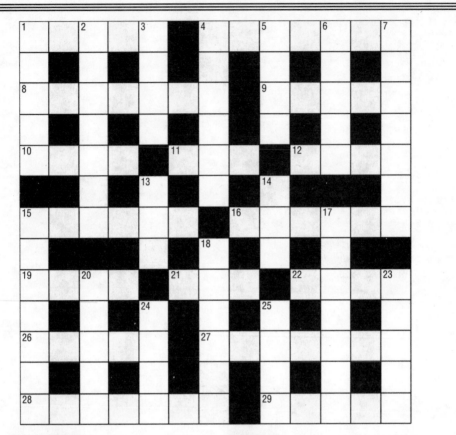

ACROSS

1 Discovered (5)
4 Pickled herring fillet (7)
8 Stripe (7)
9 Should (5)
10 Funeral pile (4)
11 Lout (slang) (3)
12 London park (4)
15 Hindu retreat (6)
16 Temptation (6)
19 Grasp (4)
21 Shake rapidly (3)
22 Medium sized (4)
26 Motion picture (5)
27 American state (7)
28 Predicament (7)
29 Malice (5)

DOWN

1 Football competition (1, 1, 3)
2 Discover (7)
3 Dressmaking tuck (4)
4 Money paid to kidnapper (6)
5 Coil (4)
6 Close (weather-wise) (5)
7 Hospital visitor? (7)
13 Possibly (3)
14 Hang low (3)
15 Embarrassed (7)
17 Kenyan capital (7)
18 African desert (6)
20 Horizontal (5)
23 Likeness (5)
24 Suture (4)
25 Prejudice (4)

The Biggest Crossword Book In The World

ACROSS
1 Formerly (10)
7 Careful and steady (8)
8 Tori - - -, American singer (4)
9 Long story or poem (4)
10 Ruler (7)
12 Texture (11)
14 The best player (3, 4)
16 Beat (4)
19 Cure (4)
20 Unrefined petroleum (5, 3)
21 Disappointed (10)

DOWN
1 Award (5)
2 Published issue (7)
3 Notion (4)
4 Final (8)
5 Rent out (5)
6 Not any person (6)
11 Muffles (8)
12 Tight necklace (6)
13 Tidiest (7)
15 Of the sun (5)
17 Scottish lord (5)
18 Sound of a contented cat (4)

The Biggest Crossword Book In The World

ACROSS

7 Obscured (8)
8 Darts player,
 - - - Bristow (4)
9 Part of a jacket (6)
10 Sailor (6)
11 Cheat, trick (4)
12 Alfred - - -,
 British poet (8)
15 Commendable (8)
19 Biting insect (4)
21 Breathe in (6)
23 Black religious music (6)
24 Royal Princess (4)
25 Fall down (8)

DOWN

1 Group of islands of the
 Cornish coast (6)
2 Somerset town (8)
3 Approval (6)
4 Thomas - - -, inventor (6)
5 Ewe's-milk cheese (4)
6 Japanese emperor (6)
13 Long thin fish (3)
14 Native of Belgrade (8)
16 Canvas shelter
 supported by
 framework (6)
17 Make whiter (6)
18 Flow over (6)
20 Opposed (6)
22 Dropped (from
 the team) (4)

The Biggest Crossword Book In The World

ACROSS

3 Area of London (9)
8 Lawsuit (4)
9 Be over-bearing (8)
10 Three times (6)
13 Arctic (5)
14 Small parcel (7)
15 Child's bed (3)
16 Miser (7)
17 Engine (5)
21 Ballet dancer,
   - - - Nureyev (6)
22 Genuine (4-4)
23 Wooded valley (4)
24 *Men Behaving Badly* star (6, 3)

DOWN

1 Coniferous tree (5, 4)
2 Study of the stars (9)
4 Instruction to
  be carried out (5)
5 Orange-coloured fruit (7)
6 Skin complaint (4)
7 Stained (4)
11 Warned (9)
12 Greatly frightened (9)
14 Long narrow
   seed case (3)
15 Fissure (7)
18 Push (5)
19 Thorny flower (4)
20 American athlete,
   - - - Lewis (4)

The Biggest Crossword Book In The World

ACROSS

1 Skinflint (5)
4 Celtic magician (5)
10 Browned bread (5)
11 Italian dish (7)
12 Impending? (2, 3, 3)
13 Fit of sulking (4)
15 A paltry amount of food? (7, 4)
19 Emblem (4)
20 Died (8)
23 Extreme (7)
24 Plea of being elsewhere (5)
25 Rimmed (5)
26 Deceive (5)

DOWN

2 Not suitable (5)
3 Establish firmly (8)
5 Baby's biscuit (4)
6 Encroach (7)
7 Wood dye (5)
8 Goodbye! (11)
9 Sporty car (5)
14 However (5, 3)
16 Looking exhausted (7)
17 Playground attraction (5)
18 Acknowledge (5)
21 Rigid (5)
22 Soreness on eyelid (4)

The Biggest Crossword Book In The World

ACROSS
1 Kinsmen (9)
8 Empty, vacant (4)
9 Contemptible person! (9)
10 Clan cloth (6)
13 Oriental boat (6)
15 European country (5)
16 Good, genuine (5)
17 Worth (5)
18 Small anchor (5)
21 London river (6)
22 Ill, sick (6)
25 Driven from a place of rest (9)
26 Cry out (4)
27 *North By - - -*, Hitchcock film (9)

DOWN
2 Heather plant (5)
3 Item of value (5)
4 Large lizard (6)
5 Slip away (6)
6 Napoleon's wife (9)
7 Go forward (7)
11 *New Statesman* star (3,6)
12 Conscious (5)
14 Variety of poplar (5)
16 Patron saint of Ireland (7)
19 Inuit (6)
20 Ruud - - -, football manager (6)
23 Extra hand of cards (5)
24 Garden vegetables (5)

The Biggest Crossword Book In The World

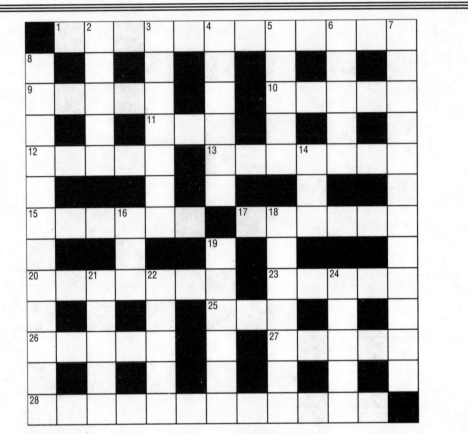

ACROSS

1 Eton or Harrow? (6, 6)
9 Billy - - -,
R & B singer (5)
10 Gloss, eg (5)
11 Sailor (3)
12 Hilltop (5)
13 Henry - - -, British
composer (7)
15 Tranquil (6)
17 Outlying district
of a city (6)
20 In arrears (7)
23 Vagrant (5)
25 Country, - - - Lanka (3)
26 Wheat used to
make pasta (5)
27 Lamp dweller (5)
28 On purpose (12)

DOWN

2 Overturn (5)
3 Portable light (7)
4 Lively and cheerful (6)
5 Cavort (5)
6 Surmise (5)
7 Nursery rhyme
character (6, 2-4)
8 Conformed (12)
14 Breed of horse (3)
16 Make a mistake (3)
18 Tense, irritable (7)
19 Court clown (6)
21 Register at college (5)
22 Disband (troops) (5)
24 Cancel (5)

The Biggest Crossword Book In The World

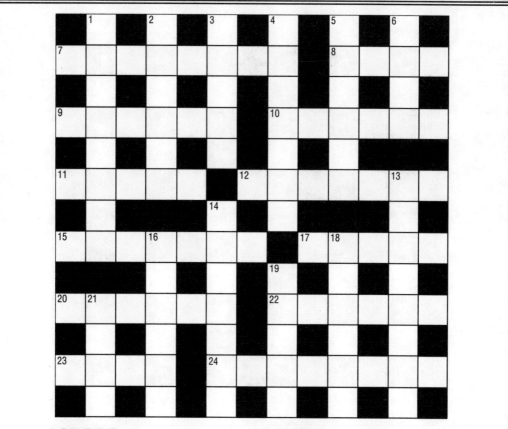

ACROSS

7 Remembered (8)
8 Patron saint of Norway (4)
9 Anti-aircraft fire (3-3)
10 French dog (6)
11 Mature (5)
12 Daphne du Maurier novel (7)
15 Grown without chemicals (7)
17 Over (5)
20 Dance? (6)
22 Sprinkler head (6)
23 Authentic (4)
24 Placed apart (8)

DOWN

1 One of the Three Wise Men (8)
2 Savoury snack before a meal (6)
3 Accidental success (5)
4 Changed (7)
5 Prairie-wolf (6)
6 Bouncy toy (4)
13 Careless, disdainful (8)
14 Russian region (7)
16 Hook and line fisherman (6)
18 Fund-raising sale of goods (6)
19 Appreciate (5)
21 Maneating giant (4)

The Biggest Crossword Book In The World

ACROSS

1 Former Bond Girl (6,7)
7 Small drum (5)
8 Magazine produced by supporters (7)
9 Unpaid sportsman (7)
10 Hissing birds (5)
11 Single eyeglass (7)
17 Din, racket (5)
18 Tease excessively (7)
20 Mammal with a long striped tail (7)
21 Thinking organ (5)
22 Musical (4, 4, 5)

DOWN

1 Optimistic (6)
2 Light shoe (6)
3 Baggy (5)
4 Irish county (7)
5 Banished from one's country (6)
6 Israeli currency (6)
8 Failed to remember (9)
12 Burdensome (7)
13 Royal prince (6)
14 Sign of the zodiac (6)
15 Water-craft (6)
16 Mean (6)
19 Visual riddle (5)

The Biggest Crossword Book In The World

ACROSS

1 Meat from a hunted animal (4)
4 Child (6)
8 Torpid, lethargic (8)
9 Mass lobby (4)
10 Johanna Spyri's alpine novel (5)
11 Governor (7)
13 Fireside (6)
15 Detest (6)
17 Tomato sauce (7)
19 To the left or right (5)
22 Nothing, nil (4)
23 Conversation (8)
24 Fee (6)
25 Sketched (4)

DOWN

2 Worship (5)
3 Boxer, - - - Holyfield (7)
4 Press (clothes) (4)
5 Adaptable (8)
6 Gentle poke (5)
7 Unruffled (6)
12 Part of the body (8)
14 Soccer team (6)
16 Leave secretly (7)
18 Woven fabric (5)
20 Playing card with two spots (5)
21 Rice wine (4)

The Biggest Crossword Book In The World

ACROSS
1 Kid's party game (5, 4, 4)
7 Greed (7)
8 Imaginary flat surface (5)
9 Scottish lake (4)
10 Unsolicited correspondence (4, 4)
12 Spouted vessel (3-3)
14 Imprison (6)
16 Native of Vienna? (8)
17 American university (4)
20 Prickly shrub (5)
21 Doctor (7)
23 Careful (13)

DOWN
1 Snake (3)
2 Scientist, Sir - - - Newton (5)
3 Leak slowly (4)
4 Way of approach (6)
5 Ignorant (7)
6 Working for oneself (9)
8 Chinese capital (6)
9 Listless (9)
11 Husky (6)
13 Loser (4-3)
15 Nonsense (6)
18 Friend (5)
19 Small piece of land (4)
22 Affirmative (3)

The Biggest Crossword Book In The World

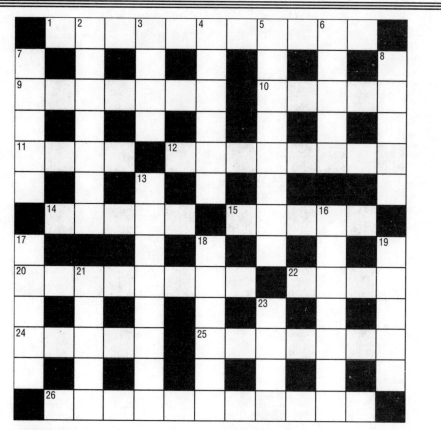

ACROSS

1 Demi Moore's ex husband (5, 6)
9 Soothing song (7)
10 Occupation (5)
11 Aquatic creature (4)
12 Waterspout (8)
14 Pass on (a message) (5)
15 Irritable (5)
20 The American government (5, 3)
22 One of the Great Lakes (4)
24 Shoulder covering (5)
25 Object (7)
26 Old-fashioned gun (11)

DOWN

2 Let go (7)
3 Hooked nail (4)
4 Attack (6)
5 Prosecute (8)
6 European country (5)
7 Coincide (5)
8 Dissuade (5)
13 Strategy (4, 4)
16 Famous London store (7)
17 Estimate (5)
18 Chattering bird (6)
19 Gauge (5)
21 Move on hands and knees (5)
23 Bedouin, eg (4)

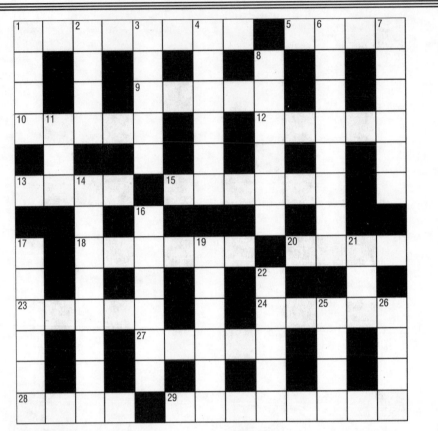

ACROSS

1 Seducer of many women (8)
5 English city (4)
9 Pulsate (5)
10 Build (5)
12 First appearance (5)
13 Cry of a cat (4)
15 Nursery for young children (6)
18 Submissive (6)
20 Slide (4)
23 Musical instrument (5)
24 Jargon (5)
27 Soak in liquid (5)
28 Simon - - -, TV and radio presenter (4)
29 Type of tree (8)

DOWN

1 Nicolas - - -, American film star (4)
2 Sour fruit (4)
3 Smart (5)
4 Church caretaker (6)
6 Sudden occurrence (8)
7 Loose garment (6)
8 Carry off, kidnap (6)
11 Fish eggs (3)
14 Usual (8)
16 From side to side (6)
17 Badge (6)
19 Servant's uniform (6)
21 Actor, - - - McShane (3)
22 Animal charity (inits)
25 Choir voice (4)
26 Butter used in Indian cooking (4)

The Biggest Crossword Book In The World

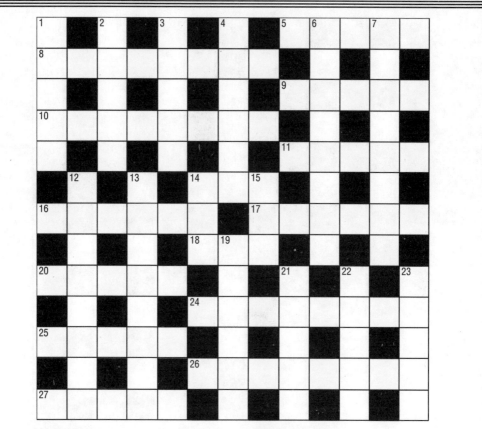

ACROSS

5 Protective garment (5)
8 Chemist's glass (4, 4)
9 Grant, allow (5)
10 Cups and plates etc (8)
11 Marriage (5)
14 Flap (3)
16 Belt fastener (6)
17 Forest worker (6)
18 Historical epoch (3)
20 Panache, elan (5)
24 Russian monk (8)
25 Rash (5)
26 Insolvent debtor (8)
27 Child's comic (5)

DOWN

1 Ordered pile (5)
2 Prestigious car,
- - - Martin (5)
3 Betting amount (5)
4 Ancient name for Spain
and Portugal (6)
6 Painful to the feelings (8)
7 Spectator (8)
12 Trunk (8)
13 Carcass (8)
14 Golfer's peg (3)
15 Woman's
undergarment (3)
19 Former US President (6)
21 Sharp point (5)
22 Dark ale (5)
23 Actress, - - - Dobson (5)

The Biggest Crossword Book In The World

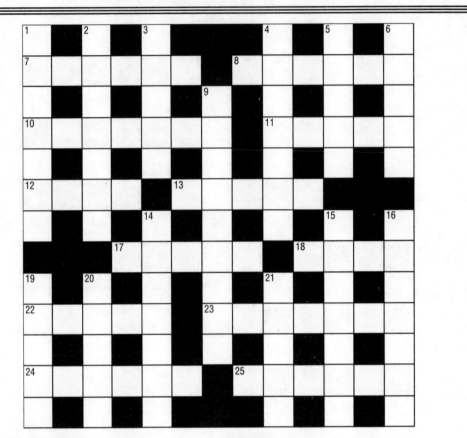

ACROSS

7 Lionel - - -, French PM (6)
8 Small pincered insect (6)
10 Skeleton (7)
11 Eating utensil (5)
12 Everyone separately (4)
13 Succulent (5)
17 Italian city (5)
18 Area enclosed by hills (4)
22 Group of singers (5)
23 Mythological nymph who kept Odysseus captive for seven years (7)
24 Rallying call (3, 3)
25 Nicosia's country (6)

DOWN

1 Expelled (7)
2 Long-legged flightless bird (7)
3 Powerful person (5)
4 Priest's garment (7)
5 Faint (5)
6 Acute pain (5)
9 Pledge (9)
14 Collection of books or records (7)
15 Defence wall (7)
16 Anguish (7)
19 Severe frown (5)
20 Slab of wood (5)
21 Welsh county (5)

The Biggest Crossword Book In The World

ACROSS
1 Chuckle, giggle (5)
4 Track beside a canal (7)
8 Breed of cat (7)
9 Wound from a bee (5)
10 Downpour (4)
11 Vase for ashes (3)
12 Recognise (4)
15 Emblem (6)
16 Team game played on a field (6)
19 Cry of a donkey (4)
21 Negative vote (3)
22 Burden (4)
26 Electronic letter (1, 4)
27 Star sign (7)
28 Scandalmonger (7)
29 Thin (5)

DOWN
1 Also-ran (5)
2 Radioactive metal (7)
3 Lean to one side (4)
4 Reasoning (6)
5 Rinse (4)
6 Foreign body (5)
7 Road (7)
13 Coal scuttle (3)
14 Edgar Allan - - -, author (3)
15 Dependant (7)
17 The most important person (7)
18 Old German emperor (6)
20 Adjust, modify (5)
23 Work of fiction (5)
24 Israel's national airline (2-2)
25 Acidic, sharp (4)

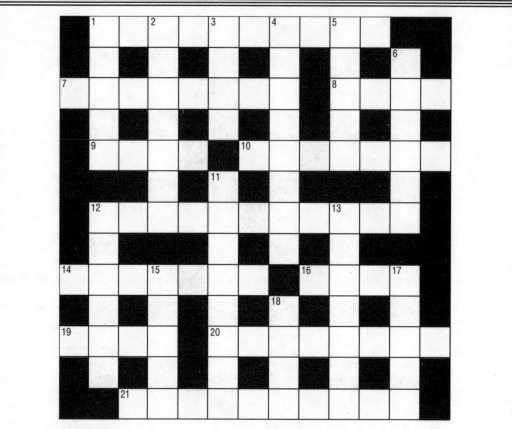

ACROSS

1 Ohio city (10)
7 Police officer (8)
8 Medical photo (1-3)
9 Quarry (4)
10 Hunting dog (7)
12 Exact (2, 3, 6)
14 Scientific study
of animals (7)
16 Shout (4)
19 Charlie - - -, fictional
detective (4)
20 Personal beliefs (8)
21 New husband ? (10)

DOWN

1 Move quietly (5)
2 Treat poorly (7)
3 Iran's neighbour (4)
4 Colourless gas (8)
5 Poison (5)
6 Series of jobs (6)
11 British pottery (8)
12 Sporting prize (6)
13 Lee - - -,
American golfer (7)
15 Passenger ship (5)
17 Desmond - - -,
TV presenter (5)
18 Aeroplane part (4)

The Biggest Crossword Book In The World

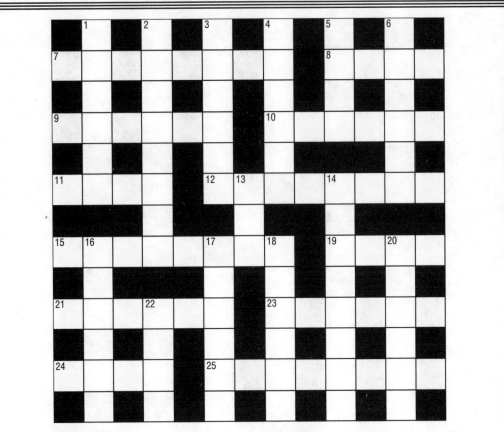

ACROSS

7 Bullfighter (8)
8 Ill (4)
9 Continually find fault (with) (6)
10 Mental institution (6)
11 Sullen in appearance (4)
12 One of the Channel Islands (8)
15 Michael - - -, cricketer (8)
19 Very old (4)
21 Customer (6)
23 Unusually large (crop) (6)
24 Seethe (4)
25 Enrolled (8)

DOWN

1 Fats - - -, R and B musician (6)
2 Indian rice dish (8)
3 Stefan - - -, tennis player (6)
4 Intricately decorated (6)
5 See at a distance (4)
6 Blame (6)
13 Flying saucer (1, 1, 1)
14 Just wide of the target (4, 4)
16 Candle ingredient (6)
17 Chuckle (6)
18 Type of cloud (6)
20 Devon town (6)
22 Jazz singer, - - - Fitzgerald (4)

The Biggest Crossword Book In The World

ACROSS

3 Grave marker (9)
8 Bicycle (4)
9 Petty quarrel (8)
10 Walk with unsteady steps (6)
13 At no time (5)
14 Illicit goods (7)
15 Swindle (3)
16 Sleeveless garment (4, 3)
17 Actor and singer, - - - Donovan (5)
21 Japanese martial art (6)
22 England's Lord Protector (8)
23 Sicilian volcano (4)
24 Figurine (9)

DOWN

1 Stubborn (9)
2 Dangerous sport (9)
4 Beginning (5)
5 US whiskey (7)
6 Musical instrument (4)
7 Void (4)
11 Girl pop goup (3, 6)
12 Food taster (4, 5)
14 Dance (3)
15 Funeral procession (7)
18 Gentleman's attendant (5)
19 Horse's pace (4)
20 Leave out (4)

The Biggest Crossword Book In The World

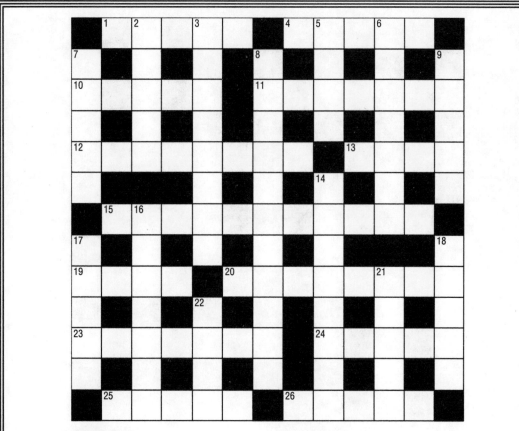

ACROSS

1 Nip (5)
4 Frank Sinatra song (2, 3)
10 John Major's wife (5)
11 Cattle farmer (7)
12 Old British coin (8)
13 Vagrant (4)
15 Former Genesis singer (4, 7)
19 Wagon (4)
20 Time-limit (8)
23 Inflatable life jacket (slang)(3, 4)
24 Lowest deck of a ship (5)
25 Water vapour (5)
26 Capital of Vietnam (5)

DOWN

2 Home of Glasgow Rangers (5)
3 Daddy-long-legs (5-3)
5 Jerk suddenly (4)
6 Paddy - - -, politician (7)
7 Grind (teeth) together (5)
8 *Runaway Train* actor (4, 7)
9 Former (5)
14 Flowering plant (8)
16 Reap, gather (7)
17 Mischievous child (5)
18 Combed, tidy (5)
21 Eskimo's hut (5)
22 Greek B (4)

The Biggest Crossword Book In The World

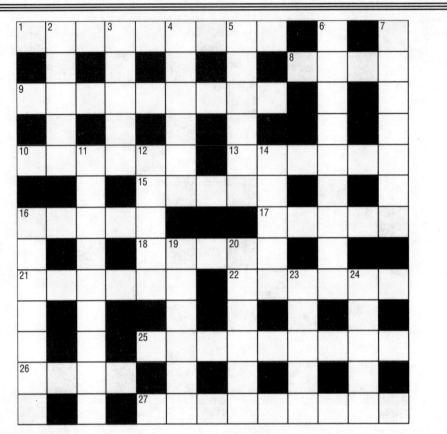

ACROSS

1 Mick Jagger's ex-wife (5, 4)
8 Music for two (4)
9 Sacred cup (4, 5)
10 Centre of a nut (6)
13 Most senior (6)
15 Jules - - -, French novelist (5)
16 Store of food (5)
17 Michael Caine film (5)
18 Regulations (5)
21 Anne - - -, second wife of Henry VIII (6)
22 Short period of rain (6)
25 Italian tenor (9)
26 Frilly (4)
27 Practice session (9)

DOWN

2 Summon up (5)
3 Synthetic fibre (5)
4 Move rapidly (6)
5 Provided (4, 2)
6 Several (5, 1, 3)
7 Take by surprise (7)
11 Remember (9)
12 All (5)
14 Dog lead (5)
16 Enclosed space (7)
19 Distress (6)
20 Get away (6)
23 Aroma (5)
24 More (5)

The Biggest Crossword Book In The World

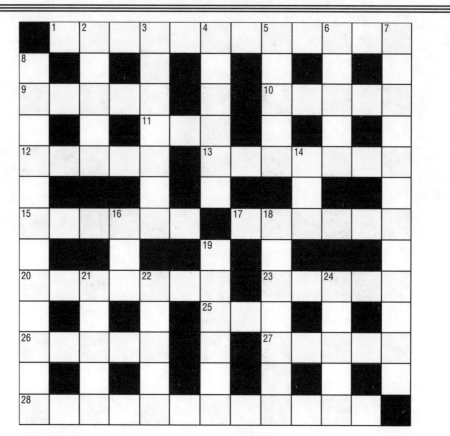

ACROSS
1 Musician and TV presenter (5,7)
9 Another time (5)
10 Jewelled headdress (5)
11 Along with (3)
12 Explosion (5)
13 Financial gift (7)
15 Heirloom left in a will (6)
17 Sell to the consumer (6)
20 Make angry (7)
23 Mediterannean island (5)
25 Indian state (3)
26 Respond (5)
27 Old-time dance (5)
28 At the same time (12)

DOWN
2 Japan's second city (5)
3 Insane (7)
4 Athletics barrier (6)
5 In the future (5)
6 Proverb, saying (5)
7 Brookside actor (4, 8)
8 Pub game (3, 9)
14 Acquire (3)
16 Unreturned serve (3)
18 Prisoner on the run (7)
19 Queen's title (6)
21 Assert one's right to (5)
22 Province of South Africa (5)
24 Oriental rice dish (5)

The Biggest Crossword Book In The World

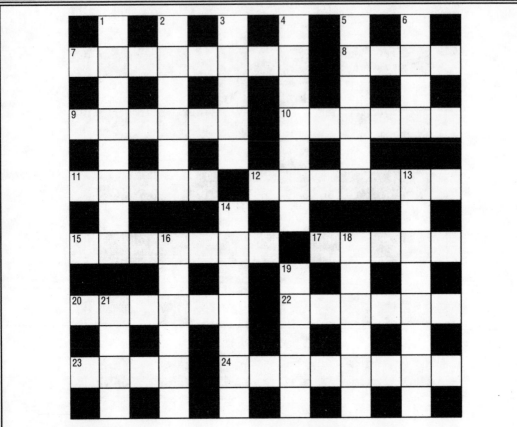

ACROSS

7 Message transmitted
   by cable (8)
8 Diesel Engined
   Road Vehicle (4)
9 Playground ride (6)
10 Tony Blair's party (6)
11 Anticipate with
    apprehension (5)
12 Sporting spear (7)
15 Eccentric person (7)
17 Hollywood film award (5)
20 Cup-shaped cake (6)
22 Spanish city (6)
23 Small flute (4)
24 Teaches (8)

DOWN

1 Hindered, prevented (8)
2 Japanese hostess (6)
3 Developed (5)
4 Alloy of mercury with
   another metal (7)
5 Fit to eat (6)
6 Pakistani language (4)
13 Thought (8)
14 False statement (7)
16 Shock absorber (6)
18 Iraqi leader,
   - - - Hussein (6)
19 Love (5)
21 Single item (4)

ACROSS

1 Not drunk! (5, 2, 1, 5)
7 Rare Chinese mammal (5)
8 Elegant management (7)
9 South American country (7)
10 Crash (a vehicle) (5)
11 *Jude the - - -*, novel (7)
17 Lag behind (5)
18 Written law (7)
20 Portentous (7)
21 Ring-shaped roll (5)
22 Norfolk resort (5, 8)

DOWN

1 Group of seven (6)
2 Twaddle (6)
3 Author, - - - Dahl (5)
4 Gin-making berry (7)
5 Dishearten, daunt (6)
6 Become visible (6)
8 Predicts (9)
12 Make an emergency parachute jump (4, 3)
13 Powerful, mighty (6)
14 Spite (6)
15 Bruce Lee's martial art (4, 2)
16 Riches (6)
19 Long-playing record (5)

The Biggest Crossword Book In The World

ACROSS
1 Jetty (4)
4 Froth (6)
8 Item of knitwear (8)
9 Change direction (4)
10 Fireplace (5)
11 Shock (7)
13 America's 'Beaver' state (6)
15 Several (6)
17 Percussion instrument (7)
19 Pal (5)
22 Coarse fibre (4)
23 Hot and humid (8)
24 Meeting for spirit contact (6)
25 Mound (4)

DOWN
2 Reversal of political policy (1-4)
3 Christmas cake (4, 3)
4 Warm affection (4)
5 Slow-moving reptile (8)
6 Young eel (5)
7 Naval jacket (6)
12 Open (8)
14 Bellowed (6)
16 Nurture (7)
18 Granny Smith, eg (5)
20 Speak slowly (5)
21 Sheltered bay (4)

The Biggest Crossword Book In The World

ACROSS

1 Roughly (13)
7 Oriental (7)
8 Rage (5)
9 Baby kangaroo (4)
10 Steady improvement (8)
12 Compensate for a loss (6)
14 Richard Attenborough film (6)
16 Jerry - - -, US TV star (8)
17 Body of water (4)
20 Zodiac sign (5)
21 Trudge (7)
23 America's highest mountain (5, 8)

DOWN

1 Overwhelming dread (3)
2 Ski slope (5)
3 Working cattle (4)
4 Overlook (6)
5 Brainy person (7)
6 English county (9)
8 Slim long-haired hound (6)
9 Capital of Israel (9)
11 Old gold coin (6)
13 Large deer (7)
15 Scottish football club (6)
18 Shock, dismay (5)
19 Floor-length skirt (4)
22 East Anglian city (3)

The Biggest Crossword Book In The World

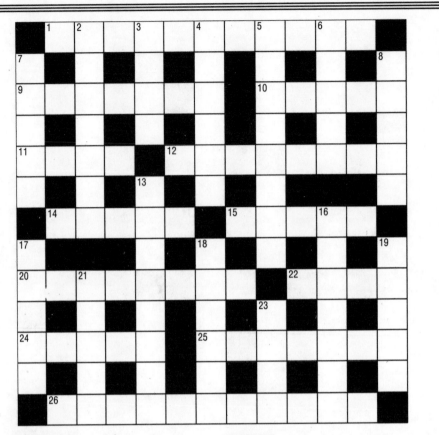

ACROSS

1 Survive (an illness) (4, 7)
9 Accounts examiner (7)
10 Concave chisel (5)
11 Ballet skirt (4)
12 Dejected (8)
14 Sunbaked brick (5)
15 Pale (5)
20 Desire for success (8)
22 Drag behind (4)
24 Frank - - -,
British boxer (5)
25 The United States (7)
26 Temperature gauge (11)

DOWN

2 Modernised (7)
3 Behind time (4)
4 Frightening movie (6)
5 Church musician? (8)
6 Dutch cheese (5)
7 Imitation jewellery (5)
8 Bills (5)
13 Slaughterhouse (8)
16 Tricky (7)
17 Jewish religious
leader (5)
18 Red salad ingredient (6)
19 Cape (5)
21 Go red (5)
23 Yield (4)

The Biggest Crossword Book In The World

ACROSS

1 Large aeroplane (5, 3)
5 Drill (4)
9 Faith, loyalty (5)
10 Fairy (5)
12 Conductor, - - - Previn (5)
13 Farmyard manure (4)
15 Modern (6)
18 Habit, practice (6)
20 Nervous (4)
23 Openmouthed (5)
24 Plague (5)
27 Care for (5)
28 Container for liquid (4)
29 Telescope part (8)

DOWN

1 Four-wheel drive vehicle (4)
2 Tailless breed of cat (4)
3 Frequently (5)
4 Develop naturally (6)
6 Obsolete (8)
7 Go beyond (6)
8 Place for worship (6)
11 Debtor's note (inits)
14 Flowering plant (8)
16 Belgian port (6)
17 Salted snack (6)
19 Large bird of prey (6)
21 Weapon (3)
22 Young dog (5)
25 Impel (4)
26 Ripped (4)

The Biggest Crossword Book In The World

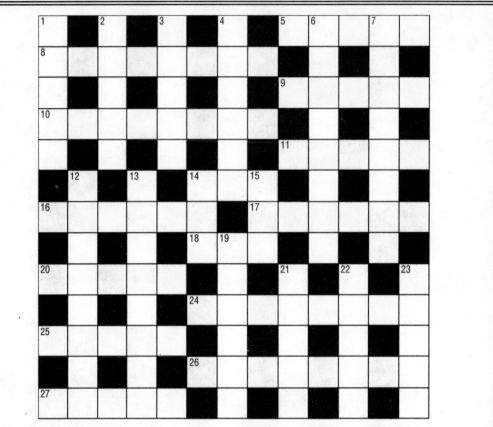

ACROSS

5 Not heavy (5)
8 Cut short (8)
9 Capital of Morocco (5)
10 Sweet-smelling (8)
11 Steps over a fence (5)
14 Sports presenter,
- - - Lynam (3)
16 Shiny metal (6)
17 Devise (6)
18 Pale (3)
20 Tell off (5)
24 Muscular man (8)
25 Children's charity (5)
26 Fire-proof mineral (8)
27 Stages (5)

DOWN

1 Cram completely (5)
2 Merciful (5)
3 Reject with contempt (5)
4 Attitude, standing (6)
6 Idle (8)
7 Newspaper title (8)
12 Stocky (8)
13 Football
competition (5, 3)
14 Early morning
moisture (3)
15 Moral crime (3)
19 Relaxed (2, 4)
21 Bid (5)
22 Fry quickly in
a little fat (5)
23 Smallest amount (5)

The Biggest Crossword Book In The World

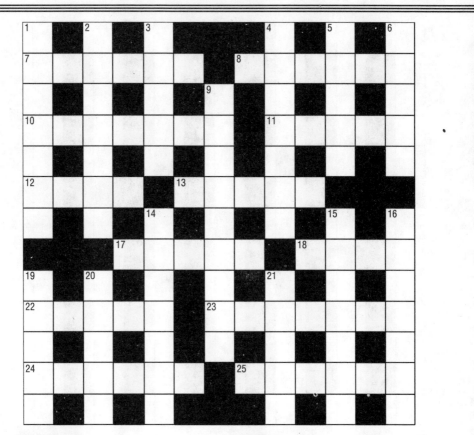

ACROSS

7 Golf club used
for tee shots (6)
8 Cream (6)
10 Sure (7)
11 In the lead (5)
12 Trampled (4)
13 Leg bone (5)
17 Hussy (5)
18 Be lost in thought (4)
22 Hooter (5)
23 Regular (7)
24 Jane - - -, British
novelist (6)
25 Fast social group? (3, 3)

DOWN

1 Teach (7)
2 Pantomime character (7)
3 Chair carried
on two poles (5)
4 North Star (7)
5 Female fox (5)
6 Insolent (5)
9 Double-dealing (9)
14 Follow a winding
course (7)
15 Japanese wrestling (7)
16 Chooses (7)
19 Written composition (5)
20 Military award (5)
21 Marvellous (5)

The Biggest Crossword Book In The World

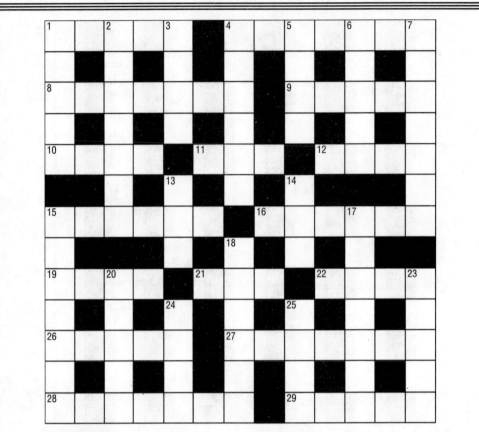

ACROSS

1 Promise on oath (5)
4 Open porch (7)
8 Increase in size (7)
9 Support for a broken arm (5)
10 Give out cards (4)
11 Large lorry (1, 1, 1)
12 Ditch (4)
15 Picture-house (6)
16 Agree to (6)
19 Nautical cry! (4)
21 Female rabbit (3)
22 Strike with open hand (4)
26 Scale (5)
27 Steal (7)
28 Ruth - - -, crime writer (7)
29 Little (5)

DOWN

1 Sliver (of glass) (5)
2 Give details of (7)
3 Mike - - -, actor and comedian (4)
4 Sea journey (6)
5 Diana - - -, Motown singer (4)
6 Deafening (5)
7 Strengthen (7)
13 Aviator, - - - Johnson (3)
14 Nourished (3)
15 *The Canterbury Tales* poet (7)
17 Romania's neighbour (7)
18 Force (6)
20 Pungent vegetable (5)
23 Dashboard (5)
24 Woodwind instrument (4)
25 Small dagger (4)

The Biggest Crossword Book In The World

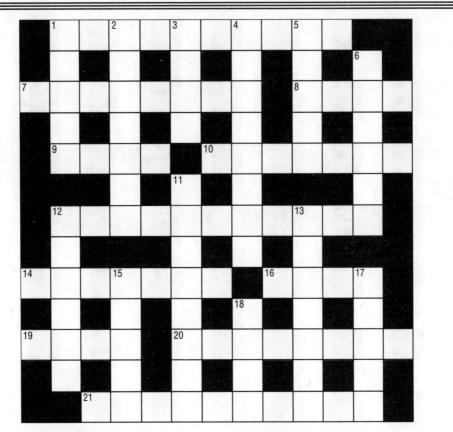

ACROSS

1 Tree fruit (10)
7 Gambling game (8)
8 John - - -, British architect (4)
9 Child's toy (2-2)
10 German town (7)
12 X-Ray specialist at a hospital (11)
14 Pungent pepper (7)
16 Surprise attack (4)
19 Unaided performance (4)
20 Worshiped (8)
21 Pitiless (10)

DOWN

1 Black wood (5)
2 Held back (7)
3 List of duties (4)
4 US lift (8)
5 Beatles' drummer, - - - Starr (5)
6 Upward slope (6)
11 Imagine, think (8)
12 Sense (6)
13 John Lennon song (7)
15 Roused (5)
17 Remains (5)
18 Protected building (4)

The Biggest Crossword Book In The World

ACROSS

7 Burger and chips, eg (4, 4)
8 Bubbly Italian wine (4)
9 Chevron (6)
10 Complete (6)
11 Potage (4)
12 Exact (2, 3, 3)
15 N American Indian's war-axe (8)
19 Concern (4)
21 Spirit communicator (6)
23 Peak (6)
24 Cathedral administrator (4)
25 Width of a circle (8)

DOWN

1 Cuban dictator (6)
2 Modern name for Abyssinia (8)
3 Precede in time (6)
4 Commercial (6)
5 Sweep smoothly along (4)
6 Hi-fi system (6)
13 Novel (3)
14 Hinder (8)
16 Followed orders (6)
17 Fleet of ships (6)
18 One of the Three Wise Men (6)
20 Attacker (6)
22 Scottish isle (4)

The Biggest Crossword Book In The World

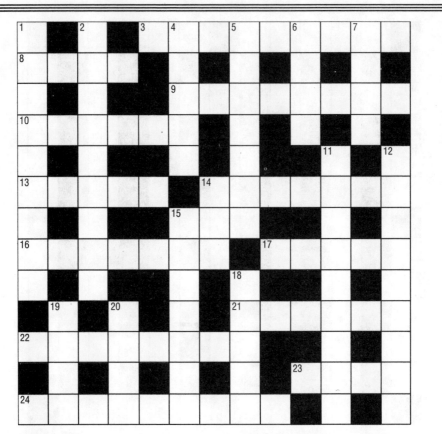

ACROSS
3 Lily-like plant (9)
8 Purposely ignore (4)
9 Ingenuity (8)
10 Mammal with
long ears (6)
13 Sing softly (5)
14 Boris - - -,
Ex Russian President (7)
15 Automobile (3)
16 Thesaurus entry (7)
17 Skirmish (5)
21 Abandon evil
practices (6)
22 Skittles (8)
23 Song of praise (4)
24 Range of chalk hills (9)

DOWN
1 Banish from society (9)
2 Shock, amaze (9)
4 Laughter (5)
5 Cattle thief (7)
6 Rough person (4)
7 Move very slowly (4)
11 Author's fictitious
name (9)
12 Getting better (2, 3, 4)
14 Tropical vegetable (3)
15 Poisonous chemical
compound (7)
18 Incendiary crime (5)
19 Wealthy (4)
20 Species of duck (4)

The Biggest Crossword Book In The World

ACROSS

1 Old Testament character swallowed by a whale (5)
4 Airman (5)
10 French fries (5)
11 Get back (7)
12 Every two years (8)
13 Rundown area (4)
15 Large store (11)
19 Woolly footwear (4)
20 Grabbed (8)
23 Stringed instrument (7)
24 Comedy play (5)
25 Escape (duty) (5)
26 Exactly (5)

DOWN

2 Oil-bearing fruit (5)
3 Missing person (8)
5 Paul - - -, England footballer (4)
6 Aviation pioneer, - - - Wright (7)
7 Aqualung (5)
8 Tolerant (5-6)
9 Muscular contraction (5)
14 Thankful (8)
16 Coarse (7)
17 Publish (5)
18 Poisonous snake (5)
21 Muslim women's quarters (5)
22 Deride (4)

The Biggest Crossword Book In The World

ACROSS
1 Nervous collapse? (9)
8 Stallion's partner (4)
9 Unofficial soldier (9)
10 Airgun shot (6)
13 Passionate (6)
15 Stretchable fabric (5)
16 Italian foodstuff (5)
17 Shockingly vivid (5)
18 Stairpost (5)
21 French painter, - - - Monet (6)
22 Whirl (6)
25 Newlyweds holiday (9)
26 Top of a building (4)
27 Poor (9)

DOWN
2 Course (5)
3 Of the ears (5)
4 Charming and delicate (6)
5 Man's name (6)
6 Self-service restaurant (9)
7 Made smaller (7)
11 Film actress (3, 6)
12 South African antelope (5)
14 Regain strength (5)
16 Image (7)
19 AA Milne's donkey (6)
20 First overlord of all England (6)
23 Send (payment) (5)
24 Game fish (5)

The Biggest Crossword Book In The World

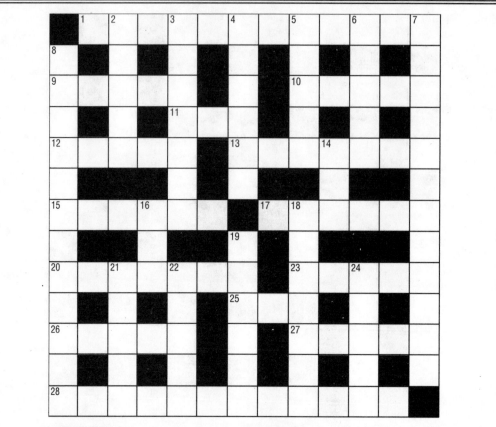

ACROSS

1 Kitchen appliance (12)
9 Memorable American battle (5)
10 Large lorry (5)
11 Perceive (3)
12 Stoke's river (5)
13 Short excursion? (3, 4)
15 Small racing vehicle (2-4)
17 Dinner jacket (6)
20 Branch of mathematics (7)
23 Houseplant (5)
25 Old distress signal (1, 1, 1)
26 Caribbean country (5)
27 Soft leather (5)
28 Gives up (12)

DOWN

2 Obliterate (5)
3 Male fowl (7)
4 Grasping (6)
5 Raring to go (5)
6 Teacher (5)
7 Gives in return (12)
8 Map maker (12)
14 Levy on income (3)
16 Hop-rich beer (3)
18 Space probe launched in 1990 to inspect the sun (7)
19 Capital of the Bahamas (6)
21 Part of a cooker (5)
22 Small child (5)
24 British town (5)

The Biggest Crossword Book In The World

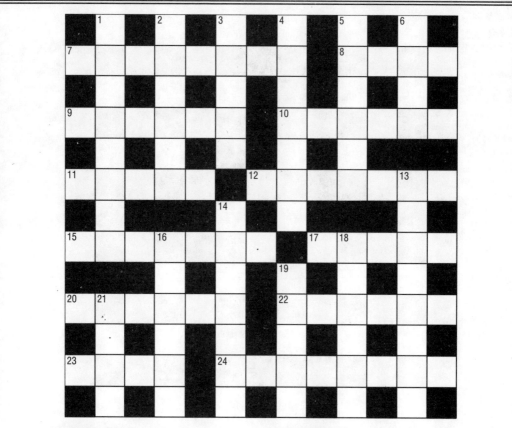

ACROSS

7 Greg - - -, British
   tennis player (8)
8 Father (4)
9 Consolation (6)
10 Card suit (6)
11 Wash (5)
12 Immature (7)
15 Ancient (7)
17 Russian spacecraft (5)
20 Marine bird (6)
22 Attractiveness (6)
23 Raise (4)
24 Articulate (8)

DOWN

1 German motorway (8)
2 Disengage
   and separate (6)
3 Daisy (5)
4 Film star, - - - Douglas (7)
5 Ligament injury (6)
6 Slight quarrel (4)
13 One of the
   deadly sins (8)
14 Pushed about (7)
16 Set fire to (6)
18 Hard to understand (6)
19 Russ - - -, star of
   September Song (5)
21 Similar, like (4)

The Biggest Crossword Book In The World

ACROSS

1 James Bond actor (6, 7)
7 Steal (slang) (5)
8 Snake (7)
9 Hiker (7)
10 North American deer (5)
11 Future (7)
17 Large steak (1-4)
18 Hand motion (7)
20 Very stupid (7)
21 Jumped (5)
22 Large body
of water (8, 5)

DOWN

1 Pie casing (6)
2 Puzzle, riddle (6)
3 Angler's basket (5)
4 Rower (7)
5 Liam - - -, *Schindler's List* actor (6)
6 Aromatic spice (6)
8 Tactical (9)
12 Premier division
soccer club (7)
13 Leader of the Huns (6)
14 Convivial (6)
15 Gas used for
cigarette lighters (6)
16 Defeated (6)
19 Volley of shots (5)

The Biggest Crossword Book In The World

ACROSS

1 Cooking chamber (4)
4 Sheen (6)
8 Area of France (8)
9 Manure (4)
10 Summarise (5)
11 Obstacle (7)
13 Hire (6)
15 Woman's undergarment (6)
17 Receive from a predecessor (7)
19 Deciduous coniferous tree (5)
22 Inexpensive restaurant (4)
23 Line on a map (8)
24 Stone effigy (6)
25 Small farm animal (4)

DOWN

2 Energy, vigour (5)
3 Sport similar to basketball (7)
4 Part of a plant's foliage (4)
5 Salty Chinese cooking ingredient (3, 5)
6 Equestrian (5)
7 Extension to a building (6)
12 Song writer (8)
14 Start of the week (6)
16 Selfish driver (4-3)
18 Occurrence (5)
20 About (year) (5)
21 Predict (4)

The Biggest Crossword Book In The World

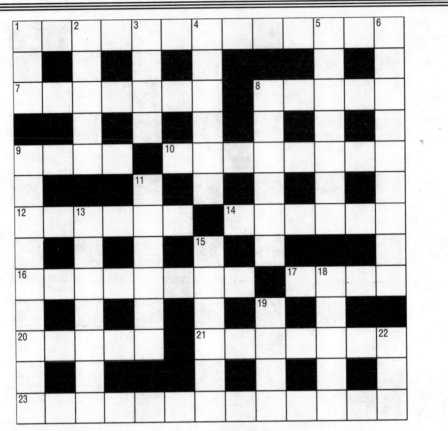

ACROSS

1 Path used to cross a road (5, 8)
7 Scheme (7)
8 Shared (5)
9 Former German chancellor (4)
10 Canadian police force (8)
12 Baby's nappy (6)
14 Sheepdog (6)
16 Senior councillor (8)
17 Electricity system (4)
20 Lurk (5)
21 Coach (7)
23 Eminent (13)

DOWN

1 Toothed clothing fastener (3)
2 Cubicle (5)
3 Smart man! (4)
4 Fixed allowance (6)
5 First (7)
6 Town in NE England (9)
8 Younger (6)
9 Abducted (9)
11 Fuel (6)
13 Harsh (7)
15 Common people (6)
18 Cattle-breeding farm (5)
19 Indian queen (4)
22 Relieve (of) (3)

The Biggest Crossword Book In The World

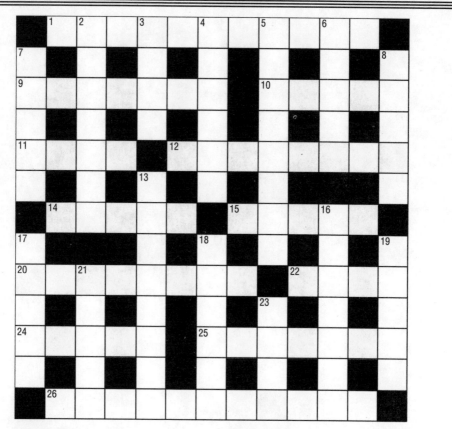

ACROSS

1 Lead singer of
   The Doors (3, 8)
9 Parachute string (7)
10 Treasure box (5)
11 A gas (4)
12 Patient (8)
14 Tired (5)
15 At an oblique angle (5)
20 Strong praise (8)
22 *My - - - Foot*, film (4)
24 Motor racing driver,
   - - - Hill (5)
25 On the way (2, 5)
26 Austere, strict (6-5)

DOWN

2 Enhance (7)
3 Arguable (4)
4 Very, very warm (3-3)
5 Become greater
   in size (8)
6 Last Greek letter (5)
7 Admit (5)
8 Declare (5)
13 Asian republic (3, 5)
16 Carry out sentence
   of death (7)
17 Garish (5)
18 Arrival (6)
19 Guide (5)
21 Heavenly body (5)
23 Operatic song (4)

The Biggest Crossword Book In The World

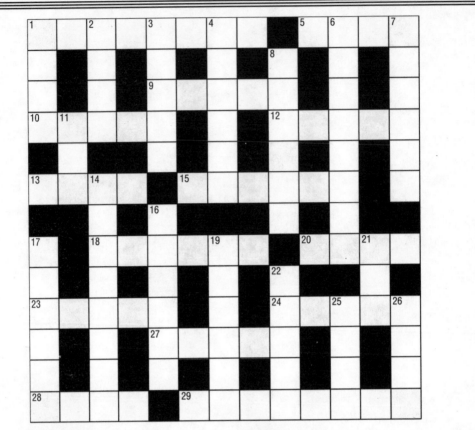

ACROSS

1 Young plant (8)
5 Not soft (4)
9 Thin (5)
10 Angry stare (5)
12 Capture (5)
13 Peruse (4)
15 Crispy salad
ingredient (6)
18 Tell (6)
20 Irritation of the skin (4)
23 Supple (5)
24 Underhand person (5)
27 Sceptic (5)
28 Tale with supernatural
characters (4)
29 False teeth (8)

DOWN

1 Hitch (4)
2 Book of the Bible (4)
3 Let down (5)
4 Compass pointer (6)
6 Purple stone (8)
7 Cricketing county (6)
8 Juicy Chinese fruit (6)
11 Untruth (3)
14 Rigorous
examination (4, 4)
16 Result (6)
17 Rarely (6)
19 Snooker player,
- - - O'Sullivan (6)
21 US spy
organisation (1, 1, 1)
22 Royal racecourse (5)
25 Always (4)
26 Touch with the lips (4)

The Biggest Crossword Book In The World

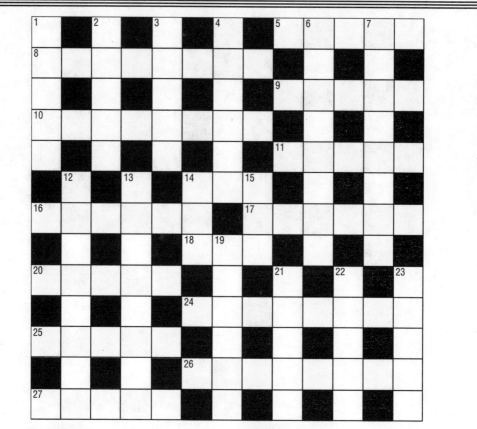

ACROSS

5 Animals in general (5)
8 Tennessee - - -, American playwright (8)
9 Wandering tribesman (5)
10 Widespread outbreak (8)
11 Banquet (5)
14 Favourite (3)
16 Live-in home help (2, 4)
17 Enclosure for birds (6)
18 Bark of a small dog (3)
20 Protective wrapper (5)
24 Central heating panel (8)
25 Meat juices (5)
26 Languid (8)
27 Severe (5)

DOWN

1 Sugary (5)
2 Weary (3, 2)
3 Underwater worker (5)
4 Drink (alcohol) (6)
6 Eating disorder (8)
7 Biblical ship (5, 3)
12 Absolute ruler (8)
13 Acquisition of a company (8)
14 Snoop (3)
15 Touch lightly (3)
19 Middle East language (6)
21 Quick, agile (5)
22 Alternative (5)
23 Alloy of copper and zinc (5)

The Biggest Crossword Book In The World

ACROSS

7 Group of relatives (6)
8 Beginner (6)
10 Quay-side post (7)
11 Foe (5)
12 Measure of land (4)
13 Social gathering (5)
17 Beethoven's last symphony (5)
18 Christmas (4)
22 King with the golden touch (5)
23 Mischievous troublemaker (7)
24 Taken illegally (6)
25 Formal (6)

DOWN

1 Unconventional (7)
2 Beg (7)
3 Wintry (5)
4 Ribbon (7)
5 Sacked (5)
6 African republic (5)
9 Benefit (9)
14 Oil often used on cricket bats (7)
15 Former Dutch currency (7)
16 Leftover material (7)
19 Break up (5)
20 Stupid person (5)
21 Devil, evil spirit (5)

The Biggest Crossword Book In The World

ACROSS

1 Flow away (5)
4 Postman's sack (7)
8 Groom's mate (4,3)
9 Happen (5)
10 Politician, - - - Blair (4)
11 Musical note (3)
12 Stake (4)
15 Safe (6)
16 Unassuming (6)
19 Chest bones (4)
21 Omelette base (3)
22 Scottish island (4)
26 Prickly part of a plant (5)
27 Tell (a story) (7)
28 Kind of sponge cake (7)
29 Poor (5)

DOWN

1 First appearance (5)
2 A deadly poison (7)
3 Too cold to feel (4)
4 Trusted adviser (6)
5 Object of veneration (4)
6 Pig meat (5)
7 Item of clothing (7)
13 Anger, wrath (3)
14 Detailed record
of a journey (3)
15 Layer of rock (7)
17 Attempt to equal (7)
18 Discussion list (6)
20 Descent, parentage (5)
23 Nail board (5)
24 Opposed to (4)
25 Smile (4)

The Biggest Crossword Book In The World

ACROSS

1 Last book of the New Testament (10)
7 Young bird (8)
8 Peer (4)
9 Dry, parched (4)
10 Competence (7)
12 The Father of the Bride? (5, 6)
14 Shameless woman (7)
16 Throw (4)
19 Tidings (4)
20 Queen of the Iceni tribe (8)
21 Very excessive (10)

DOWN

1 Sports venue (5)
2 Exterior (7)
3 Enthusiastic (4)
4 Boo Boo's buddy (4, 4)
5 Aroma (5)
6 Dish covered with breadcrumbs (6)
11 Month of the year (8)
12 Kebab spike (6)
13 Russian emperor's wife (7)
15 County (5)
17 Act of stealing (5)
18 Hindu dress (4)

The Biggest Crossword Book In The World

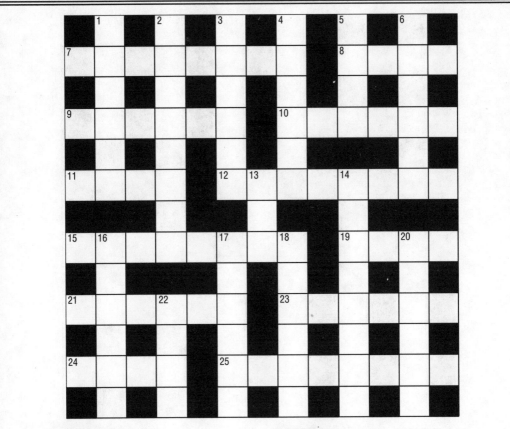

ACROSS

7 Region of Italy (8)
8 Defeat and put
to flight (4)
9 Peruvian llama (6)
10 Move about restlessly (6)
11 Scottish hill (4)
12 New York borough (3, 5)
15 Sussex seaside town (8)
19 Square (4)
21 Make oneself popular (6)
23 Root of a tropical
plant (6)
24 Talk wildly (4)
25 Disregard (8)

DOWN

1 Flour maker (6)
2 Close by (8)
3 Humphrey - - -, actor (6)
4 Suppress (6)
5 Brought up (4)
6 Soup dish (6)
13 Male pig (3)
14 Not long ago (8)
16 Happening
once a year (6)
17 Slim (6)
18 Royal seal (6)
20 Inhabitant of Brittany (6)
22 Duelling sword (4)

The Biggest Crossword Book In The World

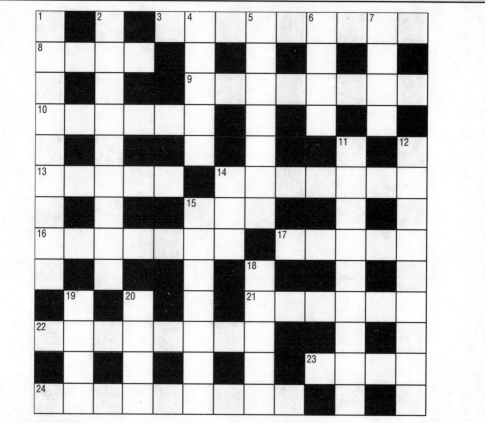

ACROSS

3 Quentin - - -, film director (9)
8 Pigeon house (4)
9 German shepherd dog (8)
10 Reply to a question (6)
13 Hit film, - - - *Dancing* (5)
14 American film star (3, 4)
15 Piece of turf (3)
16 Tolerant (7)
17 Plentiful (5)
21 Assistant (6)
22 Kitchen utensil (8)
23 Celine - - -, singer (4)
24 Sea walk (9)

DOWN

1 Alan - - -, playwright (9)
2 Children (9)
4 Separated (5)
5 Convinced (7)
6 Haul, carry (4)
7 In apple-pie order (4)
11 Indigestion (9)
12 War-time diary writer (4, 5)
14 Test for motor vehicles (inits)
15 Welsh mountain (7)
18 Small amount (5)
19 Gloomy looking (weather) (4)
20 Peaceful, placid (4)

The Biggest Crossword Book In The World

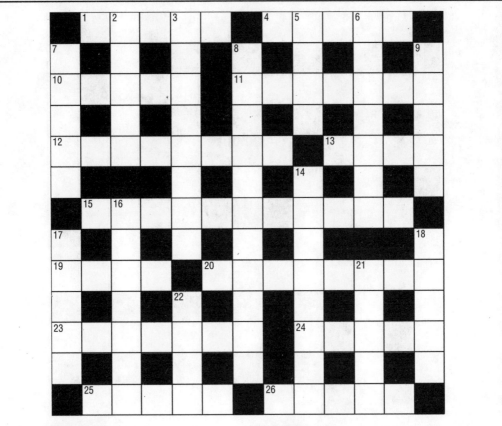

ACROSS

1 North American
Indian's tent (5)
4 Witchcraft (5)
10 Long for (5)
11 Expression of regret (7)
12 Voting event (8)
13 Travel charge (4)
15 Clarifies (11)
19 Smart (4)
20 Forefather (8)
23 French castle (7)
24 Court case (5)
25 Caper, stunt (5)
26 Guardian spirit
from heaven (5)

DOWN

2 Get away from (5)
3 Latest (8)
5 Minute portion (4)
6 Metallic period
of history (4, 3)
7 Group of eight
musicians (5)
8 Winner's tour? (3, 2, 6)
9 Welsh county (5)
14 Earn vast amounts of
money! (4, 2, 2)
16 Choose not to vote (7)
17 Aromatic flavouring (5)
18 Fancy edging (5)
21 Gardening string (5)
22 Suburban house (4)

The Biggest Crossword Book In The World

ACROSS

1 Tourist attraction (6, 3)
8 Long spar (4)
9 Perfect (9)
10 Gambling centre (6)
13 To last (6)
15 Irate (5)
16 Pansy-like flower (5)
17 Damp (5)
18 Bored (3, 2)
21 Although (6)
22 Temporary wooden
   building (6)
25 Pilgrim Father's ship (9)
26 Soft thick lump (4)
27 Fill up again (9)

DOWN

2 City in Nebraska (5)
3 New - - -,
   capital of India (5)
4 **Former** South African
   President,
   - - - Mandela (6)
5 Shellfish (6)
6 Bruise (9)
7 Notable (7)
11 Cowardly cartoon
   canine (6, 3)
12 Military shop (5)
14 Legendary maiden (5)
16 Railway bridge (7)
19 Flammable gas (6)
20 Advantageous (6)
23 Oak fruit (5)
24 Long lock of hair (5)

The Biggest Crossword Book In The World

ACROSS
1 Praised (12)
9 Revolt against those in power (5)
10 Scottish poet (5)
11 Slide on snow (3)
12 Islamic religious ruling (5)
13 Submarine's missile (7)
15 Missive (6)
17 Richard Branson's company (6)
20 Disgusting (7)
23 Rational thought (5)
25 American law enforcement agency (inits)
26 Species (5)
27 Social class in India (5)
28 Memory (12)

DOWN
2 Planet's path (5)
3 Quiver, vibrate (7)
4 Ask (6)
5 Cinder (5)
6 Concise (5)
7 Separated (12)
8 Oliver Twist character (6, 6)
14 Golf norm (3)
16 Nervous twitch (3)
18 Forbidden (7)
19 Disprove (6)
21 Computer game hedgehog (5)
22 Painting stand (5)
24 Zest (5)

The Biggest Crossword Book In The World

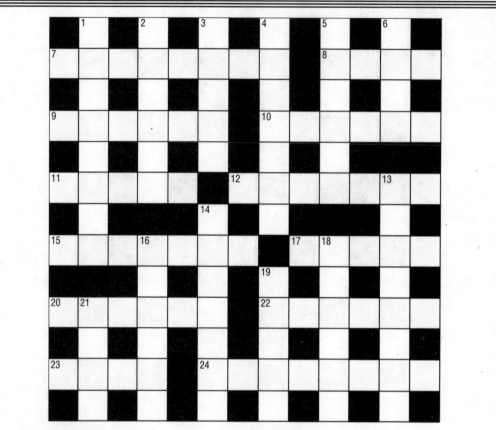

ACROSS

7 Rep (8)
8 Restaurant critic,
- - - Ronay (4)
9 Cabbage dish,
- - - and squeak (6)
10 Meryl - - -, *Out of Africa*
actress (6)
11 Emblem (5)
12 Linked computer
system (7)
15 Reserve fund (4, 3)
17 Body of employees (5)
20 Skip playfully (6)
22 Venerate (6)
23 Apple's centre (4)
24 Largest of the
Canary islands (8)

DOWN

1 Drench (8)
2 Beverage sachet (3, 3)
3 Drive forward (5)
4 Liquorice-like
flavouring (7)
5 Official language
of Israel (6)
6 Fine whetstone (4)
13 Disreputable people (8)
14 Dexterity (7)
16 Pill (6)
18 Old-fashioned pub (6)
19 Trim (5)
21 Medicinal herb (4)

The Biggest Crossword Book In The World

ACROSS
1 Precious McKenzie's sport (13)
7 A loving gift (5)
8 Small bouquet worn on a dress (7)
9 Direction on piece of mail (7)
10 An assumed name (5)
11 Member of the public (7)
17 Freshwater fish (5)
18 Stern, severe (7)
20 Quiver (7)
21 Musical drama (5)
22 Offensive retaliation (7,6)

DOWN
1 Capital of Poland (6)
2 In prison (slang) (6)
3 Hurry (5)
4 Metal melting apparatus (7)
5 Sloping (type) (6)
6 Lubricate (6)
8 Rebuke severly (9)
12 Dwell in (7)
13 Literary judge (6)
14 Rich cake (6)
15 Headquarters of many international bodies (6)
16 Perceive, notice (6)
19 Part of a teapot (5)

ACROSS
1 Soft mixture (4)
4 Prolong in duration (6)
8 Computer programme (8)
9 Apply paint (4)
10 Remove clothes (5)
11 Scout's cord (7)
13 Shooting star (6)
15 African country (6)
17 Success (7)
19 Game of chance (5)
22 Nuisance (4)
23 Imitated (8)
24 Irish PM, - - - Ahern (6)
25 Distinctive air (4)

DOWN
2 Overhead (5)
3 Direct telephone link (3, 4)
4 Academic test (4)
5 Seat of the Dutch government (3, 5)
6 Enid Blyton character (5)
7 Rotten and foul-smelling (6)
12 Quarrel (8)
14 Lace hole (6)
16 Pantomime character (3, 4)
18 Woodwork machine (5)
20 Germaine - - -, feminist (5)
21 Certain (4)

The Biggest Crossword Book In The World

ACROSS
1 Sharon Stone film (5, 8)
7 Farm vehicle (7)
8 Nellie - - -, soprano (5)
9 Television award (4)
10 Feminine (8)
12 Scatter (6)
14 Mr Hyde's doctor? (6)
16 Humorous tale (8)
17 Practice boxing (4)
20 River mammal (5)
21 Fictitious reason (7)
23 Welsh acting legend (7,6)

DOWN
1 Club (3)
2 Crowd round (5)
3 Cherubic (4)
4 Greg - - -, golfer (6)
5 Cancel (7)
6 Person on a journey (9)
8 Violent destruction (6)
9 Strive (9)
11 Bookworm (6)
13 Cynic, doubter (7)
15 Silly (6)
18 Fold (5)
19 List of meals (4)
22 Heavy weight (3)

The Biggest Crossword Book In The World

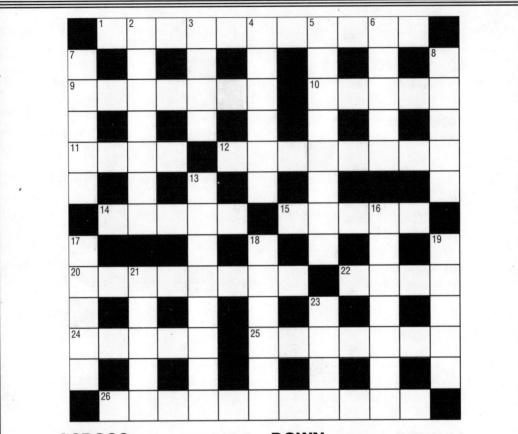

ACROSS
1 Behind time (7, 4)
9 Reached (7)
10 Darkest colour (5)
11 Heroic tale (4)
12 In an excited state (8)
14 Alternative (5)
15 Actor, - - - Bowles (5)
20 Send to jail (8)
22 Heart, hub (4)
24 Cut into two
   equal pieces (5)
25 Operating room (7)
26 Shelf above
   a fireplace (11)

DOWN
2 Erect (7)
3 Part of a church (4)
4 Doze (3, 3)
5 Manual worker (8)
6 Mannerism (5)
7 Not true (5)
8 Item of clothing (5)
13 Matter which settles to
   the bottom of a liquid (8)
16 Irregular (7)
17 Correct (5)
18 Born to die (6)
19 Force out (5)
21 Capital of the
   Balearic Islands (5)
23 Peaked cap (4)

The Biggest Crossword Book In The World

ACROSS

1 Famous orange seller (4, 4)
5 Change (4)
9 Tusk material (5)
10 Rough cloth (5)
12 Scoff (5)
13 Spandau's last inmate (4)
15 Popular 'whodunit' board game (6)
18 Violent disturbance (6)
20 Nourish (4)
23 Every 24 hours (5)
24 Garden ornament (5)
27 Seance board (5)
28 Piffle (4)
29 Mechanical sensing device (8)

DOWN

1 Nothing! (4)
2 Exist (4)
3 Adviser (5)
4 Somerset town (6)
6 Scottish winter sports resort (8)
7 Annually (6)
8 Routine (6)
11 Tiny (3)
14 False (8)
16 Coloured wax stick (6)
17 Extremely small person (6)
19 Look up to (6)
21 Tree prone to Dutch disease (3)
22 Type of quartz (5)
25 Hop drying kiln (4)
26 Islamic ruler (4)

The Biggest Crossword Book In The World

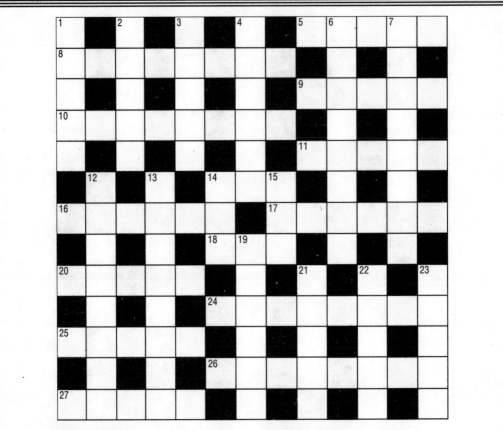

ACROSS

5 Watch band (5)
8 Swimming pool chemical (8)
9 Dr Who's enemy (5)
10 Brutal (8)
11 Theme (5)
14 Social insect (3)
16 Afterwards (6)
17 Soup ingredient? (6)
18 Civil award (1, 1, 1)
20 Dental string (5)
24 Item of jewellery (8)
25 Faithful (5)
26 Fixed (8)
27 Sullen (5)

DOWN

1 Total of points (5)
2 Shaggy-coated mammal (5)
3 Routine teaching (5)
4 Agreement (6)
6 John - - -, *Pulp Fiction* actor (8)
7 Alcoholic appetiser (8)
12 Wealthy (4-2-2)
13 Emergency medical assistance (5, 3)
14 Needless fuss (3)
15 Front of a boot (3)
19 Exchange goods (6)
21 Vamoose (5)
22 Plants of a region (5)
23 Office in the home (5)

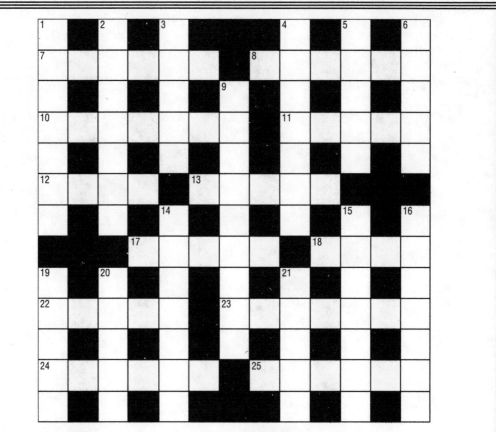

ACROSS

7 Sorrowful (6)
8 The elite (6)
10 Mechanical piano (7)
11 Record of daily events (5)
12 Prepare for publication (4)
13 Land of the Rising Sun (5)
17 Staple food (5)
18 Low dam (4)
22 Denise - - -, Tim Healy's wife (5)
23 Side by side (7)
24 Reduce in quality (6)
25 Short sleep (6)

DOWN

1 Exchanged (7)
2 Royal insignia (7)
3 Recognition (5)
4 Somerset village (7)
5 *The - - - of Dibley*, TV sitcom (5)
6 English diary writer (5)
9 Indian prince (9)
14 Ancient (7)
15 Six-sided shape (7)
16 Benjamin - - -, British composer (7)
19 Mark - - -, American author (5)
20 Petticoats (5)
21 Currency unit of Denmark (5)

The Biggest Crossword Book In The World

ACROSS

1 Small bag (5)
4 Seasoned red sausage (7)
8 Exalted (7)
9 Support (5)
10 Quantity of paper (4)
11 Uncooked (3)
12 Cordial (4)
15 A dozen (6)
16 Piercing scream (6)
19 Loud explosive noise (4)
21 Not in (3)
22 Kill time (4)
26 Strategy game (5)
27 Snooker player, - - - Hendry (7)
28 Ham it up! (7)
29 Shabby-looking (5)

DOWN

1 Tricky problem (5)
2 Resentment (7)
3 Icy rain (4)
4 Swedish tennis player, - - - Edberg (6)
5 Forbid (4)
6 Actress, - - - Dern (5)
7 Muslim veil (7)
13 First woman (3)
14 For what reason? (3)
15 Cigarette's contents (7)
17 Scott novel (7)
18 Reddish brown (6)
20 Nephew's sister (5)
23 Bitter (5)
24 Large continent (4)
25 Greek god (4)

The Biggest Crossword Book In The World

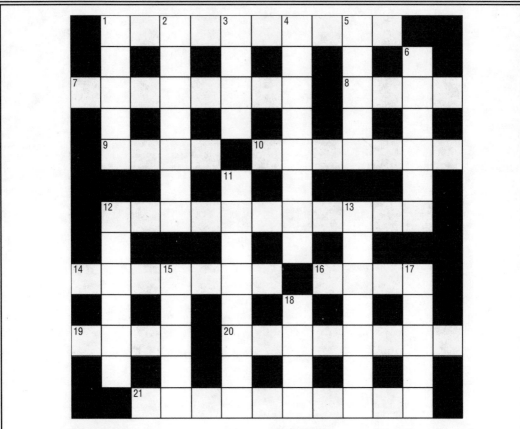

ACROSS

1 Joel Chandler
Harris tale (5, 5)
7 Practical tools (8)
8 What is owed (4)
9 Train track (4)
10 French pilgrimage
town (7)
12 Wasteful (11)
14 Lebanese seaport (7)
16 Let go (4)
19 Stimulus (4)
20 Exciting, tense (8)
21 South Coast resort (10)

DOWN

1 Make a sound (5)
2 Tell secrets (7)
3 Way out (4)
4 Establish firmly (8)
5 Beneath (5)
6 Away (6)
11 Well-to-do (8)
12 Increase suddenly (6)
13 Imaginary line around
the middle of the
planet (7)
15 Warm jacket (5)
17 Three-wheeled cycle (5)
18 Intra-office note (4)

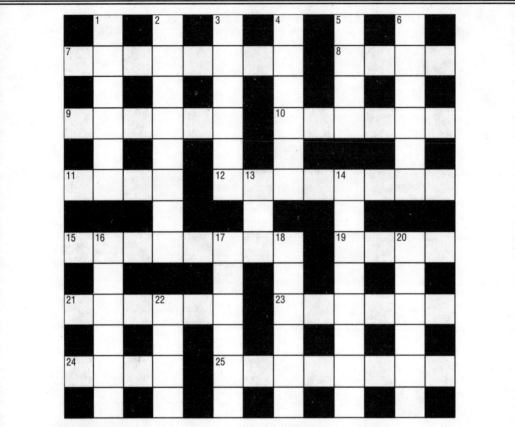

ACROSS

7 Not guilty of a crime (8)
8 Artful (4)
9 Near (6)
10 Deliver a sermon (6)
11 Satan's domain (4)
12 Mockery (8)
15 Plaited (8)
19 TV presenter,
- - - Freud (4)
21 Run and play in
a lively manner (6)
23 Servant (6)
24 Ornamental jar (4)
25 German-born genius (8)

DOWN

1 Sign of a cold (6)
2 Daughter's
husband (3-2-3)
3 Return to former
condition (6)
4 Perfect place (6)
5 Margin (4)
6 Leftover piece
of wood (6)
13 Regret (3)
14 Infinite time (8)
16 Routine (6)
17 Metal (6)
18 Purchaser's desire (6)
20 Short-sighted (6)
22 Lecherous look (4)

The Biggest Crossword Book In The World

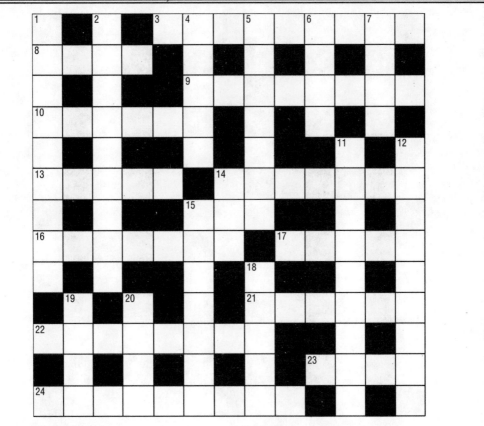

ACROSS

3 Struggles (9)
8 Crafty (4)
9 Determined (8)
10 Shock (6)
13 Jilly Cooper novel (5)
14 Pushed against (7)
15 Sink a snooker ball (3)
16 Officer in royal
household (7)
17 Metric weight (5)
21 Beginning (6)
22 Steersman of a boat (8)
23 Loud deep
hoarse sound (4)
24 Facial hair (9)

DOWN

1 Ready to wear
(clothing) (3-3-3)
2 Arthur's magic sword (9)
4 Talk show host,
- - - Winfrey (5)
5 Pedantic person (7)
6 Eric - - -, *Monty Python*
star (4)
7 London art gallery (4)
11 Catapult (9)
12 Exciting experience (9)
14 Feeling of
great delight (3)
15 In proportion (3, 4)
18 Period of time (5)
19 Extinct bird (4)
20 Upper Thames (4)

The Biggest Crossword Book In The World

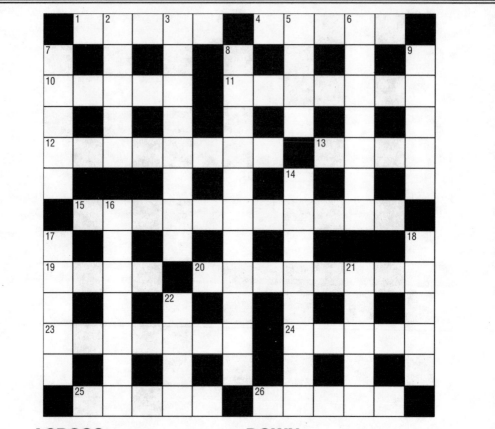

ACROSS

1 Aromatic herb (5)
4 Roadside accommodation (5)
10 Rely upon (5)
11 Gestures (7)
12 Least expensive (8)
13 Smoker's tube with small bowl (4)
15 Supply with board and lodging (11)
19 Practical joke (4)
20 Formal relationship (8)
23 Trade ban (7)
24 Drinker (5)
25 Clan (5)
26 Climb (5)

DOWN

2 Domestic building (5)
3 Figure of speech (8)
5 Cereal (4)
6 Self-admirer (7)
7 Goods kept for sale (5)
8 Soft, spongy sweet (11)
9 Paul - - -, Ex *Brookside* actor (5)
14 European sea (8)
16 Bedroom (7)
17 Small mammal (5)
18 Oyster's gem (5)
21 Asian country (5)
22 Pincered creature (4)

The Biggest Crossword Book In The World

ACROSS
1 Body spin in dancing (9)
8 Tube (4)
9 Yeoman (9)
10 Clement - - -, former British PM (6)
13 Distributor of goods (6)
15 Bedeck (5)
16 Eye shield (5)
17 Shrink in fear (5)
18 Rotate one end (5)
21 Chinese self-defence (3, 3)
22 Funeral car (6)
25 Trained fighter (9)
26 Extensive (4)
27 Staff (9)

DOWN
2 Static (5)
3 Less valuable parts of the carcass (5)
4 Deleted (6)
5 Shudder (6)
6 Golden plant (9)
7 Race official (7)
11 Evidence (9)
12 Soil (5)
14 Male relative (5)
16 Indispensably (7)
19 Jockey, - - - Carson (6)
20 Zandra - - -, fasion designer (6)
23 Grand Prix driver, - - - Prost (5)
24 Slant (5)

The Biggest Crossword Book In The World

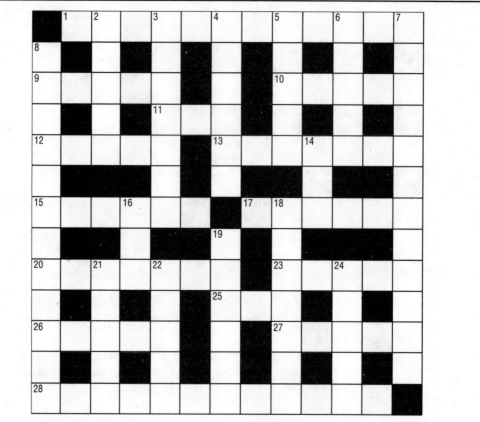

ACROSS

1 Unwelcoming (12)
9 Rowing team (5)
10 Member of the
weasel family (5)
11 Primate (3)
12 Make different (5)
13 Frank - - -, singer (7)
15 Chance to vote (6)
17 Baked - - - dessert (6)
20 Tanned skin (7)
23 Chocolate powder (5)
25 French word for 'yes' (3)
26 Honorary name (5)
27 Vanessa - - -,
TV host (5)
28 *Stir Crazy* actor (7,5)

DOWN

2 Dark period (5)
3 Canadian province (7)
4 Clergyman (6)
5 Mike - - -,
American boxer (5)
6 Upward thrust (5)
7 Fantastic show (12)
8 Formal word for
a pram (12)
14 Farmhouse cooker (3)
16 Rent out (3)
18 Satan (7)
19 Soil, earth (6)
21 Loft space (5)
22 Dog-like African
animal (5)
24 Large stringed
instrument (5)

The Biggest Crossword Book In The World

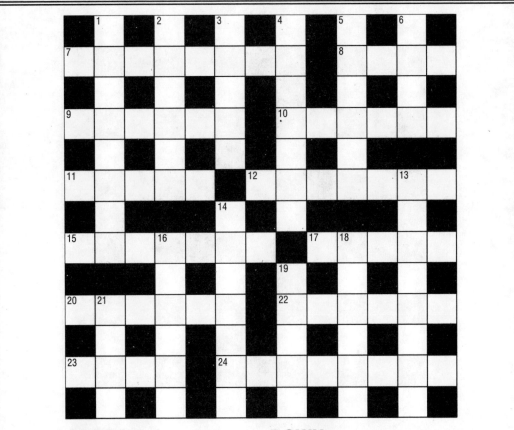

ACROSS

7 Small towns (8)
8 Silent acting (4)
9 Apparatus (6)
10 Substantial (6)
11 Cuban dictator,
- - - Castro (5)
12 Obvious (7)
15 Go down (7)
17 Pleasurable trip (5)
20 Zero (6)
22 Spider's trap (6)
23 Shawl (4)
24 Bee keeper (8)

DOWN

1 Generation (8)
2 Flatfish (6)
3 Correspond (5)
4 Road-making material (7)
5 Strong impression (6)
6 Give forth (4)
13 Balderdash (8)
14 In place of (7)
16 Baby swan (6)
18 Reddish-brown
hair colour (6)
19 Bitter, pungent (5)
21 Pale gem (4)

The Biggest Crossword Book In The World

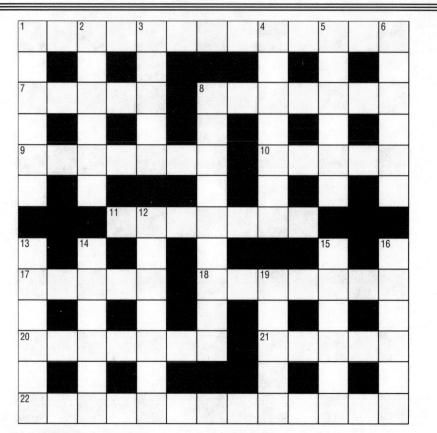

ACROSS

1 Fair grounds
   for action (13)
7 Detect a smell (5)
8 Strong desire (7)
9 From the sides (7)
10 Research deeply (5)
11 The art of Japanese
   flower arrangement (7)
17 Regal (5)
18 High-ranking naval
   officer (7)
20 Hand-thrown shell (7)
21 Princess of Wales (5)
22 Exploit for profit (13)

DOWN

1 Jolt (6)
2 Hockey-like game (6)
3 Deduce (5)
4 Owner of the lamp (7)
5 Hanging spike of
   frozen water (6)
6 Lump of gold ore (6)
8 Mark with festivities (9)
12 Irish county (7)
13 Disastrous (6)
14 London theatre (6)
15 Italian fashion
   designer (6)
16 Give satisfaction (6)
19 Newspapers,
   television etc. (5)

The Biggest Crossword Book In The World

ACROSS

1 Mix (4)
4 One or the other (6)
8 Find out (8)
9 Perfumed powder (4)
10 Take a break (5)
11 Silly (7)
13 Religious address (6)
15 Correspond (6)
17 Withdraw
   (from a deal) (4, 3)
19 Without restrictions (2, 3)
22 Quip (4)
23 Theoretical (8)
24 Cheddar or Stilton, eg (6)
25 Thin crisp biscuit (4)

DOWN

2 Two times (5)
3 Win back (7)
4 Resentment (4)
5 Small pasty (8)
6 Glorify (5)
7 Cupboard (6)
12 Protect against
   the cold (8)
14 Exhilarated (6)
16 Remove clothes (7)
18 Sailing boat (5)
20 Spanish island (5)
21 Salary (4)

The Biggest Crossword Book In The World

ACROSS

1 Spanish singer (5, 8)
7 European country (7)
8 Animal with a fox-like face (5)
9 Cry of pain! (4)
10 Capital of Finland (8)
12 Flavoured water ice (6)
14 Notice (6)
16 Draw near (8)
17 Bamboo stick (4)
20 Impression (5)
21 Infectious disease (7)
23 Soothing drug (13)

DOWN

1 Poke roughly (3)
2 Pale mauve (5)
3 American state (4)
4 Boring tool (6)
5 Huge (7)
6 Napkin (9)
8 Jockey, - - - Piggott (6)
9 Attack (9)
11 Indicate (6)
13 Exact copy (7)
15 Large prawns (6)
18 Book of maps (5)
19 Affront (4)
22 Honorary title (3)

The Biggest Crossword Book In The World

ACROSS
1 Diving platform (11)
9 Chief disciple (7)
10 Large hoisting device (5)
11 Cultivate (4)
12 Photo (8)
14 Monica - - -,
tennis player (5)
15 To such time as (5)
20 Comparative (8)
22 Hurt (4)
24 Scott's companion
to the South Pole (5)
25 Free time (7)
26 Bergerac actor (4, 7)

DOWN
2 Incense (7)
3 Small amount (4)
4 Scottish border town (6)
5 Person in place (8)
6 Arrive at (5)
7 Shooting area (5)
8 Molars (5)
13 Throw overboard (8)
16 Comprise (7)
17 Conclusive evidence (5)
18 Lightly built (6)
19 Doctrine (5)
21 Bingo-like game (5)
23 Mud from a river (4)

The Biggest Crossword Book In The World

ACROSS

1 Al Capone, eg (8)
5 Precious metal (4)
9 Ancestry (5)
10 Gambling resort,
- - - Carlo (5)
12 Demolish (5)
13 Yemen port (4)
15 Glared (6)
18 Allot (6)
20 Drunken revel (4)
23 Alarm (5)
24 Follows closely (5)
27 Enthusiastic (5)
28 Gaelic (4)
29 State robe (8)

DOWN

1 Sullen (4)
2 Midday (4)
3 Sedate (5)
4 Shameful (6)
6 Perpetrator (8)
7 Ass (6)
8 Foil, frustrate (6)
11 Ancient (3)
14 Originates (8)
16 Dozing (6)
17 Muslim temple (6)
19 Mouthwash (6)
21 Hair application (3)
22 Support, prop (5)
25 Sea-girt land (4)
26 Sodium chloride (4)

The Biggest Crossword Book In The World

ACROSS

5 Express verbally (5)
8 Fastest (8)
9 Habit (5)
10 Offended (8)
11 Vacant (5)
14 Do sums (3)
16 Victim, sufferer (6)
17 French impressionist painter (6)
18 Shy and modest (3)
20 Hysteria (5)
24 Hand and nail treatment (8)
25 Magnate (5)
26 Fleet of small vessels (8)
27 Audio recording machine (5)

DOWN

1 Cuttlefish (5)
2 Before all others (5)
3 Head? (5)
4 Go up (6)
6 Decorative item (8)
7 Mixed alcoholic drink (8)
12 Tube shaped pasta (8)
13 Mental view (8)
14 Crescent (3)
15 Dehydrated (3)
19 Soothsayer (6)
21 Breadth (5)
22 Suppress (5)
23 May 8th 1945 (1, 1, 3)

The Biggest Crossword Book In The World

ACROSS

7 Lovesong (6)
8 Eraser (6)
10 Majestic (7)
11 Light doughy cake (5)
12 Sourtasting (4)
13 Ronald Reagan's wife (5)
17 Padded quilt bed (5)
18 Mud (4)
22 Fourpenny piece (5)
23 Tool (7)
24 Motor racing competition (2, 4)
25 Cat-like (6)

DOWN

1 Extremely bad (7)
2 European country (7)
3 Adhesive sticker (5)
4 Tuft of grass (7)
5 Loathe, detest (5)
6 Salt container (5)
9 Religious building (9)
14 Seedless raisin (7)
15 Waterproof fabric (7)
16 Responded (7)
19 Supple (5)
20 Spacious (5)
21 Slanting edge (5)

The Biggest Crossword Book In The World

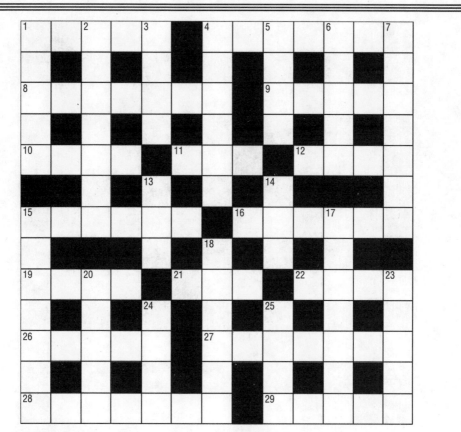

ACROSS
1 Sacred song (5)
4 Mentally accuse (7)
8 Having a liking for something, to some extent (7)
9 Sailing vessel (5)
10 French city (4)
11 A long way (3)
12 Scheme (4)
15 Powerful racing car (3, 3)
16 Defamation (6)
19 Short (skirt) (4)
21 Illness like a bad cold (3)
22 Understanding (4)
26 Bring up (5)
27 Maim (7)
28 Harrods boss, - - - Al Fayed (7)
29 Avarice, voracity (5)

DOWN
1 Part of the eye (5)
2 Heathrow, eg (7)
3 Principal (4)
4 Author, - - - Rushdie (6)
5 Breed of terrier (4)
6 Outdo (5)
7 Queen of the fairies (7)
13 Type of lettuce (3)
14 Devoured (3)
15 Dull, monotonous (7)
17 Wrestle (7)
18 Calm (6)
20 Cry of a horse (5)
23 Direction, tendency (5)
24 Microbe (4)
25 Wagner operas (4)

574

The Biggest Crossword Book In The World

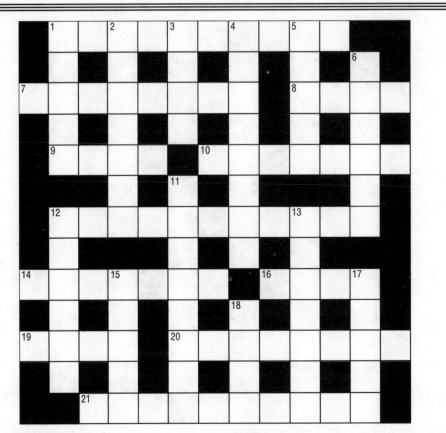

ACROSS

1 Mary - - -, decency campaigner (10)
7 Leading position (8)
8 Cart used for carrying heavy loads (4)
9 Mass of small bubbles (4)
10 Made different (7)
12 Impulse to steal things (11)
14 Unlawful (7)
16 Castle tower (4)
19 Ward off (4)
20 Badminton court boundary (8)
21 Modern (7-3)

DOWN

1 Harbour platform (5)
2 Ungrateful person (7)
3 Dutch cheese (4)
4 Previous partner (3, 5)
5 Move in a furtive manner (5)
6 Picturetaker (6)
11 The lost continent (8)
12 Murderer (6)
13 Provoked (7)
15 Type of duck (5)
17 Beatles' song, - - - *Lane* (5)
18 Abel's brother (4)

The Biggest Crossword Book In The World

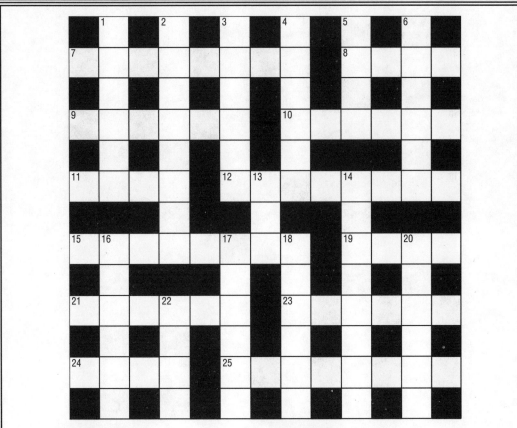

ACROSS

7 Chime used by visitors (8)
8 Italy's former currency unit (4)
9 Animal feed (6)
10 Famous London clock (3,3)
11 Ice-cream cornet (4)
12 Expand (8)
15 Former Queen (8)
19 Mountain goat (4)
21 Saunter (6)
23 Signal fire (6)
24 Sea mile (4)
25 Elegant, artistic (8)

DOWN

1 Balkan republic (6)
2 Slope (8)
3 Former Grand National winner (3, 3)
4 Worldwide (6)
5 Hit hard (4)
6 Terrible trial (6)
13 Spoon bender, - - - Geller (3)
14 Copied (8)
16 Mean, plan (6)
17 Have links (6)
18 Surprise attack (6)
20 Mass departure of people (6)
22 Vow (4)

The Biggest Crossword Book In The World

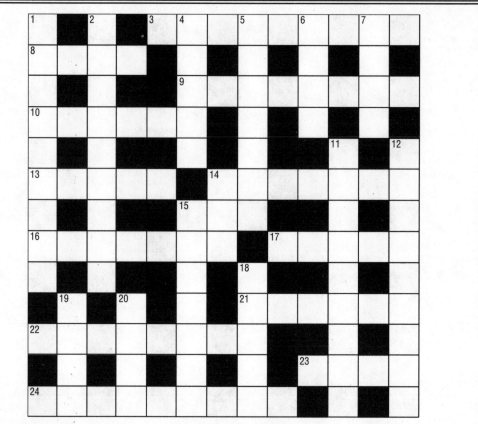

ACROSS

3 Broad avenue (9)
8 Narrow part of a violin (4)
9 Guest-house manager (8)
10 Earlier (6)
13 Put onto a surface (5)
14 Rustle (7)
15 State (3)
16 Set fire to (7)
17 Dividend (5)
21 Wine store (6)
22 Character from Mad Hatter's Tea Party (8)
23 Ballerina, - - - Pavlova (4)
24 Dog trained to find and bring in killed game (9)

DOWN

1 Russian Duchess (9)
2 Escort (9)
4 Yellow-orange colour (5)
5 Raffle (7)
6 Riverbank rodent (4)
7 Scottish dance (4)
11 Miserly person (9)
12 Top blanket (9)
14 Rotter (3)
15 Shut off (7)
18 Location (5)
19 Roused (4)
20 Actor, - - - Sharif (4)

The Biggest Crossword Book In The World

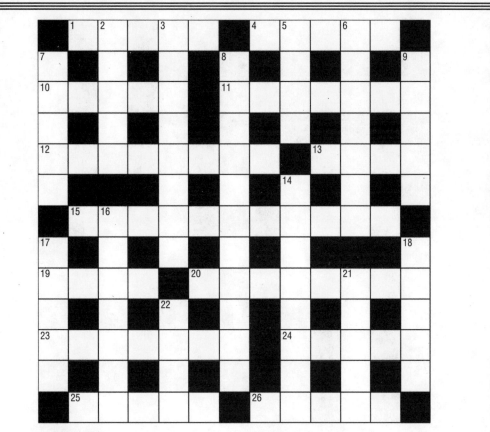

ACROSS

1 Underground room of a church (5)
4 Unfortunately (5)
10 Defective specimen (5)
11 American state, capital Montgomery (7)
12 Tory PM before Margarret Thatcher (3, 5)
13 Indian from Peru (4)
15 American singer (5, 6)
19 Put down noisily (4)
20 Wonderful (8)
23 Fail to complete (7)
24 Wicked person (5)
25 Female wren (5)
26 Pig's noise (5)

DOWN

2 Inflexible (5)
3 Went before (8)
5 Soccer pundit, - - - Hansen (4)
6 Novice driver (7)
7 Use a pen (5)
8 Competitor (11)
9 Scanner (5)
14 Protector (8)
16 Originate (7)
17 Common (5)
18 Muddle (5)
21 English county (5)
22 *East of - - -*, film (4)

The Biggest Crossword Book In The World

ACROSS

1 Take to court (9)
8 Rabbit fur (4)
9 Evaluation (9)
10 Grant authority to (6)
13 Part of a contract (6)
15 Greek A (5)
16 Odd number (5)
17 Blockade (5)
18 Swear (5)
21 Frontier (6)
22 Despicable person (6)
25 One of the Three
    Wise Men (9)
26 Fledgling's home (4)
27 Private
    coversation (4-1-4)

DOWN

2 Yorkshire racecourse (5)
3 Rub hard (5)
4 Tool (6)
5 Roof material (6)
6 Fat (9)
7 Practise of health and
    cleanliness (7)
11 Publicise (9)
12 Cavalry weapon (5)
14 Device generating
    intense beam (5)
16 Brother or sister (7)
19 Elegant (6)
20 Cover with bandages (6)
23 Perform (5)
24 Simple song (5)

The Biggest Crossword Book In The World

ACROSS

1 Horror film actor (5,7)
9 During (5)
10 Memorise (5)
11 Scarlet (3)
12 British airport (5)
13 Drastic (7)
15 Excite (6)
17 Bodyguard (6)
20 Cravat (7)
23 Michael - - -, tennis player (5)
25 Hawaiian garland (3)
26 Irish police force (5)
27 Polish (5)
28 Hallowe'en prank? (5, 2, 5)

DOWN

2 Throw out (5)
3 Endless (7)
4 London borough (6)
5 Break into parts (5)
6 Furious (5)
7 Fred Astaire's dancing partner (6.6)
8 The evening of January 5th (7, 5)
14 Move quickly (3)
16 Irritate (3)
18 Cutting tooth (7)
19 Bank employee (6)
21 Small Welsh dog (5)
22 Bless (5)
24 Scent (5)

The Biggest Crossword Book In The World

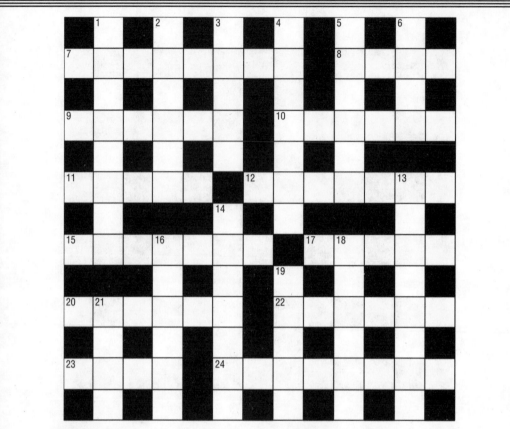

ACROSS

7 Member of the public (8)
8 Aquarium fish (4)
9 Substance made into honey (6)
10 **Former** US Vice President (2, 4)
11 Stone landmark (5)
12 Native of Newcastle? (7)
15 John - - -, author (2, 5)
17 Country divided into North and South (5)
20 Sprightly (6)
22 Prize draw (6)
23 Borrowed sum (4)
24 Ted Danson film (4, 4)

DOWN

1 Release (8)
2 Female relative (6)
3 Spun thread (5)
4 Worked (dough) (7)
5 Paying guest (6)
6 Over a great distance (4)
13 Impractical person (8)
14 Well-behaved (7)
16 Capital of New York state (6)
18 Insult (6)
19 Bread bin (5)
21 Logo (4)

The Biggest Crossword Book In The World

ACROSS

1 British actress (5, 8)
7 Pause mark (5)
8 Straight course (7)
9 Chose (7)
10 Garden toy (5)
11 Aromatic herb used in cooking (7)
17 Come clean (3, 2)
18 Insult (7)
20 Spotted feline (7)
21 Large gimlet (5)
22 *The Good Life* actress (8,5)

DOWN

1 Horse rider (6)
2 Count (6)
3 Breadmaking ingredient (5)
4 Simon - - -, *Coronation Street* actor (7)
5 Source (6)
6 Vigour, vim (6)
8 Minder (9)
12 Archangel (7)
13 Handmade cigarette (4-2)
14 Hereditary (6)
15 *Jungle Book* character (6)
16 Carbohydrate (6)
19 Thermos (5)

The Biggest Crossword Book In The World

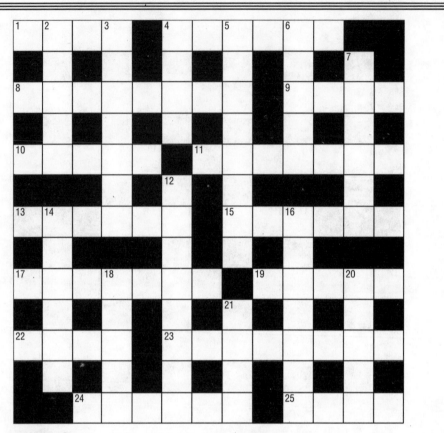

ACROSS

1 Snatch (4)
4 Limb (6)
8 Table showing months of the year (8)
9 Destroy (4)
10 Sober (5)
11 Not on either side (7)
13 Batman's city (6)
15 High respect (6)
17 Pathetic (7)
19 Resin (5)
22 Dissolve, thaw (4)
23 Evita? (3, 5)
24 Without charge (6)
25 Sweet, pretty (4)

DOWN

2 Sunday joint (5)
3 Defect, stain (7)
4 Created (4)
5 Killer (8)
6 Wading bird (5)
7 Long critical outburst (6)
12 Cheeky, pert (8)
14 Actor, - - - Tobias (6)
16 Storm (7)
18 Lay to rest (5)
20 Wear away (5)
21 Go by (4)

The Biggest Crossword Book In The World

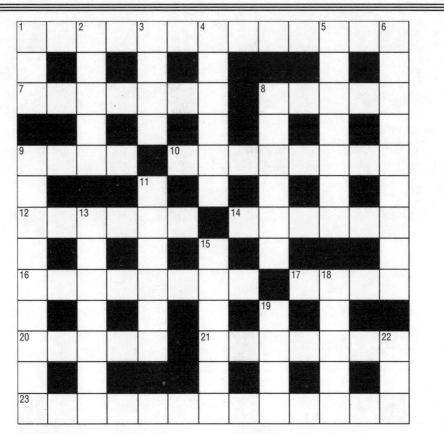

ACROSS

1 Distance around a circle (13)
7 Father and son actors, Kirk and Michael (7)
8 Dish (5)
9 Large water jug (4)
10 Souvenir, memento (8)
12 Confirm (6)
14 Something to eat (6)
16 Shrewdish old woman (8)
17 Adam's second son (4)
20 Empty, senseless (5)
21 Firearm (7)
23 Kind person (4, 9)

DOWN

1 Peace group (inits)
2 Waken (5)
3 Hideous (4)
4 Make secure (6)
5 Canadian waterfall (7)
6 Basic (9)
8 Doll controlled by strings (6)
9 Human? (9)
11 Bureau (6)
13 Twister (7)
15 Soothing ointment (6)
18 Philistine (5)
19 Fall heavily (4)
22 Holy lady (3)

The Biggest Crossword Book In The World

ACROSS
1 Chance event (11)
9 Atrocity (7)
10 Spicy meal (5)
11 Chinese dog? (4)
12 Nursing institution (8)
14 Carouse (5)
15 Proficient (5)
20 Group of spectators (8)
22 Flowing garment (4)
24 Terrible (5)
25 Police series featuring Reg Hollis (3, 4)
26 US naval base (5, 6)

DOWN
2 Result (7)
3 *ER* actor, - - - Wyle (4)
4 Coldest part of a refrigerator (6)
5 Caper, fling (8)
6 Unit of gem weight (5)
7 Sofa (5)
8 Pedalled transport (5)
13 Gem dealer (8)
16 Condition (7)
17 Large bright parrot (5)
18 Type of whisky (6)
19 British athlete, - - - Holmes (5)
21 Daniel - - -, author (5)
23 Split, rip (4)

THE
SOLUTIONS

1

```
O L W T   A M O N G
R H O D E S I A   E U
A L D R   A D M I T
T E L E G R A M   S
E Y E D   O C E A N
  D I   L E A   I N
H O A R S E   M U N I C H
  R R   T R Y   E E
A M B I T   E E S   S
  O T   T A I L B A C K
D U M A S   S O X   I
  S T   L O O P H O L E
S E V E R   N E N R
```

2

```
S   L A     M A   T
T R E A T Y   D A G G E R
E   A H A   U R   U
A C T I O N S   D W E L L
L   H S S   S L   E Y
T R E X   R I G I D
H R   J S   N D   U
  Q U O T A   M I S T
N A   K A   G L   T
U N D U E   N U R T U R E
R U   B T   E T   R
S A L O O N   S E V E R E
E   T X     T D D
```

3

```
E J E C T   H E C T A R E
L M   I   E U   B R
A L A D D I N   F R A M E
N N   Y   M F   S C
D U A L   R A P   Z E S T
    T   J N S     E
A M E L I A   P O I S E D
L   G   B S   T
G E N T   B A P   P U T T
E   O S   R T   T E
B U R S T   B R I T T L E
R M   Y   E N E N
A M A T E U R   T A R R Y
```

4

```
  A D V A N T A G E S
  F E E L P   P
O I N T M E N T   S P U N
  R E D H O   N
  E A R N   C O M M E N T
  A P U   E
  W I N N I N G P O S T
  E N H R
E A R R I N G   R I P E
V A A C F   G
M E L T   C O L L I E R Y
R I L A C E
  G O V E R N M E N T
```

5

```
  R D U E T   S
R E B E L L E D   S I T E
  G L S   I A A
B I S E C T   S C R I B E
  N G E O   L
T A T A   R E N O W N E D
  T R E
O F F E N D E R   D A U B
  E U E D N
R E N T A L   G U I N E A
  L I C A N V
C E L L   E A R L G R E Y
  R T T D S N
```

6

```
A B   A S H B L O N D E
B O U T   W A G R
Y L   E N L A R G E D
S O L A C E   L E W
S D T O S G
I V O R Y   P O T H O L E
N Z   S I N M N
I N E X A C T   A D E P T
A R R R T L
  A G O   E M P I R E
I L L I N O I S   M M
O L G I   F E T A
W E L L B E I N G S N
```

7

```
  A S L E F   F R A I L
F M N M I M R
J O I S T   A S T R I D E
O R W R E T V
R A K E I T I N   M A T E
D N A T T L
  L E V E L H E A D E D
A M D C W E
F L E X   M A G N E T I C
F R S R Y W L
I N G R A T E   O M A H A
X E G Y W I T
  A D H O C   C L I N K
```

8

```
R O A D B L O C K   C   S
  B E A R   B R O W
P E R P E T U A L   O   I
  S O T V C N
B E E T L E   A C C O R D
  R I R A T E D L
E N A C T     C H I M E
A D H A N O I L
R U I N E D   C L U E D O
M C M E T I
A A M I L L S T O N E
R O T A R O E G
K E C E N T U R I O N
```

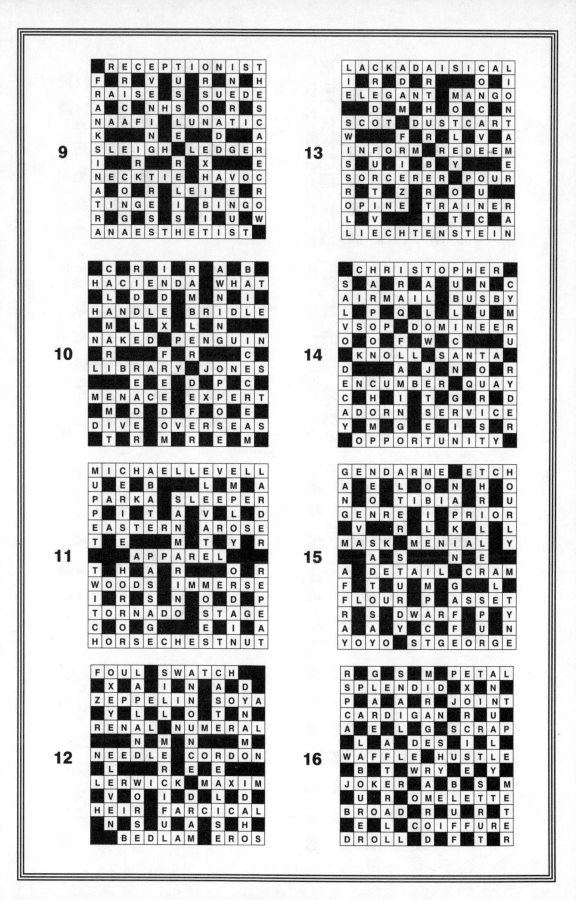

17

```
A   O   S       A   C   N
B A F F L E   A R C A D E
Y   F   O   B   I   B   P
S L I P P E R   Z E B R A
M   C   E   I   O   Y   L
A D E N   A G O N Y
L   R   I   A   A   R   S
        S T U D S   D E C K
E   E   A   I   U   L   I
R I V A L   E A R H A R T
A   E   I   R   B   P   T
S U N D A E   D A M S E L
E   T   N       N   E   E
```

18

```
B A R M Y   D E C A Y E D
L   E   I   O   E   E
E N T I T L E   D E N I M
N   I   I   P   Y   T   O
D A R N   Q P R   F L A T
    E   G   E   P   E
A N D R E W   F R I E N D
D   M   R   Y   D
M I C K   O A F   M I L D
I   O   M   G   J   T   I
R U M M Y   T U I T I O N
E   M   T   A   L   O   K
R O A D H O G   T A N G Y
```

19

```
  H E A D M A S T E R
  E   N   E   U   A   T
A N N A F O R D   S A I L
  N   R   W   D   E   N
  A R C H   R E C L U S E
  H   A   N       E
C R Y S T A L B A L L
U   H   Y   G
P R O B L E M   J O A N
  A   E   R   P   N   U
E T N A   T H E B I R D S
  E   N   O   A   S   G
  J O H N C L E E S E
```

20

```
  P   R   F   A   O   S
D E T A I L E D   G N A T
  D   S   O   J   L   L
P A M P E R   U S E F U L
  L   U   I   S       T
F O N T   N O T I F I E D
  I   I   I   I
T O W N H A L L   G O S H
  B   V   A   U   E
A L C O V E   P I R A T E
  O   M   N   T   I   T
R N L I   G R O U N D E D
  G   T   E   P   E   R
```

21

```
O   I   A R T H R I T I S
F E N D   E   A   R   D
F   D   B O R R O W E D
T R O U P E   M   N   A
H   N   L   F   R   E
E L E G Y   G U N N E L L
P   S   E E L   M   S
E M I N E N T   G R A C E
G   A   F   B   I   W
  C   A   O   L A U N C H
P R E S E R V E   D   E
  O   I   C   S   T E A R
S P E A K E A S Y   R   E
```

22

```
  S Y N O D   D R E A D
N   I   P   B   A   V   P
A V E R T   R I S S O L E
S   L   I   I   P   C   P
A B D I C A T E   L A D Y
L       I   T   H   D   S
  P A R A C E T A M O L
W   L   N   K   R       B
O P A L   C L E A N S E R
G   B   E   A   S   L   E
A B A N D O N   S N I D E
N   M   G   D   E   G   D
  W A V E R   I D I O T
```

23

```
A C T I V A T E D   C   T
  R   N   R   N   Y O G A
D A R T B O A R D   R   L
  Z   E   U   I   N   L
D E B R I S   C R A F T Y
  L   D E L H I   L   H
P R O B E       P H O T O
U   W   A M P L E   U
R E A L L Y   E N E R G Y
C   F   O   A   L   A
E   U   S P A G H E T T I
L E S S   I   U   C   E
L   E   S C I E N T I S T
```

24

```
  C H E D D A R G O R G E
A   A   I   L   Y   E   X
S W I L L   P   P E A C E
G   T   E R A   S   C   R
O P I U M   C R Y P T I C
O   M   A   I       I
D U R B A N   T E N N I S
A   U   G   S       E
S E T T L E R   T H R O B
G   A   U   A X E   O   I
O N I O N   H   F L A N K
L   L   A   A   A   S   E
D I S C R I M I N A T E
```

25

```
  G   P   S   A   T   U
F U L L S T O P   H U N G
  L   A   A   P   A   D
F L I G H T   O P T I O N
  I   U   E   I   C
A B B E Y   A N C H O V Y
  L       J   T       I
L E A R N E R   D I T C H
      O   Z   N   N   I
V O Y A G E   S P H I N X
  H   R   B   P   A   I
L I F E   E S C A L A T E
  O   D   L   C   E   Y
```

26

```
B R E C O N B E A C O N S
E   V   M     V   R   H
S T O N E   F R E D D I E
I   L   G   R   E   K
D E V I A T E   A M A Z E
E   E     I   G   L   L
      S N I G G E R
R   R   O   H     G   C
A G E N T   T O R P E D O
N   N   A   E   O   M   H
C L O B B E R   T R I K E
I   W   L       O   N   R
D I N N E R S E R V I C E
```

27

```
C A R D   D E P A R T
  M   I   O   R   O   E
M O N G O O S E   M Y N A
  U   N   R   A   E   R
B R U I N   A C R O B A T
  T   R   H       G
G R O Y N E   E N A M E L
  O   P   P   R   I
W A L K O U T   A L L O T
  C   E   L   D   M   D
T H I N   S K E L E T O N
  E   D   E   A   N   U
  L O N D O N   T O R N
```

28

```
E M I L I O E S T E V E Z
R   N   T   N     E   E
R A N G E R S   F A R C E
  E   M   U   A   T   B
P E R M   C R O U P I E R
E   S   E   C   G   U
P O T I O N   B E L O N G
R   H   P   S   T   G
E L E P H A N T   G A M E
R   B   I   I   D   L
O L I V E   P R E C I S E
N   L     E   R   G   V
I N L A N D R E V E N U E
```

29

```
P A N D E M O N I U M
R   N   E   E   O   N   B
A N T E N N A   A L I B I
J   W   Y   G   H   T   R
A P E X   P R O S P E C T
H   R   G   E   A   H
  S P O O L   B R O W N
D       V   E   K   H   H
I N C R E A S E   S I R E
V   A   R   T   B   T   A
A P R O N   E Q U A T O R
N   V   O   E   R   L   D
  R E P R I M A N D E D
```

30

```
G O L D F I S H   C R O W
R   A   I   I   S   E   A
I   T   L Y C R A   M   N
T H E F T   K   W E I R D
  A   H   L   Y   N   E
L Y N X   D E P E N D   R
  A   A   A   R   E
W   R E G R E T   G R A B
E   R   A   X   S   T
A W A I T   O   W H E E L
L   T   H E D G E   C   O
T   O   A   U   D   H   R
H O R N   A S T E R O I D
```

31

```
P   P   S   A   B H A J I
I N A C T I V E   U   U
T   P   A   E   B L A N K
T R A M L I N E   A   K
A   W   L   U   R H Y M E
  S   R   S E T   O   A
A C K A C K   U T O P I A
  H   I   Y A P   P   L
M E A N T   G   O   D   A
  D   C   L E A F L E T S
K U D O S   O   F   C   K
  L   A   A L C A P O N E
D E B T S   D   L   R   W
```

32

```
A   G   C       E   M   K
P S Y C H O   U N E A S E
O   M   A   A   H   J   A
S U N K I N G   A B O R T
T   A   R   R   N   R   S
L O S T   M E R C Y
E   T   B   E   E   R   T
      P L E A T   S O A R
A   S   A   B   M   T   U
M O W E R   L E I S U R E
I   A   N   E   X   N   M
S I M M E R   B U D D H A
S   P   Y       P   A   N
```

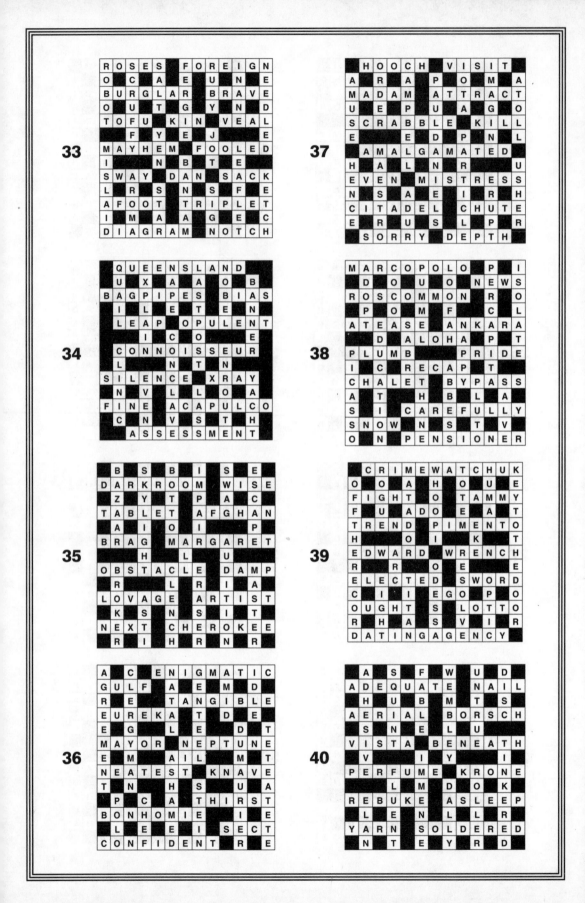

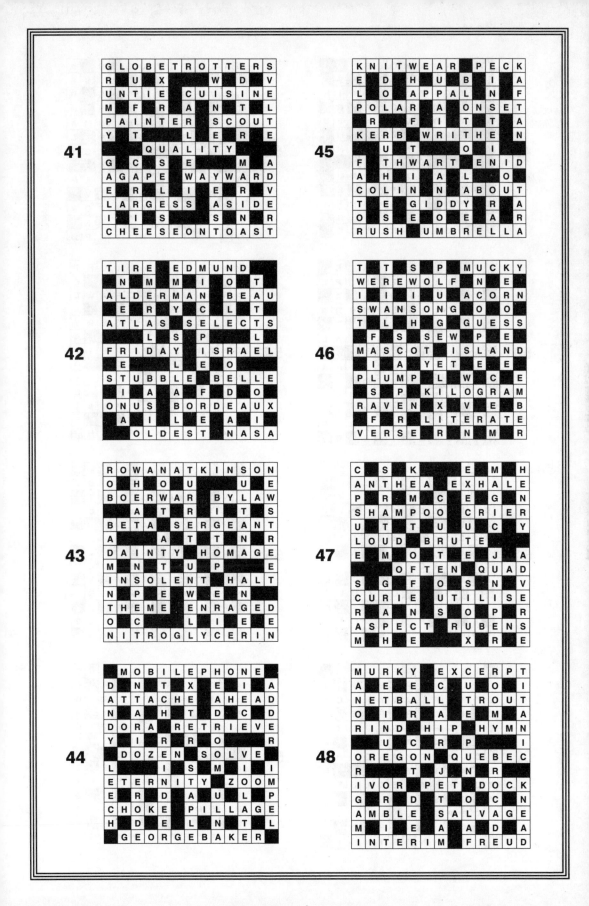

49

```
W H I T E H O U S E
R   R   D   B   W   S
B A R O N E S S   O A T H
T   N   N   O   R   R
H O A X   G L A N C E D
    G   P   E       W
  T H E P E N T A G O N
  R   D   E       E
P E R P L E X   N O R M
M   A   S   F   L   E
B O R N   T R A V O L T A
R   T   A   I   G   R
  R O L L S R O Y C E
```

50

```
  F   K   I   P   K   S
J U L I E N N E   H O P E
  T   N   T   R   A   A
W I G G L E   S E N O R A
  L   S   N   I       T
W E P T   D I A G O N A L
  O       C       N
A M U N D S E N   L I R A
  U       H   U   O   A
R E F U S E   G R O U N D
  S   R   A   G   K   T
S L I D   T E E T E R E D
  I   U   H   T   R   D
```

51

```
A   M   F R I A R T U C K
S E R F   E   L   U   O
S   S     A D M I R I N G
U P H O L D   A   N   Y
R   U   Y   N   H   S
A U D I T   M A R G A T E
N   S   S E C   R   C
C R O U T O N   F E M U R
E   N   J   O   O   E
  T   G O   C Y G N E T
P A R A Q U A T   I   A
  C   I   R   E   S C A R
F O R T U N A T E   A   Y
```

52

```
  T E X A S   F O Y E R
M   L   I   P   M   P   T
O F F E R   A V A R I C E
O   I   C   S   R   S   E
C O N G R E S S   P O E T
H   A   T   I   D   H
  C L I F F H A N G E R
S   A   T   E   N       M
T U R F   A B S O L U T E
A   G   S   U   C   N   R
S C E P T I C   E M I L Y
H   S   I   K   N   O   L
  U T U R N   S T U N T
```

53

```
D I L I G E N C E   H   A
  M   N   X   R   H U S S
G A T E S H E A D   G   P
  G   P   O   T   H   H
P E S T E R   E N I G M A
  E   S T A R E   R   L
B I G G S       E X A C T
A   R   A P H I D   N
B Y E B Y E   S Y S T E M
Y   G   T   O   H   V
G   A   W I M B L E D O N
R A T E   T   L   K
O   E   T E R R I F I E D
```

54

```
  A F T E R T H O U G H T
A   R   V   E   C   R   E
S T A V E   R   C R A W L
S   U   R U E   U   Z   L
A D D L E   S U R G E R Y
S       S   A   O   A
S H A N T Y   P U T R I D
I   I   A   N       D
N U C L E U S   C O R G I
A   L   X   T O O   U   C
T A I N T   H   V A L E T
E   F   R   M   E   S
D A F T A S A B R U S H
```

55

```
  J   I   G E   E   T
N U M B E R E D   S O U L
  V   E   A   U   K   T
B E I R U T   C L I Q U E
  N   I   E   A   M
D I N A R   O T T O M A N
  L   L   G   E   L
D E S S E R T   S C O L D
    O   E   T   A   S
N O R M A N   W A R H O L
P   B   A   I   T   U
L E E R   D A N I E L L E
  N   E   E   E   L   S
```

56

```
T Y R A N N O S A U R U S
A   O   I       B   A   E
B A T O N   A S S U R E D
A   U   T   T   T   I   U
R A N C H E R   A R T I C
D   D   O   I   Y   E
      C H I C A N E
A   M   A   I       F   O
M O O D Y   O R D E R L Y
I   U   W   U   E   I   S
D I S M I S S   I N G O T
S   S   R   G   H   E
T H E T E R M I N A T O R
```

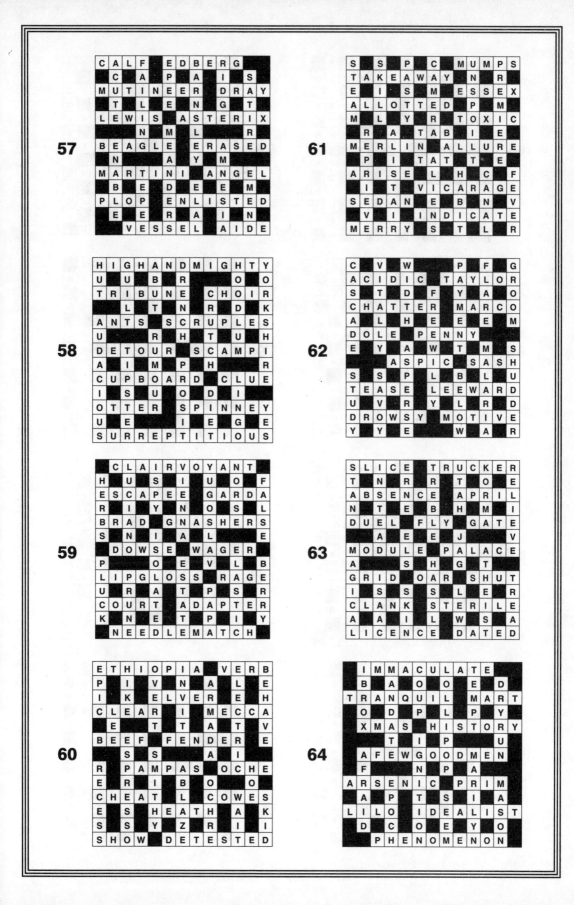

65

```
  O T A B E A
S T R A D D L E   V O T E
  T N R A E T
G A N D H I   T H R E A D
  W O F E I
H A L O   T O N Y B E N N
    R F R
D E D I C A T E   O N Y X
  U S X W O
P R E A C H   E U B A N K
  O C R M E D
S P A T   A L P H A B E T
  E S M T T R
```

66

```
O   I   S A L I S B U R Y
B O N D   L   D E   E
V   T   T R I A N G L E
I G U A N A   O D Y
O   I R T   J   D
U N T I L   D I S P U T E
S   I   R O C   D C
L O O K O U T   P R I M E
Y   N M B D I
  L R M   A C C E P T
H A Y S T A C K   N F
  V V G E   E C R U
R A S P B E R R Y   H L
```

67

```
  E N D O W   D R E A M
A E V   M E D   C
F O R G E   A L I B A B A
T V R S N M M
E X E R C I S E   W A D E
R A P E N O
M O N S T R O S I T Y
A L T O T A
B R I G   A D D I T I O N
Y V S U M N D
S C I A T I C   A W A R E
S E U E T P S
  C R U D E   H E F T Y
```

68

```
P A V A R O T T I   D   I
  L S B I   K E E N   S E
C O R P U L E N T   S   E
  N E I   G   P R
E G G N O G   L A M E N T
  E   S E W E R   R I
S O N I C       G H A N A
U E   A D I E U   D
F U R O R E   R E F O R M
F A   F R L U
O L   B A G A T E L L E
L Y L E   M N E E
K Y   H E A D S T A R T
```

69

```
  I R V I N G B E R L I N
I E C L X E I
N A I V E   A   T U N I C
T G   B E N   O I O
E R N I E   C O L O N E L
R R E U E
M A N A G E   A T T A C K
I I L Y I
T R A M P L E   P L A I D
T P O G B H L M
E X P E L   A   O U I J A
N L K C O V N
T H E L A D Y I N R E D
```

70

```
R L T T C T
A U D A C I T Y   R U I N
S R G N U D
T H R I C E   W A S H E R
H A R A O
N O R T H   A L D E N T E
U U P D R
P R I M A R Y   L O G I C
I O S B B
N E C T A R   C H E R U B
D T A R N
C A N E   T E E T O T A L
M A W N L
```

71

```
S P I K E M I L L I G A N
U N R A L O
L A D L E   T A M B O U R
L I C A P V M
E R R A T I C   O P E R A
N A T O S L
    S A L I E N T
A H M C C H
G R A D E   I N S P I R E
R R N A L R A
E R O S I O N   I N C U R
E L T N L T
D A D D Y L O N G L E G S
```

72

```
H Y D E   M O Y L E S
O N O E A R
B U L G A R I A   G R E W
T R E R L V
S H E A F   I N H E R I T
V T I V
B R E E Z E   N I P P E R
E L G R
U P D A T E D   J A S O N
O R T R L R
B R I E   E R I C I D L E
T N X F N O
M A N T L E   E S P Y
```

73

```
G L E N D A J A C K S O N
I N . I . A . . . N . . E
N A T U R A L . Y O U N G
. . E . T . O . E . G . L
G E R M . E P I L O G U E
O . . I . Y . L . L . . C
L A R Y N X . M O M E N T
D . A . V . A . W . . . E
E S T R A N G E . R E E D
N . R . D . A . T . V . .
E V A D E . S T A T I O N
Y . C . . . S . L . T . O
E L E C T R I C C H A I R
```

74

```
. M O R T A R B O A R D .
I . D . A . O . L . I . P
R A D I C A L . D I N E R
I . B . T . L . F . G . O
S I A M . W E L L T O D O
H . L . C . D . A . . . F
. G L O R Y . S M O K E .
C . . I . S . E . N . J .
O V E R C O M E . R U D E
R . M . H . O . A . C . N
F E A S T . O I L S K I N
U . I . O . T . E . L . Y
. A L A N W H I C K E R .
```

75

```
T W I T C H E R . T A N G
E . R . O . N . H . L . E
E . A . W I T T Y . T . N
M O N T E . I . B L E A T
. R . R . R . R . R . L .
A B E L . V E N I C E . .
. L . G . . . D . . G . .
B . E Q U A T E . C O S Y
U . V . I . R . T . . U .
B O A S T . A . H Y E N A
B . T . A B U S E . A . W
L . O . R . M . R . C . O
E Z R A . T A J M A H A L
```

76

```
T . V . F . G . D E U C E
E L I G I B L E . B . L .
A . G . N . O . D E L A Y
C H I V A L R Y . N . P .
H . L . L . I . P E T T Y
. C . A . S A S . Z . R .
B O U N C E . L E E W A Y
. M . A . E L Y . R . P .
V A U L T . A . S . E . U
. T . Y . L I N E S M A N
T O A S T . D . E . B . I
. S . E . G O L D L E A F
B E N D Y . N . Y . D . Y
```

77

```
E . B . E . . D . H . . Y
S T E A D Y . G R E A S E
C . L . G . R . E . L . A
A G I T A T E . D U V E T
P . E . R . Q . G . E . S
E N V Y . Q U E E R . . .
D . C . I . R . D . D . D
. . G R A S S . G O N E .
B . C . U . I . B . N . N
L I L A C . T A R R A N T
U . O . I . E . E . T . I
R E G G A E . F A M O U S
T . S . L . . K . R . . T
```

78

```
W E E D Y . A L T E R E D
O . N . O . S . A . A . A
M I S E R L Y . L U N D Y
E . N . K . L . E . G . T
N E A T . R U M . W E A R
. . R . P . M . T . . . I
S W E D E N . M O C K U P
O . . G . C . R . E . . .
L A S H . A U K . C E R T
I . H . S . R . S . P . A
C H A M P . T H E R M O S
I . M . U . L . T . U . .
T U E S D A Y . T U M M Y
```

79

```
. G A B Y R O S L I N . .
. O . A . E . T . M . V .
F R A G M E N T . P R A M
. G . H . L . R . L . C .
. E D D Y . C O P Y C A T
. . . A . O . P . . . N .
. E N D O R S E M E N T .
. A . . N . Z . D . . . .
C R O W B A R . S I N G .
. W . R . M . J . F . U .
M I N I . E X A M I N E D
. G . T . N . N . C . S .
. S E T T L E M E N T . .
```

80

```
. P . C . B . C . S . I .
T H O R O U G H . K E M P
. R . I . R . A . I . P .
N A T T E R . S Y M B O L
. S . E . O . T . . . S .
J E E R . W R E S T L E D
. I . . . U . . . E . . .
P L E A S A N T . N E S S
. A . . . C . O . T . T .
A U F A I T . G O A L I E
. R . P . U . G . C . T .
Z E U S . A L L B L A C K
. L . E . L . E . E . H .
```

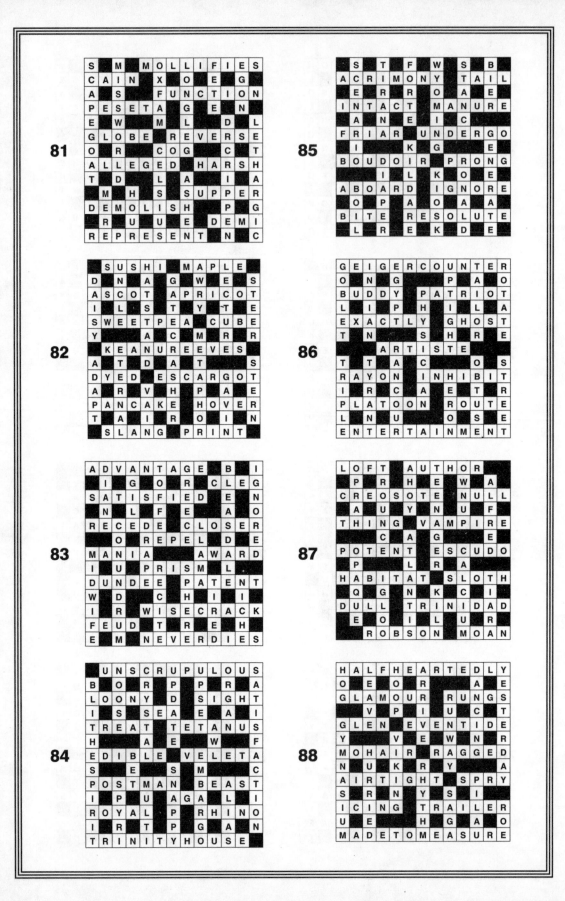

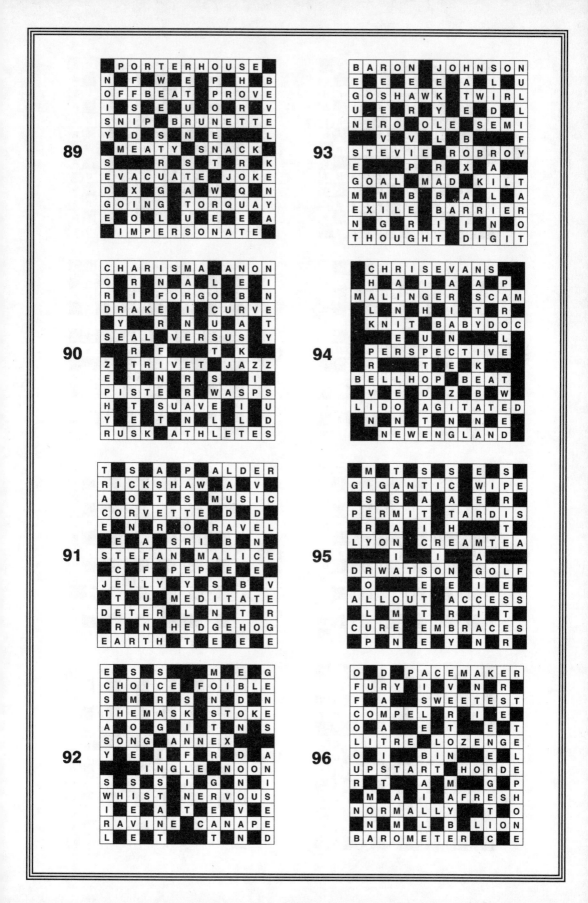

89

90

91

92

93

94

95

96

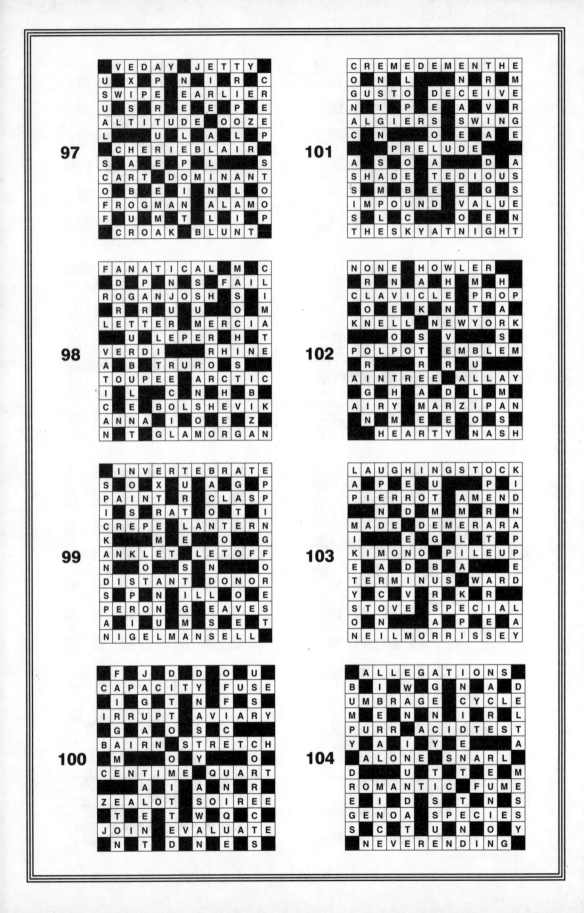

97

98

99

100

101

102

103

104

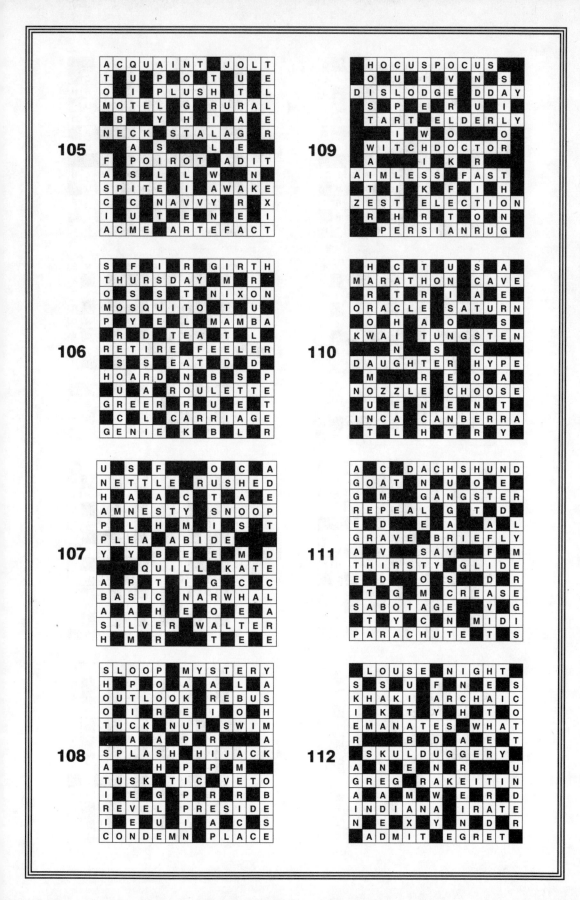

105

```
A C Q U A I N T   J O L T
T   U   P   O   T   U   E
O   I   P L U S H   T   L
M O T E L   G   R U R A L
  B   Y   H   I   A   E
N E C K   S T A L A G   R
  A   S       L   E
F   P O I R O T   A D I T
A   S   L   L   W   N
S P I T E   I   A W A K E
C   C   N A V V Y   R   X
I   U   T   E   N   E   I
A C M E   A R T E F A C T
```

106

```
S   F   I   R   G I R T H
T H U R S D A Y   M   R
O   S   S T   N I X O N
M O S Q U I T O   T   U
P   Y   E   L   M A M B A
  R   D   T E A   T   L
R E T I R E   F E E L E R
  S   S   E A T   D   D
H O A R D   N   B   S   P
  U   A   R O U L E T T E
G R E E R   R   U   E   T
  C   L   C A R R I A G E
G E N I E   K   B   L   R
```

107

```
U   S   F       O   C   A
N E T T L E   R U S H E D
H   A   A   C   T   A   E
A M N E S T Y   S N O O P
P   L   H   M   I   S   T
P L E A   A B I D E
Y   Y   B   E   E   M   D
      Q U I L L   K A T E
A   P   T   I   G   C   C
B A S I C   N A R W H A L
A   A   H   E   O   E   A
S I L V E R   W A L T E R
H   M   R       T   E   E
```

108

```
S L O O P   M Y S T E R Y
H   P   O   A   A   L   A
O U T L O O K   R E B U S
O   I   R   E   I   O   H
T U C K   N U T   S W I M
    A   A   P   R   A
S P L A S H   H I J A C K
A   H   P   P   P   M
T U S K   T I C   V E T O
I   E   G   P   R   R   B
R E V E L   P R E S I D E
I   E   U   I   A   C   S
C O N D E M N   P L A C E
```

109

```
  H O C U S P O C U S
  O   U   I   V   N   S
D I S L O D G E   D D A Y
  S   P   E   R   U   I
  T A R T   E L D E R L Y
      I   W   O   O
  W I T C H D O C T O R
  A   I   K   R
A I M L E S S   F A S T
Z   I   K   F   I   H
Z E S T   E L E C T I O N
R   H   R   T   O   N
  P E R S I A N R U G
```

110

```
  H   C   T   U   S   A
M A R A T H O N   C A V E
  R   T   R   I   A   E
O R A C L E   S A T U R N
  O   H   A   O   S
K W A I   T U N G S T E N
  N   S   S   C
D A U G H T E R   H Y P E
  M   R   E   O   A
N O Z Z L E   C H O O S E
  U   E   N   E   N   T
I N C A   C A N B E R R A
  T   L   H   T   R   Y
```

111

```
A   C   D A C H S H U N D
G O A T   N   U   O   E
G   M   G A N G S T E R
R E P E A L   G   T   D
E   D   E   A   A   L
G R A V E   B R I E F L Y
A   V   S A Y   F   M
T H I R S T Y   G L I D E
E   D   O   S   D   R
  T   G   M   C R E A S E
S A B O T A G E   V   G
  T   Y   C   N   M I D I
P A R A C H U T E   T   S
```

112

```
  L O U S E   N I G H T
S   S   U   F   N   E   S
K H A K I   A R C H A I C
I   K   T   Y   H   T   O
E M A N A T E S   W H A T
R   B   D   A   E   T
  S K U L D U G G E R Y
A   N   E   N   R   U
G R E G   R A K E I T I N
A   A   M   W   E   R   D
I N D I A N A   I R A T E
N   E   X   Y   N   D   R
  A D M I T   E G R E T
```

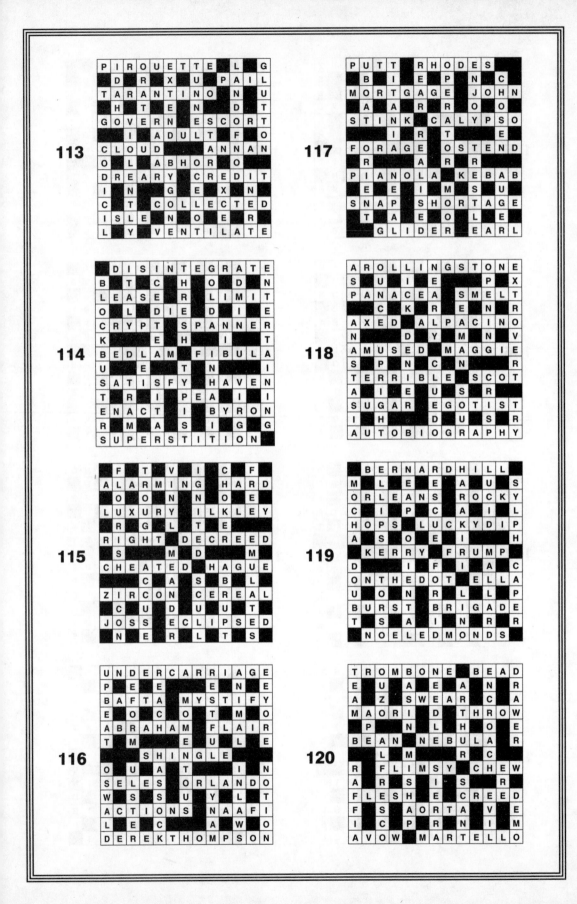

113

117

114

118

115

119

116

120

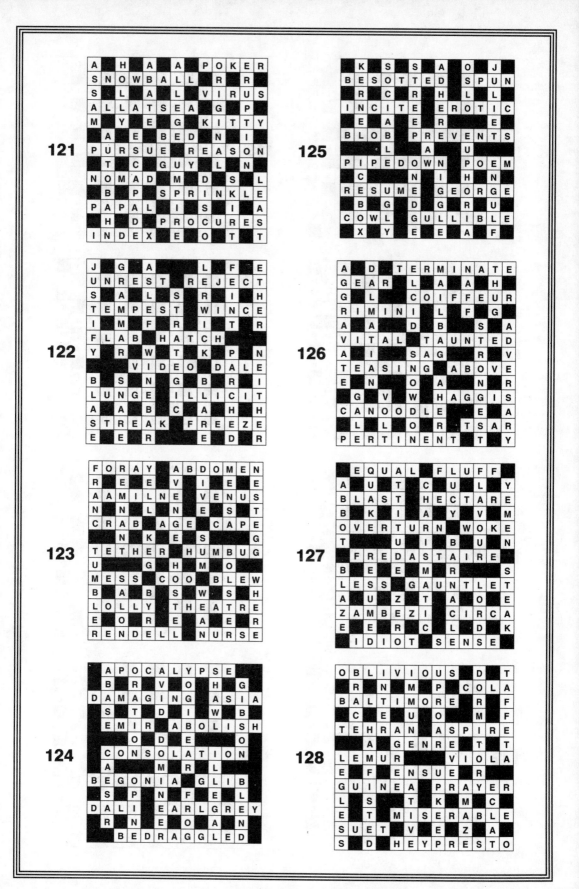

121

A	H	A		A		P	O	K	E	R
S	N	O	W	B	A	L	L		R		R
S		L		A		L		V	I	R	U	S
A	L	L	A	T	S	E	A		G		P
M		Y		E		G		K	I	T	T	Y
	A		E		B	E	D		N		I
P	U	R	S	U	E		R	E	A	S	O	N
	T		C		G	U	Y		L		N
N	O	M	A	D		M		D		S		L
	B		P		S	P	R	I	N	K	L	E
P	A	P	A	L		I		S		I		A
	H		D		P	R	O	C	U	R	E	S
I	N	D	E	X		E		O		T		T

125

K		S		S		A		O		J
B	E	S	O	T	T	E	D		S	P	U	N
	R		C		R		H		L		L
I	N	C	I	T	E		E	R	O	T	I	C
	E		A		E		R			E
B	L	O	B		P	R	E	V	E	N	T	S
	L			A		U
P	I	P	E	D	O	W	N		P	O	E	M
	C		N		I		H		N
R	E	S	U	M	E		G	E	O	R	G	E
	B		G		D		G		R		U
C	O	W	L		G	U	L	L	I	B	L	E
	X		Y		E		E		A		F

122

J		G		A			L		F		E
U	N	R	E	S	T		R	E	J	E	C	T
S		A		L		S		R		I		H
T	E	M	P	E	S	T		W	I	N	C	E
I		M		F		R		I		T		R
F	L	A	B		H	A	T	C	H		P	N
Y		R		W		T		K		P		N
			V	I	D	E	O		D	A	L	E
B		S		N		G		B		R		I
L	U	N	G	E		I	L	L	I	C	I	T
A		A		B		C		A		H
S	T	R	E	A	K		F	R	E	E	Z	E
E		E		R			E		D		R

123

F	O	R	A	Y		A	B	D	O	M	E	N
R		E		E		V		I		E		E
A	A	M	I	L	N	E		V	E	N	U	S
N		N		L		N		E		S		T
C	R	A	B		A	G	E		C	A	P	E
		N		K		E		S
T	E	T	H	E	R		H	U	M	B	U	G
U			G		H		M		O
M	E	S	S		C	O	O		B	L	E	W
B		A		B		S		W		S		H
L	O	L	L	Y		T	H	E	A	T	R	E
E		O		R		E		A		E		R
R	E	N	D	E	L	L		N	U	R	S	E

124

	A	P	O	C	A	L	Y	P	S	E
	B		R		V		O		H		G
D	A	M	A	G	I	N	G		A	S	I	A
	S		T		D		I		W		B
	E	M	I	R		A	B	O	L	I	S	H
		O		D		E			O
	C	O	N	S	O	L	A	T	I	O	N
	A			M		R		L
B	E	G	O	N	I	A		G	L	I	B
	S		P		N		F		E		L
D	A	L	I		E	A	R	L	G	R	E	Y
	R		N		E		O		A		N
		B	E	D	R	A	G	G	L	E	D

126

A		D		T	E	R	M	I	N	A	T	E
G	E	A	R		L		A		A		H
G		L		C	O	I	F	F	E	U	R
R	I	M	I	N	I		L		F		G
A		A		D		B		S		A
V	I	T	A	L		T	A	U	N	T	E	D
A		I		S	A	G		R		V
T	E	A	S	I	N	G		A	B	O	V	E
E		N		O		A		N		R
	G		V		W		H	A	G	G	I	S
C	A	N	O	O	D	L	E		E		A
	L		L		O		R		T	S	A	R
P	E	R	T	I	N	E	N	T		T		Y

127

	E	Q	U	A	L		F	L	U	F	F
A		U		T		C		U		L		Y
B	L	A	S	T		H	E	C	T	A	R	E
B		K		I		A		Y		V		M
O	V	E	R	T	U	R	N		W	O	K	E
T			U		I		B		U		N
B		F	R	E	D	A	S	T	A	I	R	E
B		E		E		M		R			S
L	E	S	S		G	A	U	N	T	L	E	T
A		U		Z		T		A		O		E
Z	A	M	B	E	Z	I		C	I	R	C	A
E		E		R		C		L		D		K
	I	D	I	O	T		S	E	N	S	E

128

O	B	L	I	V	I	O	U	S		D		T
	R		N		M		P		C	O	L	A
B	A	L	T	I	M	O	R	E		R		F
	C		E		U		O			M		F
T	E	H	R	A	N		A	S	P	I	R	E
		A		G	E	N	R	E		T		T
L	E	M	U	R				V	I	O	L	A
E		F		E	N	S	U	E		R
G	U	I	N	E	A		P	R	A	Y	E	R
L		S		T		K		M		C
E		T		M	I	S	E	R	A	B	L	E
S	U	E	T		V		E		Z		A
S		D		H	E	Y	P	R	E	S	T	O

129

```
 P R E F E R E N T I A L
A E I E E N A
S I M O N B V A L I D
T I E M U E A Y
R A T E S F O R S Y T H
O S F A
N U M B E R R E D E E M
O A R V I
M A C R A M E A U R A L
I R L S I N I T
C R U E T U D I N G O
A M E L S N
L A B O R A T O R I E S
```

130

```
D I T F A M
W I S T E R I A D E A D
S A U N J K
N A P L E S F A U C E T
G I T A S
W R E C K B R O T H E R
E R E N
D E F I C I T P O U C H
C C S B U
Z E N I T H C O L U M N
R C T O O B
C O I L E X P A N D E D
S E A E G R
```

131

```
S P I L L T H E B E A N S
E N O A B K
D U S K Y O B S E R V E
A T A B H O W
T R E L L I S F L A K E
E P C U D R
Q U I E T L Y
S M N N U M
P R O W L I N F E R N O
R S U T E B R
A N A R C H Y D E A L T
I I K U N A
N I C K Y C A M P B E L L
```

132

```
L E E K S U M M E R
N I I L S
R E U N I T E D A R C H
M G E N N H
N Y M P H F I D D L E R
I S G M
S C A N T Y H E E D E D
O L T A
O R V I L L E D R I L L
D D A S D O
N O T E B A L L R O O M
N A U A U S
C L O S E T M E E T
```

133

```
U L R I K A J O N S S O N
S E I E E O
A I L M E N T P L A I T
I V S L S R
D U C T D E C I S I V E
A M T N D D
R E C T O R A T H E N A
T O T U H M
M O N A L I S A W A V E
O F E E J L
U N I T Y F L E M I N G
T N U E B A
H I E R O G L Y P H I C S
```

134

```
B R I A N C O N L E Y
R A U E O R A
I M M O R A L A M I S S
V P A L H C K
A W A Y R A M S G A T E
L R A R A W
S T A L L A R O M A
H C W K I G
O U T D A T E D O X E N
B R P A O T A
B R U N O S T R A U S S
Y T N E C R H
C H E E R L E A D E R
```

135

```
L E M O N A D E C U B A
O I I R A L R
S L P E A R L T T
T U L I P G B E I G E
R Y O E M R
L I E D A N G I N A Y
X I T T
P P I M P L E D E E D
A L P E K R
T W I C E M O F F A L
R C D I A N A L O
O I E N L E V
N A T O E S C A L A T E
```

136

```
A I O N D E N C H
D E V I A T E D D U
O O T G B U I L D
B E R G E R A C C D
E Y S T P A N E L
D F D E S T S
B E C A M E K E E G A N
M M W R Y S C
M I N I M A G E L
J L V I O L E N C E
C O M I C S O V W
H A P I N A F O R E
A N G R Y N T Y S
```

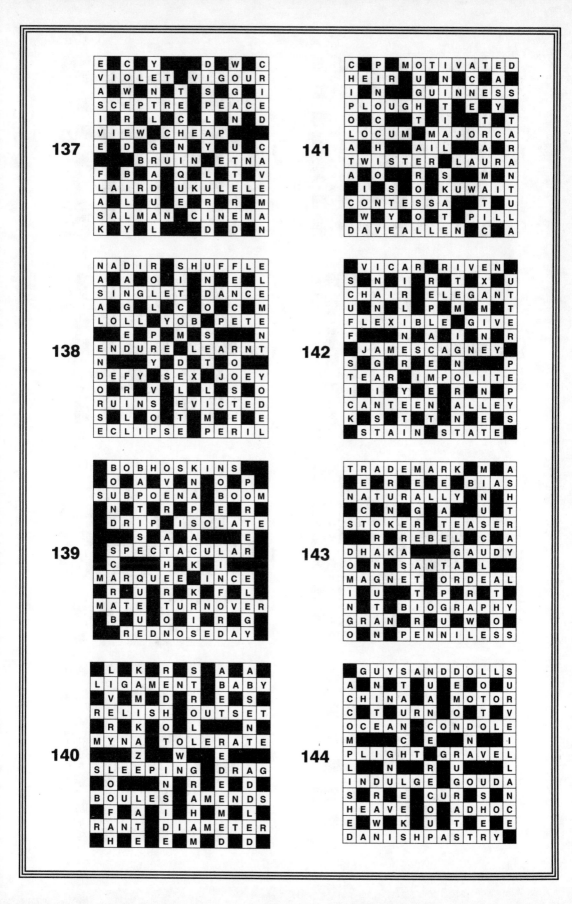

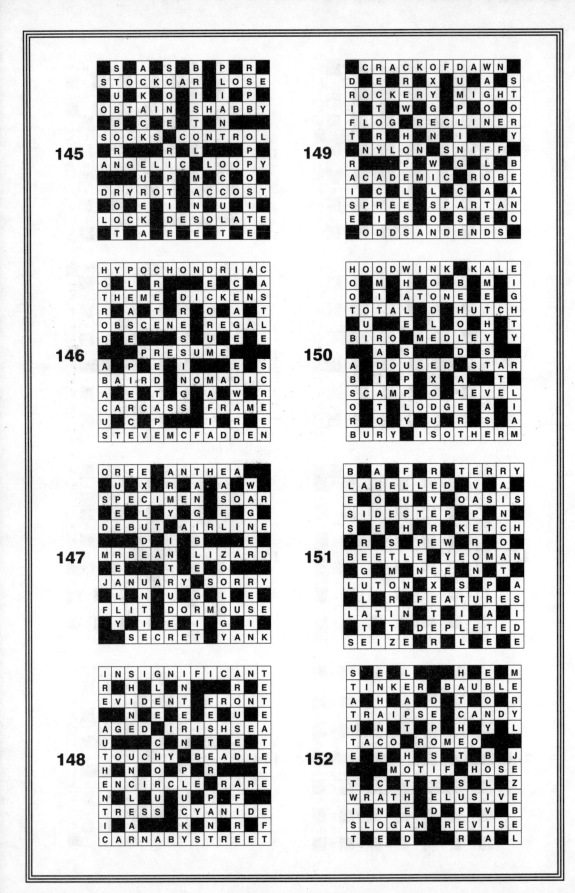

145

149

146

150

147

151

148

152

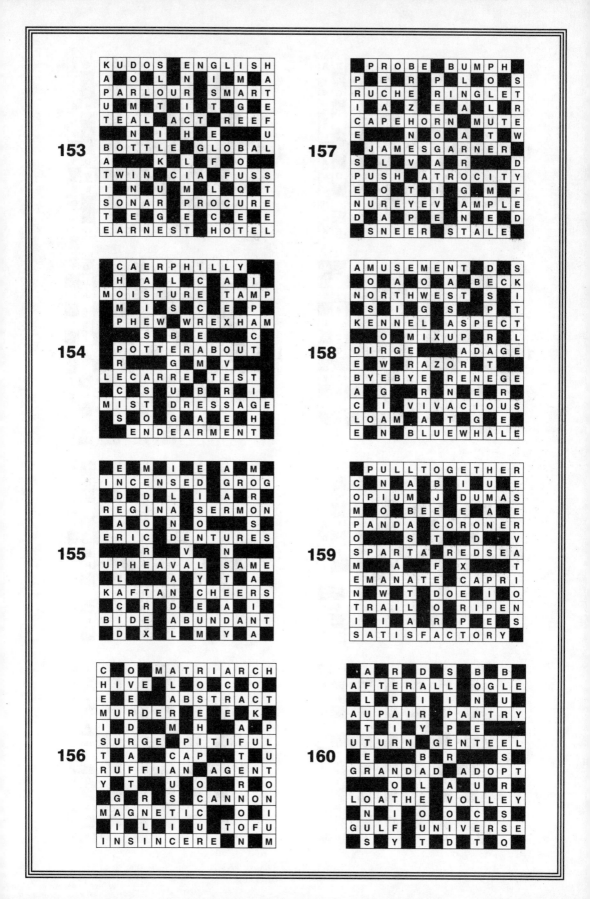

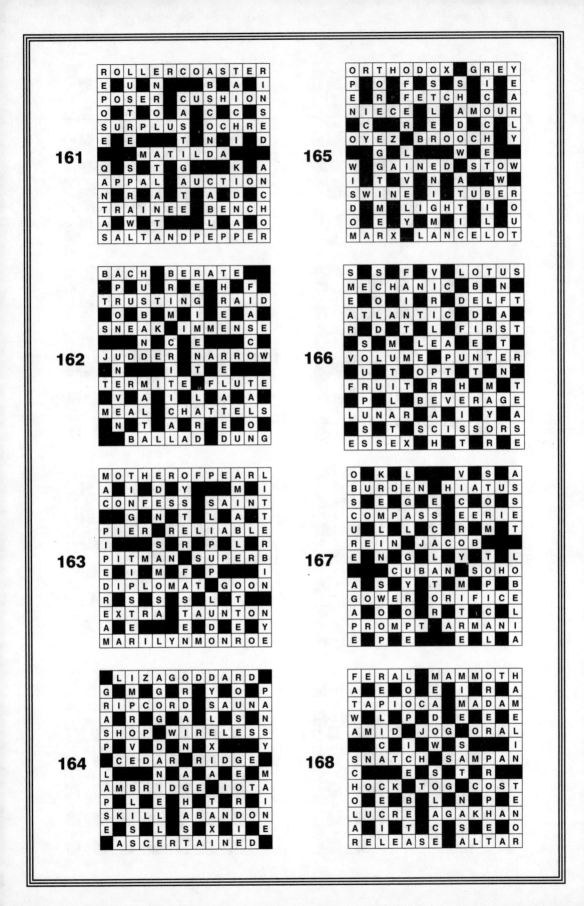

161

162

163

164

165

166

167

168

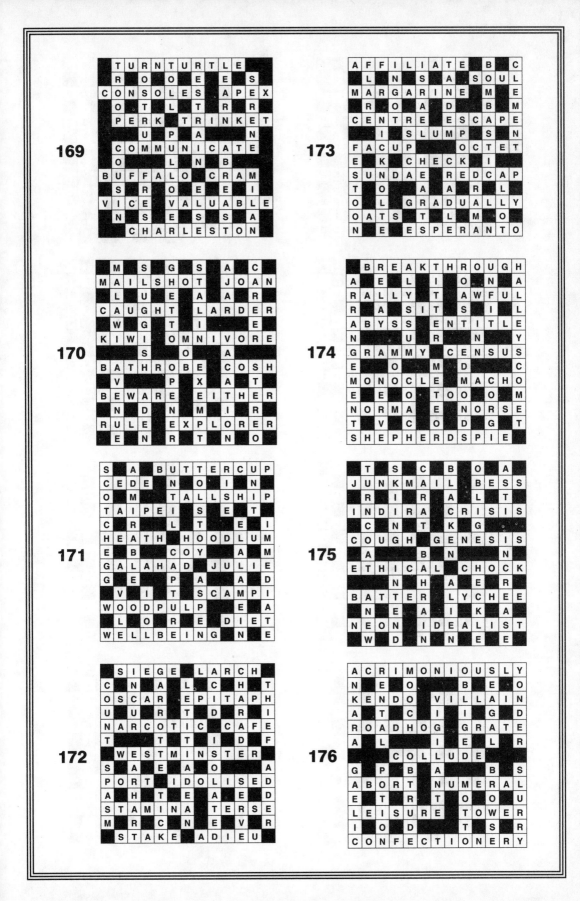

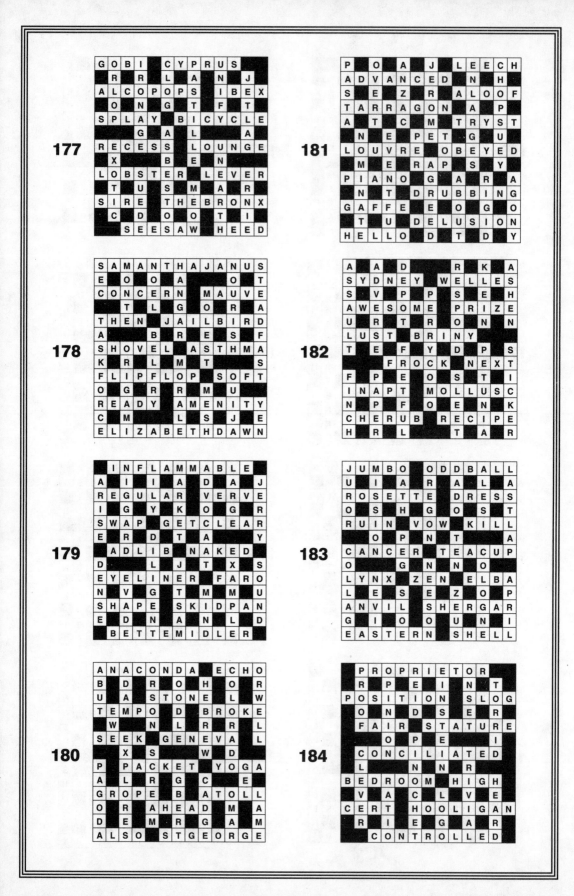

177

178

179

180

181

182

183

184

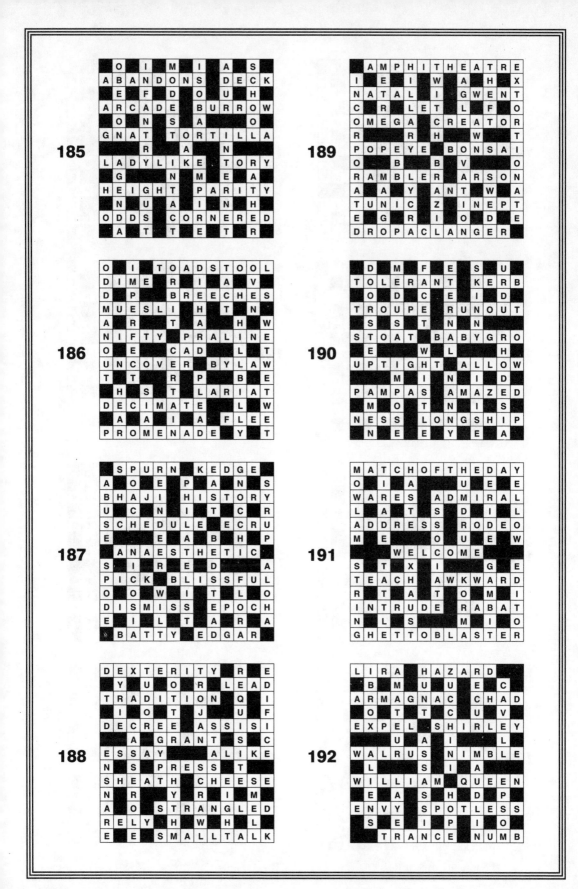

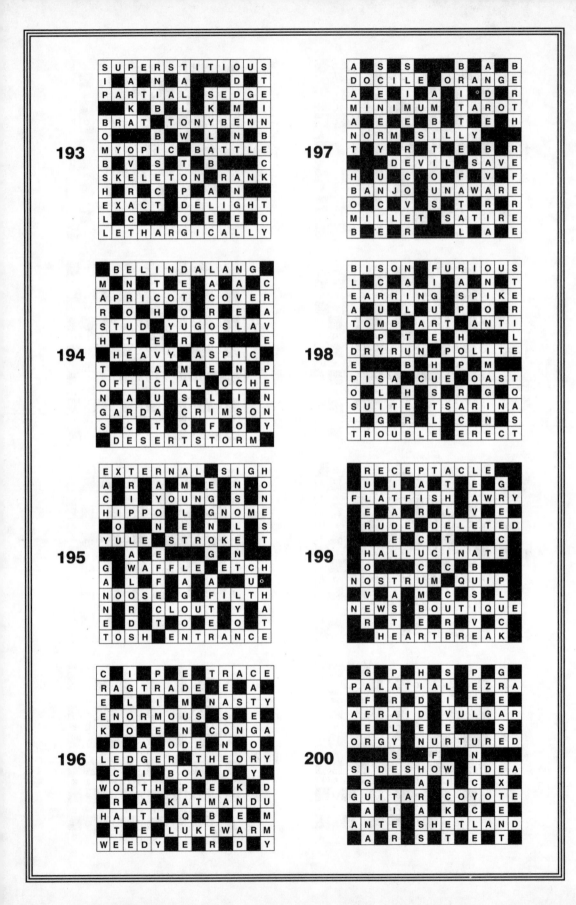

201

```
E B . B E D S P R E A D
S L U G . A . U . A . I
C L . R E N E G A D E .
A L L O U T . D . E . E
L D . H . I . D . I .
A C O R N . L A P L A N D
T Z . P A L . R . E .
E M E R A L D . O F T E N
D R . A . S . B . T .
. M W C . W H O O P I .
C A L A M A R I . A . C
Y R . R . F . A R I A .
C O M M O D I T Y . D . L
```

202

```
. T O U C H . T B O N E .
A . P . O . T . E . O . G
M U R A L . H A N O V E R
B . A . U . U . D . E . A
I N H U M A N E . F L O P
T . . B . D . S . L . H .
. I N D I G E S T I O N .
H . U . A . R . R . . .
Y A R N . O B T A I N E D
E . T . B . O . D . I . O
N E U T R A L . D E C O R
A . R . I . T . L . H . N
. F E I G N . N E W E L .
```

203

```
E D I N B U R G H . L . O
. R . E . P . I . M U F F
B O N E C H I N A . C . F
. N . D . O . G . R . B .
J E K Y L L . E S T A T E
. N . A D O R E . T . A .
C L O G S . . W H I S T .
O . T . S A U C E . V . .
M E T H O D . A R R E S T
I . Y . R . V . O . I . .
C . A . S I D E B U R N S
A P S E . F . A . T . G .
L . H . S T U T T E R E D
```

204

```
. W H O D A R E S W I N S
A . O . R . A . A . S . A
F O R T E . D . B R A W L
F . S . S K I . R . A . L
E V E N S . S K E T C H Y
C . E . H . A . G . . .
T A B A R D . K U N G F U
I . D . A . T . N . . .
O C T O B E R . E B D O N
N . H . A . M E N . R . E
A V E R T . A . S W I L L
T . R . O . G . I . V . L
E A M O N N H O L M E S .
```

205

```
. R S C S . S E . . .
M E R C H A N T . T O G A
. L . A N . A R . O . .
W I N T O N . G R E T N A
. A . H Y G E . . . .
I N F E R . B E S T M A N
. C . R . R . D . . .
D E C A Y E D . E N D O W
. W V . T U R . . .
P H R A S E . R I T U A L
. E K R U M B . . .
C A N E . S U D D E N L Y
. T N E E G E . . .
```

206

```
G R A N D N A T I O N A L
I G . W . . N E . E .
G E E S E . M A S C A R A
O N . L A T . R . D .
L O C A L L Y . A M B L E
O Y . . F N . Y . R .
. . A T H L E T E . . .
P I . A O . . S . S
H A R E M . W O R S H I P
O R . B E . A . E . E
B O U D O I R . B E L L E
I P . U . . B . V . D
A L T E R N A T I V E L Y
```

207

```
S P R Y . P A N A M A .
. H U . A . E A . T .
W O R L D C U P . S O Y A
. T E . T . O O . P .
M O U L D . S T E N C I L
. O . G . I . . . N .
O R I G I N . S I L A G E
E . . A . M . E . . .
A G E L E S S . L A D L E
G . A . H . Y . R . I
C A M P . E T E R N I T Y
E . E . R . A . E . R
. C L O S E R . R E E K
```

208

```
K E L L Y M C G I L L I S
I . E O . O . . E . P
T A N T R U M . P R O V E
. I . K . P O T . C
R U N G . E L E P H A N T
E . P . Y L . R . A
H U N G R Y . B A N D I T
E . A E . T . R . O
A Z N A V O U R . P E E R
R . K I . X . C . R
S T E I N . E N L A R G E
A . E . . D . I . O . E
L A N C E C O R P O R A L
```

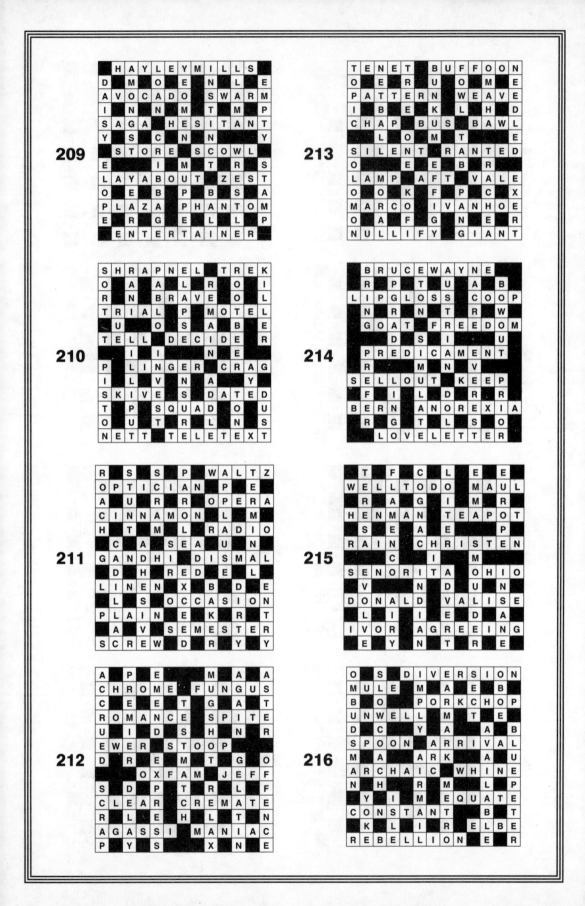

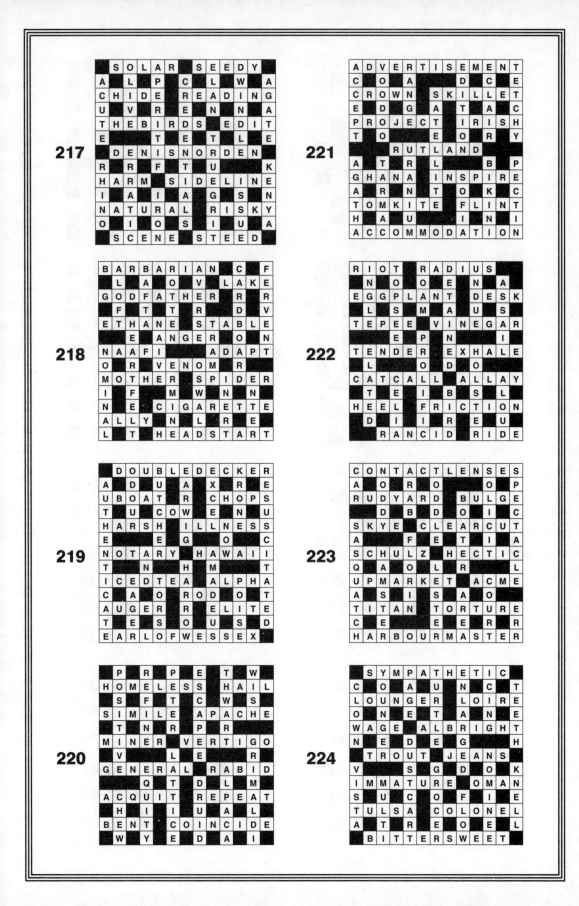

217 218 219 220 221 222 223 224

225

```
O P I N I O N S   O U S T
O D R I R P T R
Z L A R G U E T A
E V E N T G F J O R D E
  I E L U D E R
J E E R G E I S H A R
  N M E T
R T R I V E T S E E D
U R L X R R
S W E L L P H A D E S
H N E V E R Y O T
E C R R M O I
D A H L S T R E A M E R
```

226

```
P S A C P U N C H
R A T I O N A L P E
O A R M P R I N T
N I N E T E E N I S
G D A R A S C O T
C I B A T I R
W H E N C E R U N N E R
L T N A Y G D
L O W E R M C A S
R R H O R R I F I C
L I V E R U Y F O
N S U N S P O I L T
D E P T H T T X T
```

227

```
A S P J I D
B I C K E R P U D D L E
R O T R S I L
A P O S T L E T R O T H
H T Y P I T I
A B E L B U N C H
M R D L E C R
B A L S A A L O E
A C W I C I G
B O A R D V E R A N D A
A I L E E T T
T U R K E Y S P R O U T
E N R T N A
```

228

```
T Y S O N T A R N I S H
E H E A A D A
P R O W E S S S T A I D
I R D S H H D
D A T A N E W S O L O
E D L T C
S E N T R Y A N O R A K
T Y L T E
E V E N K I P E D A M
T N G A R C E
S N A I L B L O W O U T
O C I L S A E
N O T A B L E S I T A R
```

229

```
R O U N D A B O U T
E T A R N P
I N C I S I V E D O R A
A L L T E O
L A I R S H E R I F F
S I R I
T H E I N T E R N E T
U D N I
A R S E N I C F A L L
P J R Z G U
B I T E E L E G A N C E
N C C R R K
S T A T I O N A R Y
```

230

```
P S S A E S
D E C A N T E R D O M E
D T R T G I
N A T U R E F I E S T A
L R W U H
S O F A N E L L G W Y N
T V L
A N T E A T E R A R I D
E R E S T
L A U R I E S A N D A L
R O B E O L
S L I T L A N D S L I P
Y A E T T C
```

231

```
B B A E R O D R O M E
L E E R G P A O
A A R E T R I E V E
C O R P S E I L E
K N T M T S
P L A T O L U L L A B Y
O I A I M L N
O B S E R V E P O L K A
L E E O S G
N T R B I S T R O
R E C R E A T E O G
R A G S F R A U
C O M P L E T E D Y E
```

232

```
B A R M Y S I O U X
S H E M S N S
C L E F T A P P O I N T
O R A I Y C I
P I N G P O N G S O I L
E H T C R E
J E R O M E F L Y N N
A L R N I A
D R E Y H A N N I B A L
E V S N I R T
P L A S T I C C R A Z E
T T A E A C R
M E R G E F L E E T
```

233

```
S H E F F I E L D . E . V
O . U . C . E . . T I L E
B R O N Z E A G E . D . H
D . G . B . A . . E . I .
M E X I C O . C H I R A C
Y . . O X E Y E . D . L .
M E L B A . . . A L O N E
I . O . S H E A R . W . .
R E P U T E . S T A N C E
A . H . R . P . M . U . .
C . O . S O L I T A I R E
L E N S . I . R . S . I .
E . E . A C C E S S I O N
```

237

```
R A M P . C Y G N E T . .
. G . O . A . R . L . A .
P R E S T I G E . E M M Y
. E . T . N . E . C . E .
R E V U E . S T A T E L Y
. . . R . A . I . . . I .
S O L E M N . N E C T A R
U . . . D . G . . U . . .
S T O P P E R . A R O S E
. L . U . R . G . A . Y .
P A C K . S C R U T I N Y
Y . K . O . I . O . O . .
. C A T N A P . R O D E .
```

234

```
. E A U D E C O L O G N E
A . U . O . H . E . R . X
B Y R O N . E . D E A L T
O . A . A I R . G . F . R
V A L E T . I N E R T I A
E . . . O . E . U . . . G
A S H O R E . Z A N D R A
R . I . . L . . L . . . G
E X P L A I N . C I R C A
R . S . U . D U O . I . N
A W A R D . I . P A N I C
G . L . I . G . O . G . E
E M M A T H O M P S O N .
```

238

```
U N C O M F O R T A B L E
S . H . E . D . . R . L .
A G I T A T E . S U A V E
. M . T . S . P . V . M .
F L E X . E S C A L A T E
I . . M . A . R . D . N .
T O P H A T . E S C O R T
A . T . G . E . . . . A .
O U T B R E A K . R E E L
D . R . O . Z . M . V . .
R E I G N . E V A S I V E
O . O . B . R . T . Y . Y
P E T T I C O A T L A N E
```

235

```
. E . D . V . E . B . M .
E X H I B I T S . L E E K
. P . V . N . C . O . A .
L O V E L Y . A T T E N D
. S . R . L . P . T . T .
P U T T Y . R E M O R S E
. R . . F . D . . . N . .
D E F I C I T . M E T A L
. . R . D . S . N . T . .
A R N O L D . T H A T C H
. E . N . L . E . M . H .
M A X I . E B E N E Z E R
. R . C . R . R . L . D .
```

236

```
D E T E R M I N A T I O N
E . O . E . . R . D . . E
P L U M P . O U T L I N E
U . P . E . L . I . O . D
T R E B L E D . C A C H E
Y . E . . . B . L . Y . D
. . . E N R A G E D . . .
T . V . E . I . . . V . P
I B I Z A . L I B R A R Y
T . C . T . E . U . C . T
B A T T E R Y . R E A C H
I . I . S . . . M . N . O
T I M O T H Y D A L T O N
```

239

```
. R E V E R B E R A T E .
K . S . X . R . O . O . I
O U T R A G E . L U P I N
A . O . M . T . L . E . T
L U R E . C O N C O R D E
A . I . E . N . A . . . R
. P L U S H . F L A I L .
F . C . P . L . R . S . S
L A B R A D O R . D E B T
A . R . P . L . P . L . E
S C U B A . P L A C A T E
H . N . D . O . P . N . P
. R O B E R T H A R D Y .
```

240

```
R U M I N A N T . R O L F
O . E . O . O . B . M . O
A M . B E R R Y . E . . R
D R O O L . M . G O L D A
. I . E . A . O . E . . G
T O S S . P L A N E T . E
. T . P . E . . E . . . .
F . T A R I F F . K E L P
E . R . I . I . P . . E .
A W O K E . N . L O S E R
R . P . S H A D E . I . A
E . E . T . L . A . Z . N
D O Z Y . S E A T B E L T
```

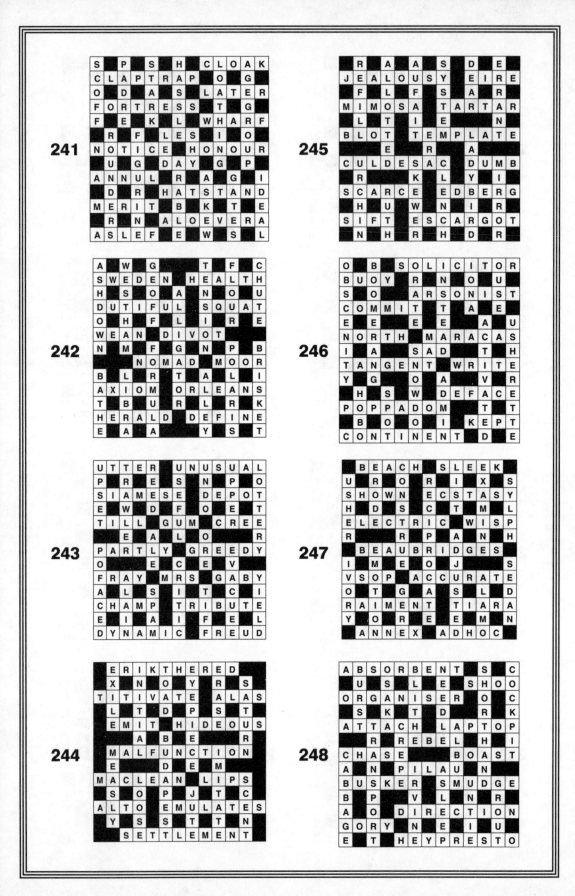

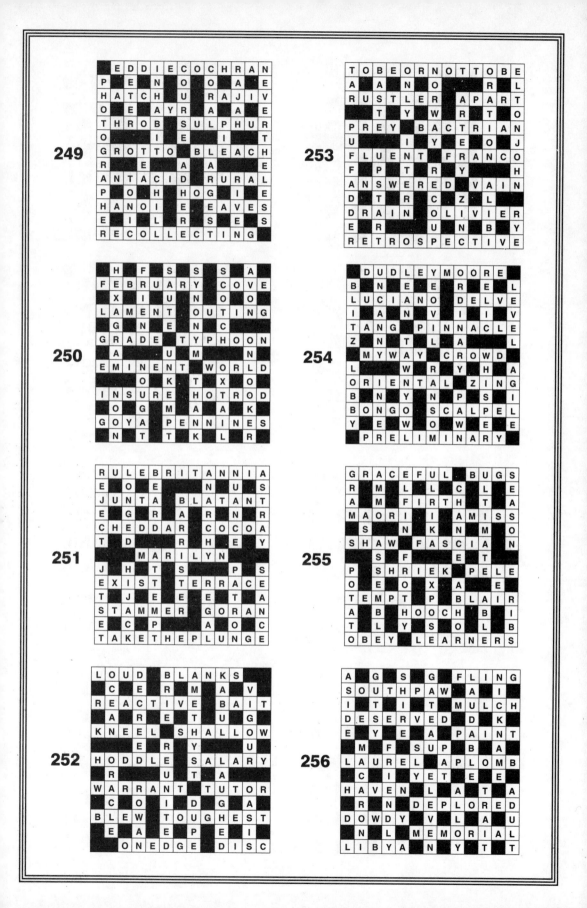

249

```
. E D D I E C O C H R A N
P E N . O . O . A . . . E
H A T C H . U . R A J I V
O . E . A Y R . A . A . E
T H R O B . S U L P H U R
O . . . I . E . I . . . T
G R O T T O . B L E A C H
R . . . E . A . A . . . E
A N T A C I D . R U R A L
P . O . H . H O G . I . E
H A N O I . E . E A V E S
E . I . L . R . S . E . S
R E C O L L E C T I N G .
```

250

```
. H . F . S . S . S . A .
F E B R U A R Y . C O V E
. X . I . U . N . O . O .
L A M E N T . O U T I N G
. G . N . E . N . C . . .
G R A D E . T Y P H O O N
. A . U . M . . . N . N .
E M I N E N T . W O R L D
. O . K . T . X . O . . .
I N S U R E . H O T R O D
. O . G . M . A . A . K .
G O Y A . P E N N I N E S
. N . T . T . K . L . R .
```

251

```
R U L E B R I T A N N I A
E . O . E . N . U . . . S
J U N T A . B L A T A N T
E . G . R . A . R . N . R
C H E D D A R . C O C O A
T . D . R . R . H . E . Y
. . M A R I L Y N . . . .
J . H . T . S . . . P . S
E X I S T . T E R R A C E
T . J . E . E . E . T . A
S T A M M E R . G O R A N
E . C . P . . . A . O . C
T A K E T H E P L U N G E
```

252

```
L O U D . B L A N K S . .
. C . E . R . M . A . V .
R E A C T I V E . B A I T
. A . R . E . T . U . G .
K N E E L . S H A L L O W
. . . R . Y . . . U . .
H O D D L E . S A L A R Y
R . . U . T . A .
W A R R A N T . T U T O R
. C . O . I . D . G . A .
B L E W . T O U G H E S T
. E . A . E . P . E . I .
. . O N E D G E . D I S C
```

253

```
T O B E O R N O T T O B E
A . A . N . O . . R . . L
R U S T L E R . A P A R T
. T . Y . W . R . T . . O
P R E Y . B A C T R I A N
U . . I . Y . E . O . . J
F L U E N T . F R A N C O
F . P . T . R . Y . . . H
A N S W E R E D . V A I N
D . T . R . C . Z . L . .
D R A I N . O L I V I E R
E . R . . . U . N . B . Y
R E T R O S P E C T I V E
```

254

```
. D U D L E Y M O O R E .
B . N . E . E . R . E . L
L U C I A N O . D E L V E
I . A . N . V . I . I . V
T A N G . P I N N A C L E
Z . N . T . L . A . . . L
. M Y W A Y . C R O W D .
L . W . R . Y . H . . . A
O R I E N T A L . Z I N G
B . N . Y . N . P . S . I
B O N G O . S C A L P E L
Y . E . W . O . W . E . E
. P R E L I M I N A R Y .
```

255

```
G R A C E F U L . B U G S
R . M . L . L . C . L . E
A . M . F I R T H . T . A
M A O R I . I . A M I S S
. S . N . K . N . M . . O
S H A W . F A S C I A . N
. S . F . . . E . T . . .
P . S H R I E K . P E L E
O . E . O . X . A . . . E
T E M P T . P . B L A I R
A . B . H O O C H . B . I
T . L . Y . S . O . L . B
O B E Y . L E A R N E R S
```

256

```
A . G . S . G . . F L I N G
S O U T H P A W . A . . I .
I . T . I . T . M U L C H .
D E S E R V E D . D . . K .
E . Y . E . A . P A I N T .
. M . F . S U P . B . A .
L A U R E L . A P L O M B .
. C . I . Y E T . E . E .
H A V E N . L . A . T . A
. R . N . D E P L O R E D .
D O W D Y . V . L . A . U .
. N . L . M E M O R I A L .
L I B Y A . N . Y . T . T .
```

257

```
S . T . S . . . G . S . B
T R E A T Y . U L S T E R
U . R . O . P . A . O . O
T O R Q U A Y . C O M M A
T . A . T . R . I . P . D
E V I L . Y O D E L . . .
R . N . H . M . R . A . P
. . V O C A L . L I A R .
S . E . R . N . J . N . E
L O V E R . I D I O T I C
O . I . I . A . F . R . E
P A C I F Y . O F F E N D
E . T . Y . . . Y . E . E
```

261

```
P . A . O B V I O U S L Y
H A S H . E . M . R . A .
Y . T . R A M S G A T E .
S T R I P E . O . E . E .
I . O . T . R . T . A . .
C Y N I C . M A U G H A M
I . O . A I L . R . S . .
A D M I R E R . H O I S T
N . Y . R . A . L . E . .
. L . S O . M E L L O R .
L I C E N S E E . I . D
. O . V . O . N . A N N A
I N T E R L U D E . G . M
```

258

```
R U I N S . B L A N K E T
O . P . N . R . F . A . E
M I S S I L E . A S T O N
E . W . P . W . R . I . D
O M I T . P E W . H E R R
. . C . A . R . S . . . I
S C H E M E . F O R M A L
I . Y . D . W . E . . . .
B L U E . A I D . D A N K
E . N . D . S . W . S . A
R A I S E . P E R J U R Y
I . T . E . E . I . R . A
A B Y S M A L . T W E A K
```

259

```
. R E A L E S T A T E . .
. H . C . A . H . U . U .
W I T H D R A W . L I N K
. N . I . N . A . I . I .
. E V E R . P R O P O S E
. . V . S . T . . . O . .
. O V E R T H E M O O N .
. P . . U . D . N . . . .
W E S T E R N . N A F F .
. N . I . G . C . S . I .
S L I P . E N L I S T E D
. Y . S . O . O . I . N .
. . H Y P N O T I S E D .
```

262

```
. M O O D Y . S K U L L .
S . U . I . C . N . O . D
M I N U S . A P O L O G Y
A . C . C . L . X . K . F
S H E R L O C K . V O T E
H . O . U . A . U . A . D
. C O N S O L I D A T E .
A . P . E . A . J . . . D
D U E L . S T R A N G E R
O . N . F . I . C . R . O
P L A C E B O . E M A I L
T . I . T . N . N . I . L
. B R E A K . A T O N E .
```

263

```
E N E R G E T I C . P . E
. U . E . N . N . C Y A N
P R I M I T I V E . G . C
. S . I . I . A . M . L .
B E T T E R . D Y N A M O
. . I . M E L E E . L . S
D U N C E . . . N O I S E
O . O . R O B O T . O . .
Z E P H Y R . C L I N I C
E . E . I . C . N . N . .
O . N . R E G U L A R L Y
F L E A . N . L . N . E .
F . R . S T A T U E T T E
```

260

```
. L . A . S . . . A . S .
B Y G R A V E S . D Y C E
. C . A . E . L . I . R .
P E N C I L . A N T H E M
. U . H . T . N . E . . .
O M E N . E L D O R A D O
. I . . I . . I . A . . .
G R A D U A T E . D E A N
. E . B . X . I . L . . .
V A P O U R . T R A U M A
. G . A . U . O . T . O .
B A C K . P O R P O I S E
. N . S . T . T . R . T .
```

264

```
. P A T R I O T G A M E S .
A . L . O . B . O . O . U
B L O O M . J . O A T E S
S . N . A G E . S . O . A
O R G A N . C H E V R O N
L . . I . T . . I . . N .
U N S E A T . A R M A D A
T . V . A . E . . . H . .
E N C A S E D . T A R D Y
Z . L . P . M A R . I . O
E B O N Y . I . E L V E R
R . U . R . R . A . A . K
O L D W I V E S T A L E .
```

265

```
  O   A A S S   S   S
E P I D E M I C   K I T E
  P   V O A   A   U
G O V E R N   R E T I N A
  S   N   G P   E
G I R T H   F E R R A R I
  T       R   R   O
R E P L I E D   R O G U E
      A   C   S R   L
G L I D E R   K E N N E L
  O   D   U I   A   T
W A D E   I R R I T A T E
  M   R   T T   E   E
```

266

```
A C U P U N C T U R I S T
P   N   P     P   N   R
P U R G E   G I R A F F E
L   E   N     I   E   M
E V A N D E R   G E C K O
S   L   M     H   T   R
      B A T I S T E   T
S   A   L     N   V   T
T I B I A   A N N U I T Y
R   S   D     Y   E   R
O V E R D U E   M E N S A
N   N   I     P   N   N
G E T I N O N T H E A C T
```

267

```
D A Z E   E I F F E L
  Z   N   N   A   R
B U D D H I S M   S N O B
  R   O   D   I   E   N
Z E B R A   I N K L I N G
      S   L   I   I
A L L E G E   N U M B E R
  E   E   M   E   A
B A B Y L O N   B E A N O
  G   E   N   P   S   I
C U B A   A F L U T T E R
  E   T   D   O   R   C
  O S T E N D   O V E R
```

268

```
C O M P L I M E N T A R Y
U   E   O   E       N   A
B E R M U D A   C A T E R
  Y   T   D   O   E   D
E L L A   T O M H A N K S
M   S   W   E   N   T
B I S Q U E   A R M A N I
A   A   M   G   E       C
R E M E M B E R   T A C K
R   U   O   N   R   E
A P R O N   T R A N S I T
S   A   N   R   K   O   I
S H I R L E Y T E M P L E
```

269

```
  A C R I M O N I O U S
H   O   C P   N   N   C
A I R P O R T   S H I N E
N   D   N I   U   T   A
D R I P   B O U L D E R S
Y   A   E N   A       E
  C L I M B   S T A F F
S   A   C E   L   L
L U M I N O U S   V A S E
I   O   A C   C   V   P
D I G I T   K A R A O K E
E   U   E O   I   U   R
  G L A S T O N B U R Y
```

270

```
A D D I T I O N   V E A L
G   I   A B   E   T   A
O   V   R A T T Y   C W
G R E E R   U   E N E M Y
  A   Y   S   L   T   E
S T A R   R E N E G E   R
  R   T       T   R
D   K U W A I T   D A R T
E   A   E   M   N   A
A N N A N   M   S W A M P
R   S   T H U M P   T O
T   A   Y   N   C   O O
H I S S   N E W C O M E R
```

271

```
P   D   A   A   A M O U R
A E R O B I C S   A   P
R   E   O C   M I G H T
T O A N D F R O   N C E
Y   M   E U   S T E A M
  P   B   D E S   A   V
S A L U T E   A N I M A L
  N   I   E S P   N   L
D O L L Y   H   D   A   G
  R   D   W A R R A N T Y
R A V E L   D   E   D   P
  M   R   C O N G R E S S
C A U S E   W   S   S   Y
```

272

```
A   O   C       A   A   C
R U M B L E   G L A D L Y
R   I   O T   M   O   M
A T T A C H E   A M B E R
N   T   K   L   N   E   U
G L E N   R E P A Y
E   D   G P   C   B   R
      C R E A M   S A K E
T   S   A   T   A   L   C
W O M A N   H O L D A L L
I   E   Y   Y   I   N   A
S H A N T Y   T A I C H I
T   R   E       S   E   M
```

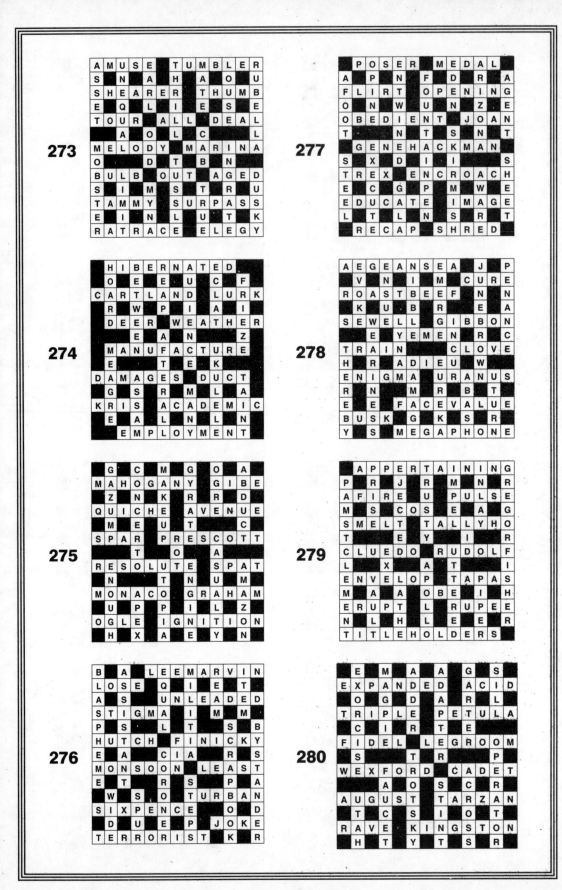

273

Across: AMUSE, TUMBLER, SHEARER, THUMB, TOUR, ALL, DEAL, MELODY, MARINA, BULB, OUT, AGED, TAMMY, SURPASS, RATRACE, ELEGY

277

POSER, MEDAL, FLIRT, OPENING, OBEDIENT, JOAN, GENEHACKMAN, TREX, ENCROACH, EDUCATE, IMAGE, RECAP, SHRED

274

HIBERNATED, CARTLAND, LURK, DEER, WEATHER, MANUFACTURE, DAMAGES, DUCT, KRIS, ACADEMIC, EMPLOYMENT

278

AEGEANSEA, CURE, ROASTBEEF, SEWELL, GIBBON, YEMEN, TRAIN, CLOVE, ADIEU, ENIGMA, URANUS, FACEVALUE, BUSK, MEGAPHONE

275

MAHOGANY, GIBE, QUICHE, AVENUE, SPAR, PRESCOTT, RESOLUTE, SPAT, MONACO, GRAHAM, OGLE, IGNITION

279

APPERTAINING, AFIRE, PULSE, COS, SMELT, TALLYHO, CLUEDO, RUDOLF, ENVELOP, TAPAS, OBE, ERUPT, RUPEE, TITLEHOLDERS

276

LEEMARVIN, LOSE, UNLEADED, STIGMA, HUTCH, FINICKY, CIA, MONSOON, LEAST, TURBAN, SIXPENCE, JOKE, TERRORIST

280

EXPANDED, ACID, TRIPLE, PETULA, FIDEL, LEGROOM, WEXFORD, CADET, AUGUST, TARZAN, RAVE, KINGSTON

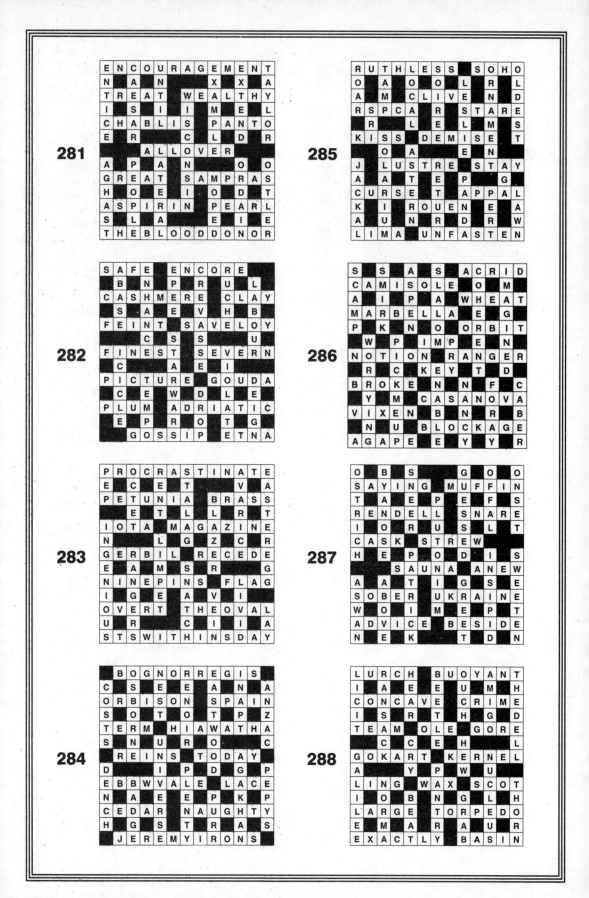

281

```
E N C O U R A G E M E N T
N   A   N     X   X   A
T R E A T   W E A L T H Y
I   S   I   I   M   E L
C H A B L I S   P A N T O
E   R   C   L   D   R
  A L L O V E R   O   O
A   P   A   N     O   O
G R E A T   S A M P R A S
H   O   E   I   O   D T
A S P I R I N   P E A R L
S   L   A     E   I   E
T H E B L O O D D O N O R
```

282

```
S A F E   E N C O R E
  B   N   P   R   U L
C A S H M E R E   C L A Y
  S   A   E   V   H B
F E I N T   S A V E L O Y
  C   S   S     U
F I N E S T   S E V E R N
  C   A   E   I
P I C T U R E   G O U D A
  C   E   W D   L E
P L U M   A D R I A T I C
  E   P   R O   T G
  G O S S I P   E T N A
```

283

```
P R O C R A S T I N A T E
E   C   E   T     V   A
P E T U N I A   B R A S S
  E   T   L   L   R   T
I O T A   M A G A Z I N E
N   L   G   Z   C   R
G E R B I L   R E C E D E
E   A   M   S   R   G
N I N E P I N S   F L A G
I   G   E   A   V   I
O V E R T   T H E O V A L
U   R   C   I   I   A
S T S W I T H I N S D A Y
```

284

```
  B O G N O R R E G I S
C   S   E   A   N   A
O R B I S O N   S P A I N
S   O   T   O   T   Z
T E R M   H I A W A T H A
S   N   U   R   O   C
  R E I N S   T O D A Y
D   I   P   D   G   P
E B B W V A L E   L A C E
N   A   E   E   P   P
C E D A R   N A U G H T Y
H   G   S   T   R   S
  J E R E M Y I R O N S
```

285

```
R U T H L E S S   S O H O
O   A   O O   L   R   L
A M   C L I V E   N   D
R S P C A R   S T A R E
  R   L   E L   M   S
K I S S   D E M I S E T
  O   A     E   N
J   L U S T R E   S T A Y
A   A   T   E P   G
C U R S E   T   A P P A L
K   I   R O U E N   E A
A   U   N   R D   R   W
L I M A   U N F A S T E N
```

286

```
S   S   A   S   A C R I D
C A M I S O L E   O   M
A   I   P   A   W H E A T
M A R B E L L A   E   G
  W   P   I M P   E   N
N O T I O N   R A N G E R
  R   C   K E Y   T   D
B R O K E   N   N   F C
  Y   M   C A S A N O V A
V I X E N   B   N   R B
  N   U   B L O C K A G E
A G A P E   E   Y   Y R
```

287

```
O   B   S     G   O   O
S A Y I N G   M U F F I N
T   A   E P   E   F   S
R E N D E L L   S N A R E
I   O   R   U S   L   T
C A S K   S T R E W
H   E   P   O   D I S
    S A U N A   A N E W
A   A   T   I G   S E
S O B E R   U K R A I N E
W   O   I M   E   P T
A D V I C E   B E S I D E
N   E   K     T   D N
```

288

```
L U R C H   B U O Y A N T
I   A   E E   U   M   H
C O N C A V E   C R I M E
I   S   R T   H G   D
T E A M   O L E   G O R E
    C   C E   H   L
G O K A R T   K E R N E L
A   Y   P W   U
L I N G   W A X   S C O T
I   O   B N   G L   H
L A R G E   T O R P E D O
E   M   A R   A U   R
E X A C T L Y   B A S I N
```

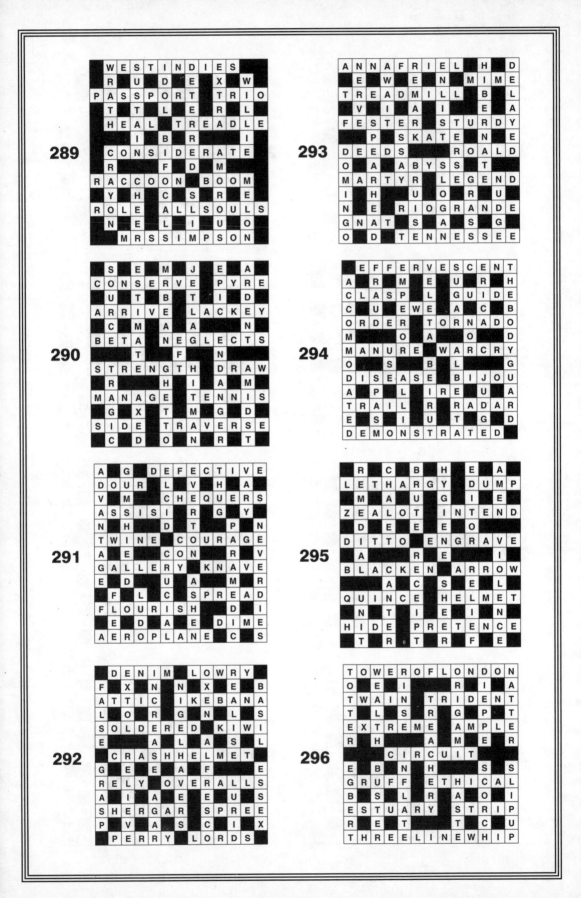

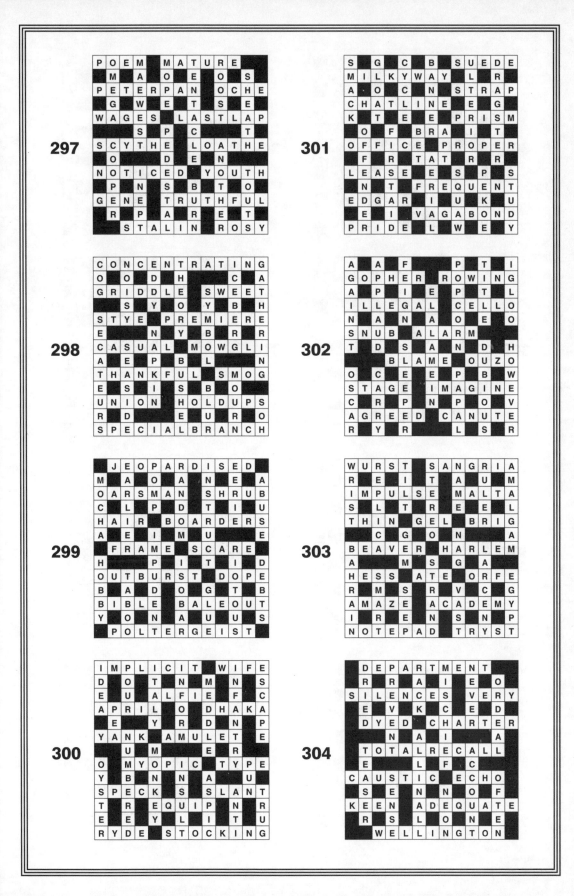

305

```
  M   A   C     P   G
C I R C U L A R   L Y L E
  K   I   I   A   E   O
H A N D L E   S H A B B Y
  D   T   N   E       A
L O N E   T O R T I L L A
      S   W       N
T E E T E R E D   F O A L
  X       A   A   I   L
S T A T I C   M I N G L E
  E   I   K   S   I   O
A N T E   E V E N T F U L
  T   R   T   L   E   T
```

306

```
I   A   D E D I C A T E D
C E D E   L   T   R   C
  E   J   G R A S M E R E
H O O P L A   L   Y   U
O   U   R   I   K   O
C O R F U   M A S T I F F
K   N   C A N   D   F
E M E R G E D   H I N G E
Y   D   R   A   A   N
  H   S   T   R U M P U S
S U B T R A C T   P   I
  L   E   I   I   D E R V
H A R M O N I C A   D   E
```

307

```
  S A T A N   D I T C H
S   L   L   C   B   U   L
K N E A D   O V E R S E E
I   S   E   S   X   H   V
E M I G R A T E   B I D E
R   M   A   J   O   R
  F I N A L D E M A N D
L   M   N   E   B   C
A L P S   C L E A N S E R
P   R   S   S   R   I   E
S C O R P I O   R I D G E
E   V   I   L   I   L   L
  H E A V Y   S E V E N
```

308

```
J O H N A D A M S   D   G
  P   A   I   O   V I E W
G R O T E S Q U E   S   Y
  A   A   T   S   H   N
S H E L V E   S T O O G E
  X   A L D E R   N   D
V I T A L       A H E A D
I   R   I S A A C   S
A G E N D A   S E T T E E
D   M   V   C   O   Y
U   I   P A P E R W O R K
C O S Y   G   N   E   I
  T   T   P E R T U R B E D
```

309

```
  I M O G E N S T U B B S
S   A   A   O   U   A   H
T R I A D   U   D I S C O
R   Z   D O G   O   I   R
A R E N A   H A R I C O T
I   F   T       R   C
T U R N I P   E S K I M O
J   E   I   C       M
A B S T A I N   R A B B I
C   O   D   S P A   R   N
K E N D O   E   P R A N G
E   I   R   R   E   N   S
T I C K E T T O R I D E
```

310

```
  A   B   B   P   A   A
A D E L A I D E   B U S H
  M   Y   Z   N   S   T
V I R T U E   S T U D I O
  R   O   T   I   R
P I A N O   H O O D L U M
  N   A   N   N
A G E L E S S   M A N G O
  E   S   S   P   A
R E D S E A   P L A C I D
  R   S   U   O   T   N
L I N O   L O O P H O L E
  K   N   T   L   Y   Y
```

311

```
I R R E S P O N S I B L E
N   A   L   I   E   X
T R I K E   M U N D A N E
A   S   P   A   A   C   M
C H E E T A H   T R O O P
T   D   A   R   N   T
    B O E R W A R
O   A   R   A   S   W
F O R C E   J U B I L E E
F   M   G   A   L   E   A
S T O M A C H   E V E N S
E   Ü   N   S   V   E
T O R T O I S E S H E L L
```

312

```
K H A N   W A R B L E
  Y   O   O   E   A   D
B E E T R O O T   S T E W
  N   H   L   I   E   P
F A K I R   A C C R U E D
  N   A   E   N
P L I G H T   N E V A D A
  O   T   T   A
A U C T I O N   A N G R Y
  V   H   R   O   T   U
E R S E   N O R M A L L Y
  E   M   E   A   G   E
  J E K Y L L   E A S Y
```

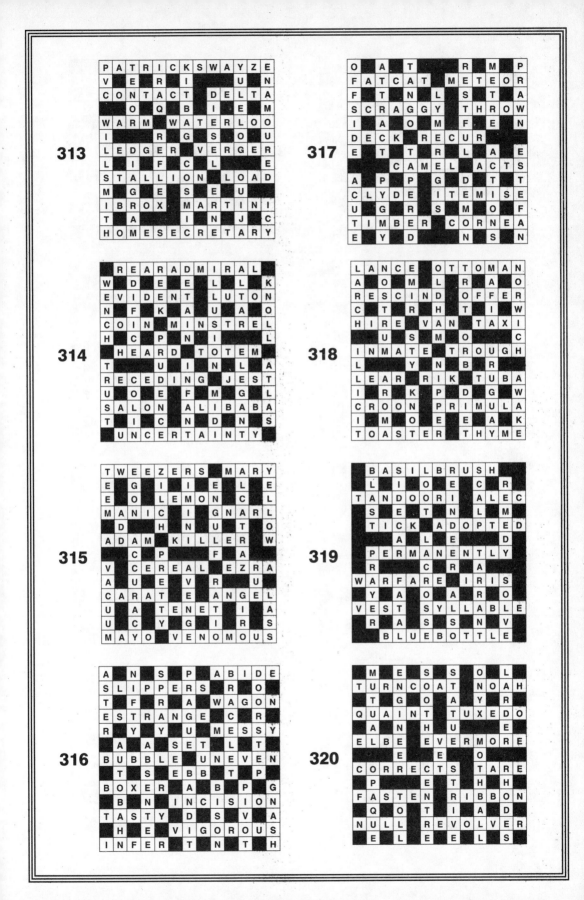

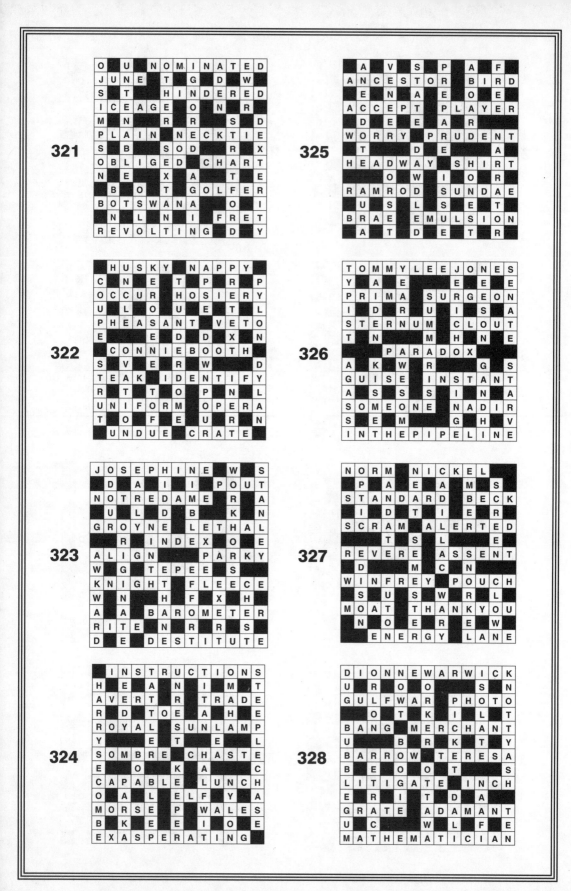

329

```
K E V I N K E E G A N
J X T I V L P
E N T I C E D A L I V E
T R H N P E T
T E A R H A Z E L N U T
Y C I P R Y
S T I N K T O N G S
G T M N R A
L A B U R N U M K E R B
O R U P E N B
B U I L D P I L L A G E
E N E E A D Y
D E E R S T A L K E R
```

330

```
D O M E S T I C C H A D
O O I N A A E
O S M U S I C L X
M E T R O I U N F I T
R N D M T E
Z E R O S E V E R E R
E I N R
P H A M L E T S M U G
I E P N G F
S P A T E S E N R O L
T R D R I V E N O
O S E G S L U
N O E L I N F E R I O R
```

331

```
A I D A T I R E D
U N D E R A G E R L
G I U E B R E E D
E M O T I O N S I C
R T D C A G A T E
I L B Y E A I
A N G I N A R A T I O N
S T P E R E N
M O N E T L S R J
M R M A R C I A N O
S N E A K T O B K
I T D E S O L A T E
D A L E K D T T R
```

332

```
U A F L S E
N A P L E S P E A N U T
I R A A G I H
C R I M S O N A N D R E
O C T I L E R
R I O T A M B L E
N T B O Y B S
C R U S T Z E S T
C G E I L A A
A O R T A T H I N N E R
B I K Y M B T
B E L I E F A B L A Z E
Y L R O G R
```

333

```
S E I N E L U G G A G E
H M V E I L L
A I M L E S S V A L V E
R E N T E O C
P U R L D E N S W O T
S N R G E
G A E L I C A B R O A D
I T D H B
G U S T D U B T S A R
G A G R B C A
L A T C H B O U Q U E T
E I E A N R E
D U N G E O N G U E S S
```

334

```
T R E M E N D O U S
E X D O N N S
I N T H E A I R D R E W
C A M M E A
H A U L C O M R A D E
S C U O
I N T E R E S T I N G
T I E R
G A Z E T T E R O P E
L L I O N M
K I L O C O L L A T E S
C P A A G N
S E L L A F I E L D
```

335

```
E V C A F S
I N F A M O U S L A K E
S L B H I I
O U T L A W O B T A I N
R E E R N
N E T T B R E A K A G E
T U N
D R E A D I N G A S I A
O N R P C
P L O U G H A U S T E N
L G A M A B
V E I L L A M B C H O P
R Y E Y K X
```

336

```
C O N A R C I S S U S
R O B E B H A L
A J A L A R M I N G
B R E A S T U E A
A C E C P C
P E T E R B E T R O T H
P I C A R L I
L E O T A R D B R A C E
E N O A R F
D R A S O R B E T
P E D A N T I C E A
M N I O S A R I
V I G I L A N T E R N
```

337

```
G U I L D   Q U O T A
T N   E   T   R   E   P
R H I N O   E N D L E S S
A F   N   A   U   N   A
S O Y S A U C E   G A L L
H   R   H   A   G   M
  K I N D H E A R T E D
D   N   O   R   B     D
E N V Y   E S P R E S S O
P   O   S   P   O   U V
T R I C K L E   A I S L E
H   C   I   T   T   H R
  P E N N Y   C H A I N
```

341

```
C A T H E R I N E P A R R
O   U   B       A L   H
F I R E D   D I S P L A Y
F   R   O   E   I   U   T
E T E R N A L   E A R T H
E   T       I   S   E M
    C H A R I T Y
I   A   O   I     S   F
G I L L S   O P T I C A L
U   W   T   U   U   A   O
A M A D E U S   L E M U R
N   Y   S       S   P   I
A S S A S S I N A T I O N
```

338

```
M A S C U L I N E   N M
R   I   O   E   T O R E
D I S G U I S E D   S A
S   A   T   D   T   N
H E A R S E   E D W A R D
  T   P R U D E   L   E
M E R G E     A N G E R
U   O   L A P E L   I
R E C A L L   S T R A I N
D   I   A   T   O   N
O   O   E S M E R A L D A
C L U B   K   E   S   I
H   S   D A L M A T I A N
```

342

```
W E P T   C L I C H E
  N   R   H   N O   O
N A P O L E O N   T H U D
  N   C   L   W U   E T
S T A L K   T E L L O F F
E   I       N   I
C A N Y O N   D E M O T E
  C   C   V   O   O
P I T C H E R   Q U I T O
  D   R   N   E N   H
F I N E   T E L E T H O N
  C   D   O   S   I N
  H O A R S E   E D G E
```

339

```
  Q U A R T E R S T A F F
L   B   E M   T   L   A
A B O U T   P   A T O L L
U   A   I L L   L   H K
R O T O R   O V E R A L L
E   E   Y   A   L   A
N O B O D Y   S I N B I N
B   U   K   N       D
A R T I S T E   D R E S S
C   O   W   E M U   X W
A L P H A   G   L Y C R A
L   A   R   A   G   E R
L I Z A M I N N E L L I
```

343

```
R E P R E H E N S I B L E
I   R   X   N   R   L
P R O R A T A   H E A V E
  W   M   M   E   V   M
C A L L   B E V E R A G E
U   S   L   D   D   N
T R A V E L   R E S O R T
T   M   Q   M   D   A
H O N D U R A S   G I L L
R   E   I   S   S   R
O R S O N   T H E B I L L
A   I   I   M   S   E
T R A F F I C L I G H T S
```

340

```
  T P   P S   E   E
V I G I L A N T   F U M E
  R   S   N   I F   E M
W A S T E S   L E E W A Y
  M   O   Y   T   C
V I L L A   R O U T I N E
  S   S   N       O
O U T B A C K   S C E N E
    R   R   S   U   S
F E D O R A   T E T H E R
L   K   T   I   L   N
M A R E   C O N V E R S E
N   R   H   G   T   E
```

344

```
  F O S B U R Y F L O P
L   R   A E   E   N   J
E V I C T E D   S L I M E
A   F   H E   T   O   L
S K I D   R E G I O N A L
H   C   A M   V   Y
  S E E D Y   F A I R Y
C   O   S   L   A   A
R E C O R D E R   F R O G
I   H   A N   B   E   R
S Q U I B   T H I M B L E
P   T   L R   E   I   E
  J E R E M Y B R E T T
```

Crossword Solutions

345

```
C U C U M B E R . F I R E
O O I Q R D X
S L R O U S E E P
H E A R T A P R A T E
. V H T O L R
J E E P . J E T S K I T
. M A E S
I . B U C K E T . E T O N
N R C N B R
D I A N E D A L T E R
I C S W E A T R A
G E S A O O I
O D D S . T R I N I D A D
```

349

```
T R A N S L A T E D
A R W G J D
Z U C C H I N I E D I T
N H M T C O
T R A Y E A S T E N D
I P T N
P I C T U R E S Q U E
I L S U
I L L N E S S C A I N
L O A B R A
P O L O T H E B R O N X
W S E R E N
P E R S O N A L L Y
```

346

```
S U V C W O U N D
N A T I O N A L V I
I T D M R E A C T
F R E C K L E S R O
F R A R P L A T O
G M S A S O I
R E M O T E E R R A N D
N V A R C D E
S E W E R E E T E
R M B A L M O R A L
W A T E R S P A A
T N C O N T E M P T
H E F T Y N Y P E
```

350

```
V M D A A R
G E R A N I U M W H E N
S L N U O V
A S S I G N S A L L O W
E N E E K
C L O G R E D E E M E D
E Y N
H E B R I D E S L O C K
X I E A L
M O R T A R D U R H A M
T E E U G R
V I S A C O C K E R E L
C T T E S T
```

347

```
E A D A C S
M A G G I E A F L O A T
B I A S F L U
R O T U N D A A D O R N
A A A T B N T
C U T E Q U I L L
E E P R E S F
U R B A N B O A R
U C E T M L E
S E L E S E P I S O D E
U W S D M M D
A S Y L U M K I M O N O
L D P C N M
```

351

```
A E U N L I M I T E D
M A C E O G V X
U C B O N H O M I E
S H E K E L I R T
E N E T T S
M A T C H J E F F R E Y
E R S A D U N
N E I T H E R W A N D A
T C C S C G
S B L P E D A L O
A L T I T U D E T G
U A D E P E R U
C R E S C E N D O S E
```

348

```
R E I G N H E N P E C K
A M E U A R I
P A P Y R U S P E R O N
I O O T E O N
D R U B H O T E R G O
N L N E C
F O D D E R A N O R A K
R E S D I
E T C H G E T K N O B
E H G P R G I
B L A R E T R A W L E R
I I R E I E T
E A R N E S T N O T C H
```

352

```
S O P P Y S K I L L
P T R C E E S
L I T H E O B E L I S K
E E A N P S I
A T R O C I T Y T U R N
T H A G R T
H E L E N M I R R E N
U X R I O C
S C A M E N C U M B E R
H M M A N O E
E M I N E N T D R O N E
R N N E E T P
R E V U E I D A H O
```

353

```
S E G R E G A T E . G . M
. L . I . A . I . J U D O
N E W F O R E S T . A . N
. C . L . I . S . R . A .
S T R E S S . U N F A I R C
. E . T H R E E . N . . .
C E L I A . . W I T C H .
H . U . M A P L E . E . .
E X C E P T . A L I E N S
D . T . T . T . R . I .
D . A . M I N T S A U C E
A C N E . R . E . T . H
R . T . R E T R I E V E R
```

354

```
. T H U N D E R S T O R M
A . E . E . X . T . D . O
B A L S A . P . R O D I N
S . L . T E E . U . I . K
E R O D E . C O M P E T E
N . . . S T . T . O . Y
T A H I T I . S E E S A W
M . C . T . X . . . R
I N F E R N O . P R O N E
N . L . I . P A L . C . N
D R O W N . H . A D H O C
E . S . G . A . I . R . H
D I S C O N T I N U E D .
```

355

```
. E . G . O . M . S . G
D Y S L E X I A . M A R K
. E . A . F . R . U . I
G L E N D A . S E D A T E
. I . C . M . H . G .
E N T E R . H A T E F U L
. E . C . L . . . P
A R D U O U S . L E A R N
. . . S . R . A . C . I
P E S E T A . M O L E S T
. I . F . T . B . A . I
F R A U . O P I N I O N S
. E . L . R . T . R . G
```

356

```
C L A R E N C E H O U S E
O . S . P . . A . R . I
G U S T O . A C R O B A T
N . U . C . D . V . A . H
A B R A H A M . E R N I E
C . E . I . S . E . R
. . . R U G R A T S . .
B . R . S . A . . . C . G
O X E Y E . B L E T H E R
N . F . L . L . A . E . I
S Q U E E Z E . V E R S E
A . N . S . . . E . U . V
I N D I S P E N S A B L E
```

357

```
M E A D . T O U C A N .
. R . E . I . N . B . T
B A R B A D O S . H O U R
. S . A . Y . T . O . R
H E N C E . Y E A R N E D
. . . L . S . A . . E
T A L E N T . D O M I N O
. M . . A . Y . A . .
Z O O L O G Y . S T R A W
. U . O . N . S . I . M
U N D O . A T L A N T I S
. T . S . T . A . E . S
. J E R E M Y . E A S T
```

358

```
M E T E O R O L O G I S T
A . B . B . B . . N . R
P R O V O K E . B A I Z E
. N . E . Y . R . T . A
C R E W . D E R E L I C T
O . R . D . T . A . M
R E C K O N . C O L L I E
K . O . M . C . N . N
S Y M P A T H Y . L E N T
C . I . N . U . M . X
R O C K Y . R E A D I N G
E . A . C . I . S . U
W O L V E R H A M P T O N
```

359

```
. C O M B I N A T I O N .
C . R . A . E . E . R . K
A N D O R R A . S H A D E
D . E . E . R . T . T . N
G U R U . F L A T T E R Y
E . L . O . Y . U . . A
. S Y R U P . I B I Z A .
Y . . . T . P . E . E . A
E N L A R G E D . G A O L
A . L . A . C . G . L . L
S L A N G . T W O S O M E
T . M . E . I . L . U . Y
. H A R D A N D F A S T .
```

360

```
M O N G O O S E . R U B Y
E . A . U . E . S . N . O
E V . G I A N T . C . N
T E E T H . R . A L O U D
. K . T . C . P . U . E
M E O W . P H I L I P . R
. F . E . . E . L . .
L . F A M O U S . T E R N
O . I . B . L . S . . Y
C E C I L . R . W A R E S
U . I . E X I L E . E . A
S . A . M . K . D . S . N
T A L C . T A L E N T E D
```

361

```
S K M R . P E C A N
T I N K E R E D . C . B
O E R P . G L A S S
A G E G R O U P . I . T
T L Y T . S P A R K
. D I . T E A . S . A
Y E O M E N . W R E T C H
. L B . T I N . D . T
L A T E X . R A W . J
. W C . M O R T G A G E
R A D I O . N . H . V . M
. R L . L I N O L E U M
F E V E R . C . S . R Y
```

362

```
S . P . S . . C A . B
A G A T H A . L O D G E R
T . R . E . A . M . I . E
C R A V I N G . P O L K A
H . B . K . G . A . E . K
M U L L . W R O N G
O . E . T . E . Y . B . B
. . L A U G H . Y O Y O
S . A . V . A . B . R . U
W E D G E . T U R M O I L
O . D . R . E . A . U . D
O B L O N G . J I N G L E
P . E . A . . N . H . R
```

363

```
P I N C H . A N G E L I C
A . U . E . N . I . O . O
S U M M A R Y . R E A L M
T . E . T . O . L . T . P
A C R E . I N N . O H I O
. . A . P . E . A . . . S
S U L L E N . I G N O R E
U . . T . R . O . P
S N O W . S E W . R E A D
P . P . S . C . D . N . W
E V I C T . O P E R A T E
N . U . A . R . E . I . L
D A M A G E D . P E R I L
```

364

```
. L A R Y N G I T I S
. E . O . A . N . N . R
L O V E B I R D . A L O E
. N . D . L . I . N . A
. E V E R . S C R E E C H
. . A . J . A . . . H
. C O N C E N T R A T E
. U . . T . E . D
F R I G A T E . S A V E
. T . E . I . P . P . B
C L A N . S O L U T I O N
. Y . R . O . U . E . N
. R E D N O S E D A Y
```

365

```
. F . S . B . S . R . A
P I C K W I C K . S O D A
. G . E . G . I . V . V
G U L L E T . N E P H E W
. R . E . O . N . . . R
L E F T . P L Y M O U T H
. . . O . . O . . N
S C H N A P P S . L O S S
. H . . . I . I . O . L
G I B S O N . G L O R I A
. R . H . C . N . K . V
M A N E . E B E N E Z E R
. C . D . R . T . R . R
```

366

```
S . S . F I R E W O R K S
P I T T . M . A . M . E
E . U . P A S T I L L E
A R T F U L . T . T . P
K . T . Y . E . S . R
E V E R Y . A R M O U R Y
A . R . S I N . P . A
S L E N D E R . S H E E N
Y . D . M . S . R . G
. D . I . I . M U E S L I
H E L S I N K I . T . G
. N . I . A . L . F A N G
N E W S T R E E T . R . S
```

367

```
. C H U N K . S A I N T
S . A . E . M . V . A . A
M A G I C . E D I T I O N
A . U . K . R . D . R . G
S H E R L O C K . C O I L
H . . . A . H . A . B . E
. A L E C B A L D W I N
L . A . E . N . V . . . A
A R N E . A D J O U R N S
S . T . D . I . C . O . K
S P E C I E S . A Z U R E
O . R . S . E . A . N . W
. K N A C K . S T U D Y
```

368

```
N E G L E C T E D . S . O
. V . I . O . N . S H I P
D A R T M O U T H . O . U
. D . R . K . I . R . L
S E R E N E . R A T T L E
. . O . A R I E S . W . N
A D U L T . . . L E A P T
M . T . T E N S E . V
B O L E Y N . O F F E N D
R . E . R . W . L . I
O . . D . C A R E T A K E R
S A G O . G . T . R . C
E . E . R E C O V E R E D
```

Crossword Solutions

369

```
  S T R I N G F E L L O W
S A L   R   M   U     E
A N N U L   E   B A C O N
R   G   W O E   E   R   D
S P Y R I   D O D D E R Y
P E B B L E   W H O O P I
A   I     P   A       C
R A M B L E R   N E I G H
I   O   A   E G G   N   A
L I G H T   C   M O T O R
L   U   I     A   E     D
A L L A N D S U N D R Y
```

373

```
C R O S S Q U E S T I O N
U   W   T   N     N   O
P U N J A B I   G W E N T
    U   N   T   L   X   O
K E P T   D E B O N A I R
A     P   D   V   C   I
M A R G I N   S E E T H E
P   A   E   H   S     T
U P M A R K E T   S P R Y
C   B   C   A   W   I
H A L V E   L E A F L E T
E   E     T   R   A   A
A U D R E Y H E P B U R N
```

370

```
    C   A   S   P   T   O
C O N F E T T I   W A V E
    L   R   E   N   I   E
P O P E Y E   S U N D R Y
    R   S   R   E   G
M A T H S   U N K E M P T
    D     S   T     R
C O R S I C A   A D M I N
    H   E   K   E   N
L E G I O N   N U A N C E
    R   N   E   O D   E
L I L T   R E C K L E S S
    C   Y   Y   K   Y   S
```

374

```
  T O B A C C O N I S T
W   B   R   L   E   E   C
R O S S I N I   G I D D Y
E   E   D   Q   L   G   M
C O R D   M U T I N E E R
K   V   J   E   G       U
  R E B U S   K E L L Y
T   L   D   E   O   S
R E T A I L E R   C O S T
U   Y   E   V   P   K   O
R E S I N   O R I N O C O
O   O   N   U   N   U   P
  I N T E R R O G A T E
```

371

```
R E V O L U T I O N A R Y
E   E   U     V   U     E
G O R A N   F R E E S I A
I   O   G   R   R   T   R
N U N N E R Y   D R I L L
A   A   I     U   N     Y
    S P I N N E Y
O   A   H   G     S   B
B E N N Y   P U L S A T E
J   G   S   A   O   F   A
E R O S I O N   T O A S T
C   R   C     U   R   E
T R A N S G R E S S I O N
```

375

```
S E L E C T E D   G R U B
N   O   O   S   B   O   E
O   G   M I T R E   M   A
B O O Z E   A   H O A R D
  I     T   T   I   N   L E
C L I P   R E N N E T
    N   S       D   I
P   H A P P E N   S C A N
O   E   E   G   V     P
D I R G E   G   I N L E T
I   E   D I N A R   A   E
U   N   Y   O   G   V   X
M Y T H   I G N O R A N T
```

372

```
N E E D   K I T T E N
  M   E   N   O   G   A
C A M P B E L L   R O S S
  I   O   E   E   S
P L U S H   F R E T F U L
  I   S     A       M
A R C T I C   T I C K E T
  E     R   E   L
R A M A D A N   R I G I D
  G   M   M   S   M   C
T A C O   B U L G A R I A
  N   U   L   O   T   N
  B R E E Z E   E D G Y
```

376

```
C   S   C   S   M I N C E
L O C A L I T Y   N   O
I   A   A   R   C H O M P
M O N S I E U R   U   P
B   T   M   C   S M A L L
  H   L   S K Y   A   E
D E S I G N   O R N A T E
  I   S   P U B   E   E
F R O T H   N   B   S   I
  L   L   I S O L A T E D
Y O D E L   E   A   A   E
  O   S   M A G N O L I A
A M A S S   T   D   L   L
```

377

```
C I D     D       B     A   P
H I N D E R   L I N G E R
O   H   V   M   Z   O     A
P I A N O L A   A N N A N
E   B   N   N   R   Y     K
R   E M I T   T H E R M
    T   K   A   E   D     O
    V I S T A     P E A R
I   U   L   T   D   V     L
N E P A L   A B U S I V E
G   S   J   N   R   A     A
O C E L O T   S U L T A N
T   T   Y       M     E   S
```

381

```
A   A   B O X I N G D A Y
G A M E   P   N   E     L
I   B   I N H E R I T S
N E L S O N   I   M   O
C   E   E   B   P     S
O A S I S   M I N O R C A
U   I   C O T     O     L
R E D C O A T   L I M I T
T   E   R   A   E     P
    F   H   D   G R A N G E
F I G U R I N E     A   T
    F   R   A N   A D U R
R E P L I C A T E   E   E
```

378

```
M O V I E   Q U I E T L Y
U   I   N   U   N   O   E
D E S P I S E   C A N A L
D   I   D   B   E   N   T
Y E T I   K E W   N E W S
A   O   R   C   R     I
P O R T E R   A U T U M N
A   X   I   M   T     N
S U M P   A N Y   S I G H
S   O   M   C   G   L   U
A N N O Y   O R A T I O N
G   T   N   M   F   S   C
E L E V A T E   F R E S H
```

382

```
  P U L S E   E L F I N
A   T   A   P   U   N   A
D A U N T   R E L A T E D
E   R   U   E   L   R   D
P A N O R A M A   M U S E
T   T   A   O   C   D   R
  M A R T I N S H E E N
C   T   E   I   R     S
R U T H   A T T I T U D E
U   E   O   I   S   N   V
M E M E N T O   R A I S E
B   P   U   N   E   T   R
  S T A S H   R A V E N
```

379

```
  O C C A S I O N A L
  U   E   W   M   P   L
E N V I S A G E   P R A Y
  C   L   G   L   L   U
  E V I L   N E W Y O R K
      N   D   T     I
  R E G R E T T A B L E
  E   S   E   L
B A R O N E T   S O N G
  D   A   R   W   S   R
S E T T   T E A M S T E R
  R   E   E   R   O   E
  A S T R O N O M E R
```

383

```
D A L A I L A M A   Q   S
  M   L   Y   E   D U S T
D U P L I C A T E   A   E
  S   O   H   T   A S   P
F E T T L E   L A V I S H
  A   Y E M E N   M   E
L E N I N       T R O O N
O   T   A L I B I   D
T R A U M A   A C C O S T
T   L   R   T   O   T
E   I   P I S T A C H I O
R I S K   A   E   O   L
Y   E   E T E R N A L L Y
```

380

```
  D   C   M   S   A   A
T A I L B A C K   F A S T
  M   O   Y   A   A   S
P A R I S H   T H R E A T
  G   S   E   E     I
S E A T   M A R T E L L O
    E   L     C
U M B R E L L A   S O R T
  I   I   N   T   E
B R A H M S   S W A T C H
  R   E   B   W   T   E
M O D E   O B E D I E N T
  R   L   N   R   C   T
```

384

```
  H O R S E A N D C A R T
A   S   C   R   I   B   E
C H A F E   R   N O B E L
C   K   P I E   G   O   L
E X A C T   S H O R T L Y
L   I   T   I   I     S
E N R I C H   S A M O S A
R   O   R   I   I     V
A U G U S T A   L I B R A
T   E   U   T O M   R   L
I N C U R   H   E V I T A
N   K   G   E   N   D   S
G L O B E T R O T T E R
```

385

```
  L  A  G     D  O     A
H OGMANAY     F ACE
  N  E  O  N     F  M
B EDLAM     A RCHER
  S  I  E  S  U
R OWAN     S TATION
  M     S  Y        P
V ERDICT     A ZTEC
     R  O  G     I  R
G AZEBO     R AGBAG
  B  A  T  E     Z  T
H ELM     E LEVATOR
  T  T     R  D  G  R
```

386

```
JASPERCARROTT
I  E  R     A  R     I
GRAZE     DOVECOT
S  M  C  O     I  H  T
ADAPTER     OLIVE
W  N     M     L  D  R
     SATIRIC
S  P  V  T        D  P
WORSE     OUTSIDE
I  O  R     R  A  V  P
TOPIARY     SWEEP
C  E  G        T  R  E
HELTERSKELTER
```

387

```
WATT     CAUGHT
  P  U  O  N     I  A
WRESTLED     TILL
  O  C  T  E     C  F
INLAY     ARCHERY
  N     I  A        E
MAGYAR     RESIDE
  R     R  M     P
BAVARIA     FATTY
  F  L  T  M     N  O
GAVE     ALIENATE
  T  R  T     L  E  A
  ATTEND     RULE
```

388

```
ROYALAIRFORCE
A  E  Y     B     O  N
PENANCE     DELFT
  T  X  R  O     L  E
BOLT     MISNOMER
E     H  A  A     O  T
TAIPEI     UTOPIA
R  N     A  B  E     I
OUTBREAK     THEN
T  E  T     S  N  E
HARSH     SWAHILI
E  I        E  S  D  A
DEMONSTRATION
```

389

```
   JANESEYMOUR
D  S  S     N  A  P  S
INSIPID     GREET
V  U  Y  U     I  N  E
EARL     ERICIDLE
R  E  P  E     I     P
  ADMIT     CABIN
P     N  R  N     D  J
ANTEATER     RIFE
U  H  F  C  G     O  R
SLIGO     EQUATOR
E  E  R  D  L     I  Y
  AFTEREFFECT
```

390

```
REACTION     SOLD
O  D  O  B     M  R  I
M  I  DELVE     N  T
PITTA  I     DEATH
V     Y  G  I     M  E
BYRE     BEMUSE     R
     E  S        M  N
T  TATTOO     ITEM
E  R  R  B     E     R
ASIDE     CREAM
B  E  AURAL     D  E
A  V  M  O     A  E  A
GLEE     INSTINCT
```

391

```
A  A  S  A     ROMAN
SEDATIVE     V  L
W  O  O  E     BENDY
ALPACINO     R  E
  C  I  FEW     O  N
ORANGE     HOOTER
  E  T  DRY     K  Y
LOWER     A  A  G  N
  S  R  GNASHERS  S
DOWNY     T  H  N  P
  T  E  CELERIAC
HEATH     D  N  E  C
```

392

```
S     S  D        G  W  C
THWART     ARMADA
E  A  A  B     A  S  U
RIPTIDE     PEPYS
I  P  N  T     P  S  E
LEER     WHELK
E  D  D  L     E  D  P
   METER     SUDS
S  C  S     H  D  S  Y
THEFT     ERRATIC
U  A  R  M     E  P  H
MOSCOW     HAWAII
P  E  Y philosophy M  N  C
```

393

```
S A U C E . P I V O T A L
C T P L E R E
R E T S I N A . A B O V E
U E C N L L W
M E R E . F E Z . E L S A
. E . E . T H . . A R
T O D D L E . A G E O L D
E . M . C V . I
S A S H . N A Y . P L O T
T H E R P S E
I N A P T . P R I C K L E
N W N E E I N
G A L L A N T . R O N A Y
```

394

```
. E X A G G E R A T E .
L C O A A N
B A C C A R A T . C O O K
N L Y I K T
D R A B . C O P Y C A T
I A N R
F A M I L I A R I T Y
A T L N
B R O T H E R . P E E P
R E R F R H
R O T A . E V E N T U A L
W S G E I S
S E C O N D R A T E
```

395

```
I E V U S M
A D D I T I O N W O O D
I N C W I R
C O R S E T E I G H T Y
C T I L A
H Y P E M U L T I P L Y
I S N
R E U N I T E D D U M P
X R E I E
M O B I L E S T R O L L
D O N P E L
R U I N C H O W C H O W
S A H T T W
```

396

```
S V W I L T S H I R E
T R I M M O E H
A O A P P A L L E D
B E L O N G C D A
I E E O P A
L U N A R B A I L I F F
I T C U T P T
T E L F O R D P A S T E
Y Y U T Q R
M B C A U B U R N
H A R A K I R I E O
K S A L F A R O
N E W S F L A S H K N
```

397

```
. R U C H E . J U L I E
S N O R T N C
T U T O R . E V A N D E R
Y I R C H I I
L I L L I P U T . B A L E
E F P C N D
. P O L I C E W O M A N .
S B C R N A
P U L P . F A S T F O O D
E I F T E V I
A C Q U I R E . S I E G E
R U D D S R U
. F E W E R . F A I T H
```

398

```
G U N P O W D E R . I S
N U A L K N O W
M I L K F L O A T S A
T K T P O G
G Y R A T E . S T A L A G
E O R D E R E E
B R A V O . I N N E R
A L T H R O B C
B L I T H E . R E N E G E
Y S R W U E
G T G A B E R D I N E
R A I L L L G U
O C E D E L W E I S S
```

399

```
C L I F F R I C H A R D
B E R I A N I
R S P C A P N E V I S
U E G Y P O I A
C O R G I L O N G L E G
E L E O R
F A T H E R W A D D L E
O U T D E
R E B E C C A M A D A M
S R A U R I R E
Y E A T S R R O U E N
T W T U E N T
H U N G E R S T R I K E
```

400

```
I A A S C S
U N C L E S A M H O W L
C P P O R A
P I R A T E T R O U P E
D C N H M
D E C A Y V E T E R A N
N A R R
S T A T E L Y B E E C H
R L S A H
S N E E Z E T O R R I D
O M G E W V
S U M O R E A L I S E D
S R O M G S
```

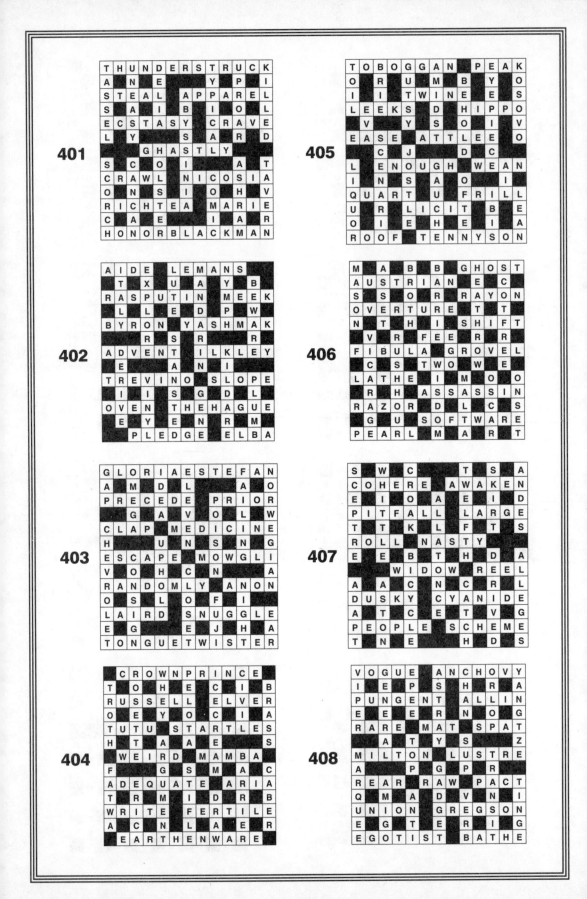

401

402

403

404

405

406

407

408

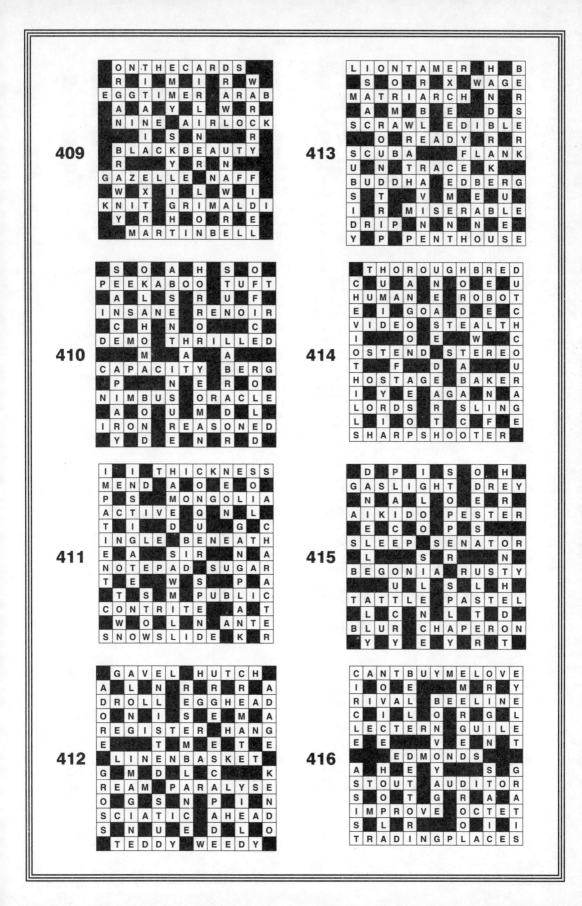

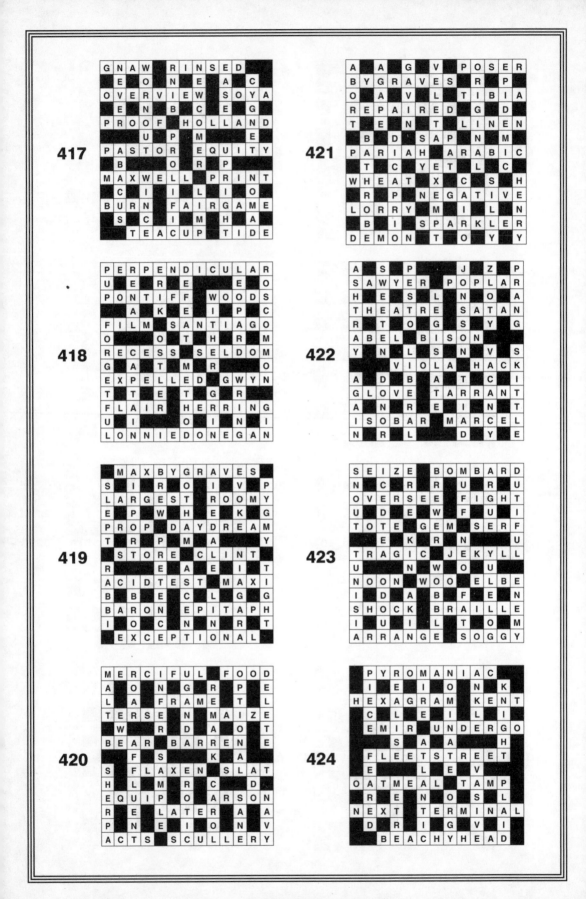

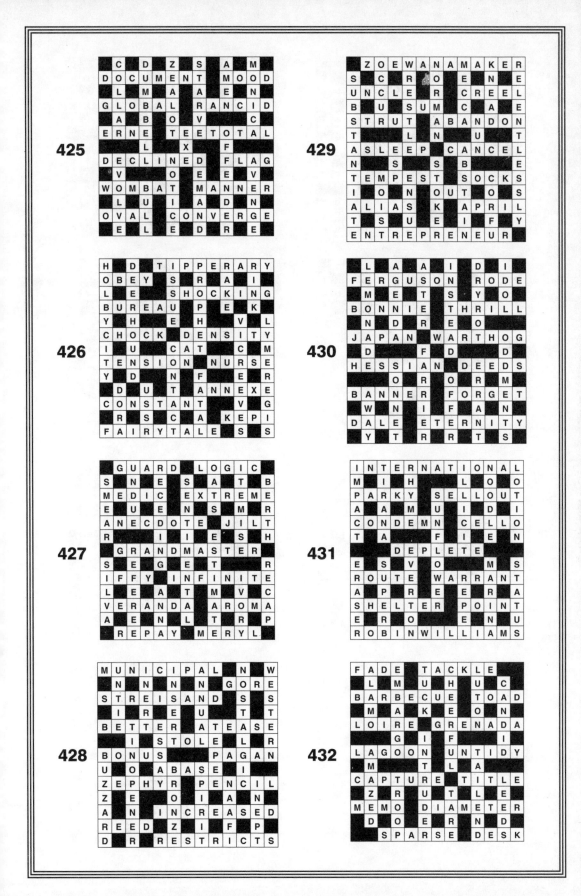

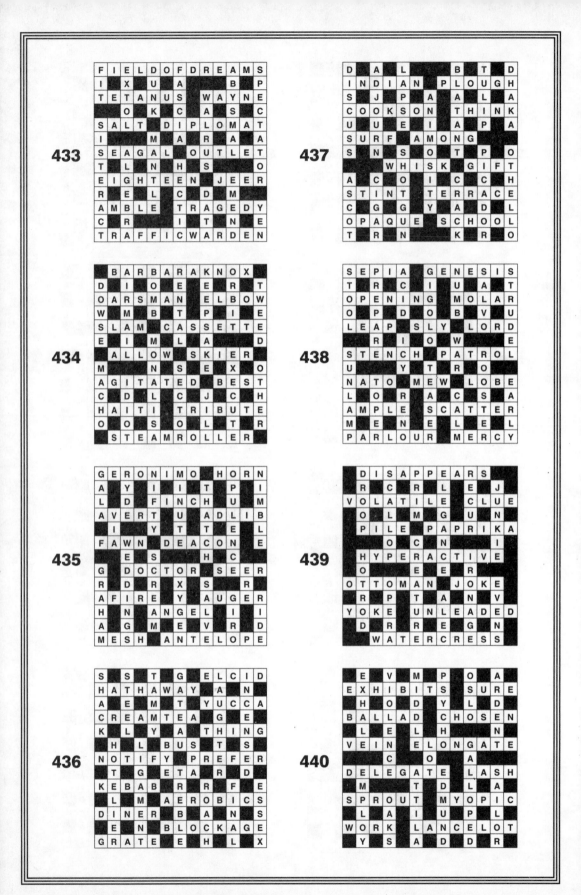

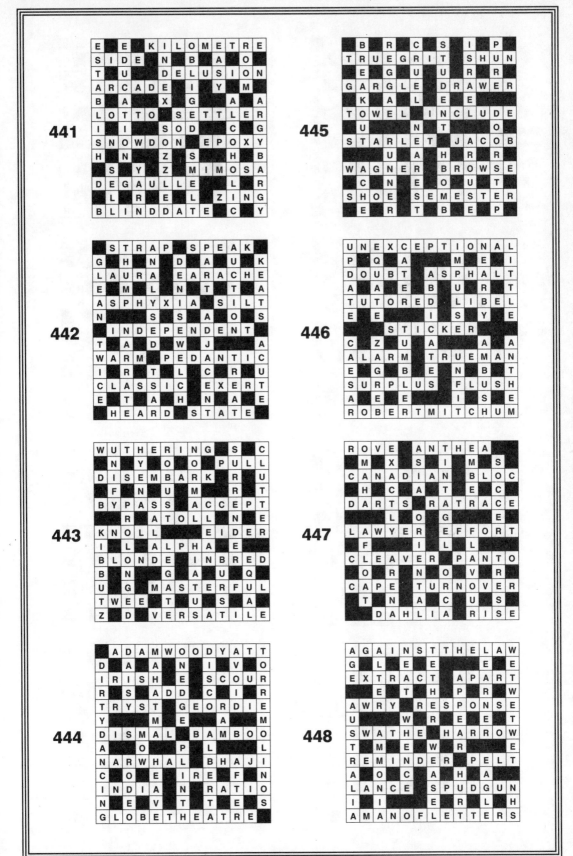

441 442 443 444 445 446 447 448

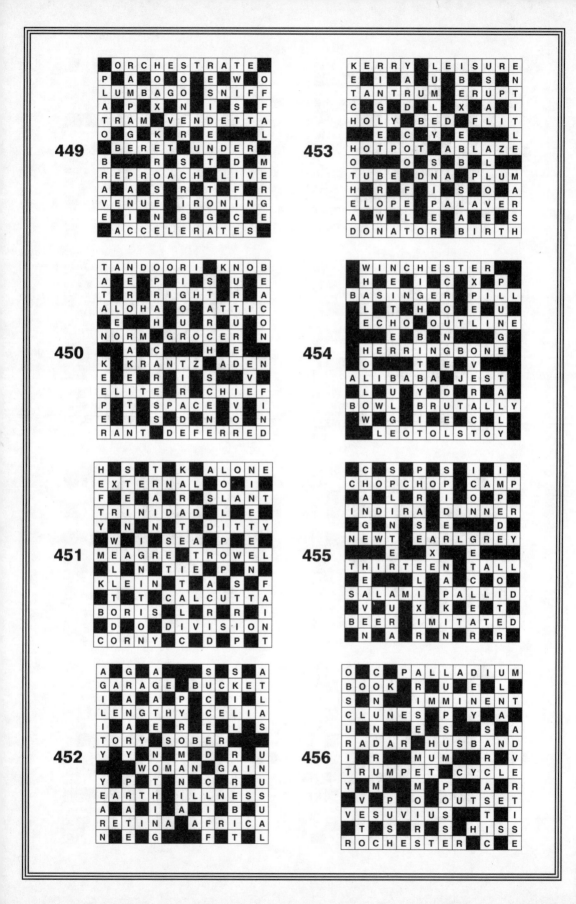

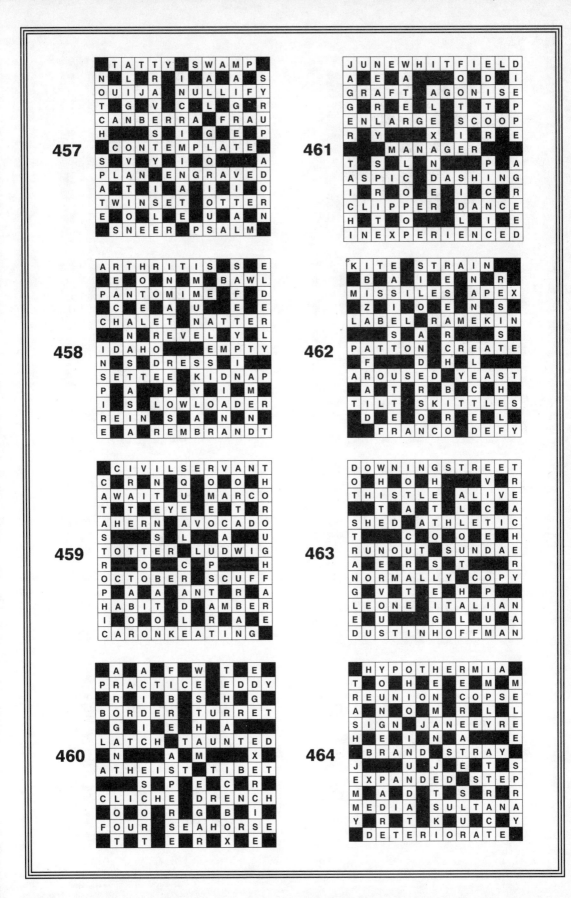

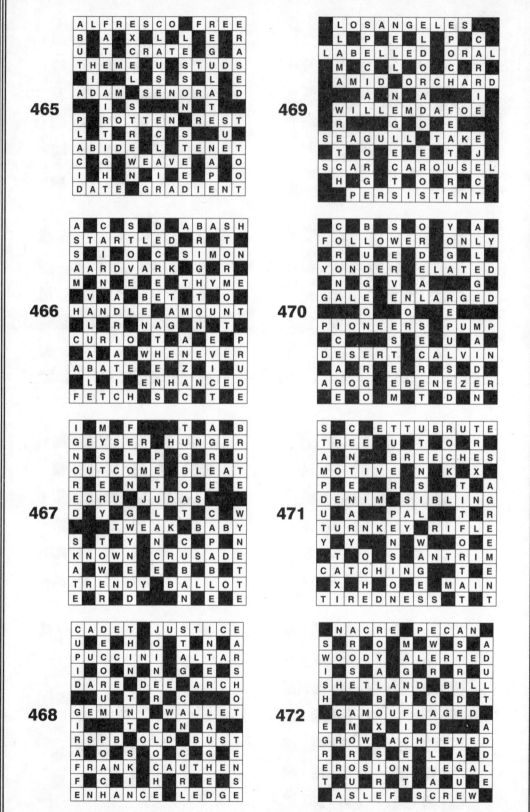

473

```
C H O C O L A T E   P   A
  O   A   I   H   G A N G
S A N D S T O R M   N   A
  R   G   T   U   A   A K
A D H E R E   S T I T C H
    O   O R A T E   E   A
K O R E A       P Y L O N
I   S   S P Y R I   L
T R E A T Y   E D W A R D
C   P   T   M   H   E
H   C H R O N I C L E
E D A M   O   V   R   I
N   Y   I N T E R L O C K
```

477

```
S O U L   H O T D O G
  R   E   E   H   C   S
B L A C K I C E   H O P S
  O   A   R   S   R   A
S N A R E   A P P E A R S
    R   P   I       T
R E V E A L   A F F R A Y
  N       E   N   R
R A I L W A Y   P E R O N
  B   I   S   A   E   W
B L A B   U P R I S I N G
  E   Y   R   M   I   U
    S A F E T Y   A L P S
```

474

```
  R E L I N Q U I S H E D
F   B   C   U   N   E   R
L O D G E   E   L U N G E
E   O   B A N   E   N   S
  E R N I E   C U T L A S S
T   R   H   I   I
W H I N G E   K I T T E N
O   E   A   N       G
  O R L E A N S   S C R A G
D   O   M   C O P   A   O
M O C H A   E   E N D O W
A   U   Z   N   C   I   N
C O M M E N D A T I O N
```

478

```
M A I D O F O R L E A N S
A   D   P   R       D   T
P R E T E N D   A T O N E
    A   N   A P P   P   A
B A L I   D I S P U T E D
U   R   N   E   E   E   F
C O R N E T   Z A N D R A
N   H   G   M   L       S
A Q U A R I U S   W A N T
N   B   E   S   A   M
E N A C T   S E L F I S H
E   R   E   E   A   S   A
R O B E R T L I N D S A Y
```

475

```
  D   P   M   H   P   T
S E N O R I T A   H O U R
  L   T   N   L   I   R
V A C A T E   I S L A N D
  W   T   R   B   I
H A V O C   S U R P A S S
  R   R   N   T       E
R E T I R E D   F U D G E
    N   U   S   N   M
G A M B I T   M O T L E Y
  G   O   R   A   R   N
L A I R   A C C O U N T S
  R   N   L   K   E   S
```

479

```
  T E L E T U B B I E S
F   X   L   N   Y   L   S
E M A N A T E   T H E R M
N   M   N   V   H   C   E
C O I L   P E D E S T A L
E   N   P   N   W       L
  D E B I T   S A I N T
J   T   P   Y   U   S
O B T A I N E D   C R E W
N   H   L   C   S   E   O
E X I L E   T A L L Y H O
S   G   S   I   I   E   P
  C H A S A N D D A V E
```

476

```
W O R D P R O C E S S O R
A   A   H   N   U   A
R H I N O   M O R N I N G
H   S   T   O   A   T
O R I N O C O   G L O B E
L   N   N   E   R   D
      O B T R U D E
A   A   U   A   B   R
R O T O R   K A R A O K E
C   T   G   E   U   N   C
T R A I L E R   L A S S O
I   I   A   E   A   I
C O N T R O V E R S I A L
```

480

```
M A L A Y S I A   W I M P
A   U   O   N   U   N   O
I   N   D O V E R   S   U
D R A K E   E   C L O W N
  I   L   S   H   L   C
U G L Y   A T T I R E   E
  I   S       N   N
S   A S P E C T   S T A B
C   I   O   R   A   Y
O R S O N   E   G N A R L
T   O   G L A Z E   M   E
C   N   E   S   N   M   N
H O S T   B E E T R O O T
```

481

```
C E D F . F A U L T
R E V E I L L E . P . I
I . I . A . E . M E A N T
M U T I N E E R . R . O
E . A . E . C . S T A L L
. . J . A . P E P . U . E
F E R G I E . . V E R S U S
R . I . R O C . E . M . U
D O T T Y . R . G . V . U
. B . A . C I V I L I A N
B O O T Y . E . R . R . I
. A . E . I N S T R U C T
A M U S E . T . H . S . E
```

482

```
E . F . F . . H . S . S
T E L L E R . H A P P E N
E . U . R . A . L . I . A
R U T L A N D . F U N G I
N . T . L . J . W . E . L
A R E A . L O U I S
L . R . S . U . T . E . F
. . W H E R E . U N D O
T . L . U . N . D . D . R
R O U N D . E P I S O D E
U . N . D . D . G . R . V
R O C K E T . T I S S U E
O . H . R . . T . E . R
```

483

```
L E E C H . A G I T A T E
A . L . E R . S . B . M
P I E B A L D . P L U M P
E . G . T O . Y . S . A
L E A K . R U T . T E X T
. . N . A R . C . . . H
I N T A C T . L U X U R Y
N . T . G . E . S
H A I R . L E S . V E I L
I . N . F . N . G . L . I
B U G L E . T O R R E N T
I . O . E . R . A . S . R
T O T A L L Y . B A S T E
```

484

```
. I C E S K A T I N G
. N . S . E . A . A . B
P L A T Y P U S . D O O R
. A . U . T . M . I . W
. Y E A R . W A R R I O R
. . R . S . N . . . U
. A S Y O U L I K E I T
. B . . . B . A . L
O R I G A M I . G A R B
. U . E . E . G . S . I
S P I N . R O A S T I N G
. T . R . G . I . I . G
. R E C E P T A C L E
```

485

```
M . D . L . B . . A . L
B A S E B A L L . . B I E R
. L . T . P . O . E . T
V A C A N T . T E T C H Y
. G . I . O . T . . . A
Y A W N . P R O M P T L Y
. . E . . . A . . . L
B A N D A N N A . A V O W
R . . . U . C . T . P
A N K A R A . C L O S E R
O . L . N . E . N . N
P L E A . C O N S I D E R
. D . S . E . T . C . R
```

486

```
O . E . G A R I B A L D I
B O S S . L . N . N . I
T . C . L A S V E G A S
R O A C H E . I . W . S
U . L . Y . P . V . S
S L A S H . H I L L A R Y
I . T . S A D . L . N
V I E T N A M . A D E P T
E . D . R . E . N . H
. D . S D . N E T T L E
P I N P O I N T . I . T
. V . O . N . E . R N L I
S A L T P E T R E . E . C
```

487

```
. R E V U E . N A V E L
A . X . L . B . P . A . S
S T A R T . R E S E R V E
W . C . E . A . E . H . V
A S T E R O I D . S A V E
N . . . I . N . U . R . R
. U N F O R T U N A T E
A . O . R . E . D . . . G
F O R M . T A K E A W A Y
F . W . G . S . R . H . P
I M I T A T E . A R I E S
X . C . Z . R . G . S . Y
. C H E E R . J E T T Y
```

488

```
D E T E C T I V E . C . P
. Y . L . R . O . T O Y S
P R A G M A T I C . M . Y
. I . A . D . C . M . C
D E G R E E . E N R I C H
. R . C R E D O . T . I
K N E L L . . . O P T I C
A . A . A B Y S S . E
R O T A T E . C E R E A L
L . D . F . R . E . Z
O . A . P O T A S S I U M
F O N T . R . P . I . R
F . E . A E G E A N S E A
```

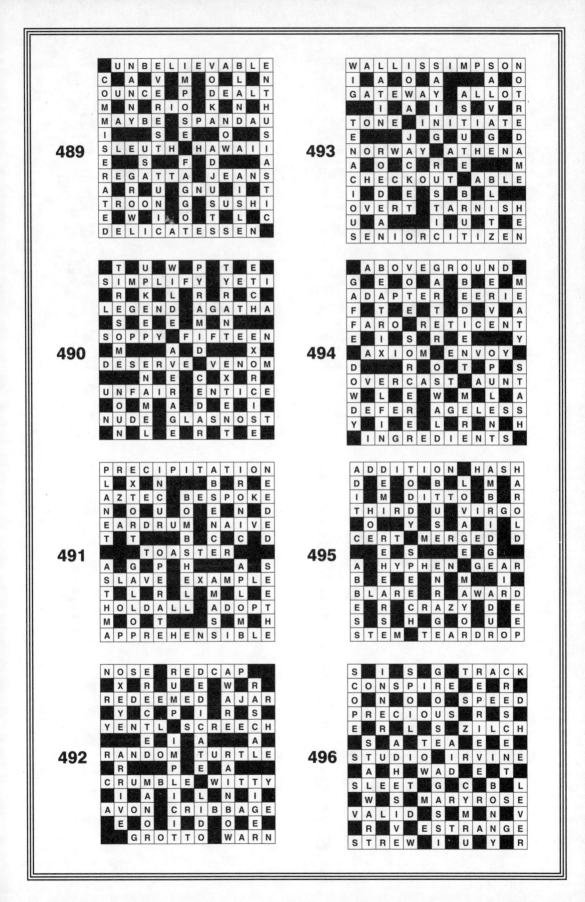

489

490

491

492

493

494

495

496

497

```
P   S A     L   C
R O W I N G   W A N D E R
E   A   N   B   C   H   E
S U R F A C E   Q U O T E
I   T   N   A   U   C   K
D A H L   A N N E X
E   Y   T   F   R   M   D
    G E N E S   F A M E
E   C   R   A   G   R   L
G L O O M   S E R V I C E
Y   U   I   T   I   T   T
P A R I T Y   B E C A M E
T   T   E     F   L   D
```

501

```
S A   D O C K L A N D S
C A S E   R   C   Y
O   T   D O M I N E E R
T H R I C E   Q   E   D
S   O   R   U   C   T
P O L A R   P A C K A G E
I   O   C O T   U   R
N I G G A R D   M O T O R
E   Y   E   P   I   I
  R   C   V   R U D O L F
B O N A F I D E   N   I
  S   R   C   S   D E N E
L E S L I E A S H   D   D
```

498

```
F O U N D   R O L L M O P
A   N   A   O   U   A
C H E V R O N   O U G H T
U   A   T   S   P   G   I
P Y R E   Y O B   H Y D E
    T   M M   S   N
A S H R A M   M A G N E T
S   Y   S   G   A
H O L D   W A G   M I D I
A   E   S   H   B   R   M
M O V I E   A R I Z O N A
E   E   A   R   A   B   G
D I L E M M A   S P I T E
```

502

```
  M I S E R   D R U I D
S   N   N   A   U   N   C
T O A S T   R I S O T T O
A   P   R   R   K   R   U
I N T H E A I R   H U M P
N   N   N   V   A   D   E
  C H I C K E N F E E D
S   A   H   D   T     A
L O G O   D E C E A S E D
I   G   S   R   R   T   M
D R A S T I C   A L I B I
E   R   Y   I   L   F   T
  E D G E D   B L U F F
```

499

```
  P R E V I O U S L Y
  R   D   D   L   E   N
D I L I G E N T   A M O S
  Z   T   A   I   S   B
  E P I C   E M P E R O R
    O   S   A   D
  C O N S I S T E N C Y
  H   L   E   E
T O P S E E D   M A U L
K   O   N   P   T   A
H E A L   C R U D E O I L
R   A   E   R   S   R
  F R U S T R A T E D
```

503

```
R E L A T I V E S   J   A
  R   S   G   L   V O I D
P I P S Q U E A K   S   V
  C   E   A   P   E   A
T A R T A N   S A M P A N
  I   W A L E S   H   C
P U K K A     P R I C E
A   M   K E D G E   N
T H A M E S   U N W E L L
R   Y   K   L   I   E
I   A   D I S L O D G E D
C A L L   M   I   O   K
K   L   N O R T H W E S T
```

500

```
  S   M   A     E   F   M
E C L I P S E D   E R I C
  I   N   S   I   T   K
S L E E V E   S E A M A N
  L   H   N   O   D
H Y P E   T E N N Y S O N
  A   E   U
L A U D A B L E   G N A T
W   L   N   O   V
I N H A L E   G O S P E L
I   X   A   U   L   R
A N N E   C O L L A P S E
G   D   H   F   V   E
```

504

```
  P U B L I C S C H O O L
C   P   A   H   A   P   I
O C E A N   I   P A I N T
R   N   T A R   E   N   T
R I D G E   P U R C E L L
E       R   Y   O   E
S E R E N E   S U B U R B
P   R   J   P   N   O
O V E R D U E   T R A M P
N   N   E   S R I   N   E
D U R U M   T   G E N I E
E   O   O   E   H   U   P
D E L I B E R A T E L Y
```

505

```
   M  C  F  A     C  B
 R E C A L L E D   O L A F
   L  N  U  A     Y  L
 A C K A C K   P O O D L E
   H  P  E     T  T
 R I P E N   R E B E C C A
   O     S  D        A
 O R G A N I C   A B O V E
      N  B     E  A  A
 B O O G I E   N O Z Z L E
   G  L  R  J  A     I
 T R U E   I S O L A T E D
   E  R  A  Y     R  R
```

509

```
   B R U C E W I L L I S
 C  E  L  A     I  T  D
 L U L L A B Y   T R A D E
 A  E  W  L  I  L  T
 S E A L   G A R G O Y L E
 H  S  G  Y  A        R
   R E L A Y   I T C H Y
 G     M  M  E     A  M
 U N C L E S A M   E R I E
 E  R  P  G  A  R  T
 S H A W L   P U R P O S E
 S  W  A  I  A  D  R
   B L U N D E R B U S S
```

506

```
 U R S U L A A N D R E S S
 P  A  O     O  X        H
 B O N G O   F A N Z I N E
 E  D  S  O  E  L        K
 A M A T E U R   G E E S E
 T  L     G  A  D        L
       M O N O C L E
 A  P  N  T        P     S
 N O I S E   T O R M E N T
 D  S  R  E  E  D        I
 R A C C O O N   B R A I N
 E  E  U     U  L        G
 W E S T S I D E S T O R Y
```

510

```
 C A S A N O V A   Y O R K
 A  L  A  E  A  U        A
 G  O   T H R O B   T     F
 E R E C T   G   D E B U T
 O     Y  E  U  R        A
 M E O W   C R E C H E   N
    R  A        T  A
 E   D O C I L E   S K I D
 M  I  R     R  A
 B A N J O   V   S L A N G
 L  A   S T E E P   L     H
 E  R  S  R  C  T        E
 M A Y O   S Y C A M O R E
```

507

```
 G A M E   I N F A N T
   D  V  R  L     U  S
 C O M A T O S E   D E M O
   R  N  N  X     G  O
 H E I D I   V I C E R O Y
   E     S  B        T
 H E A R T H   L O A T H E
   L     O  E     B
 K E T C H U P   A S I D E
   V  L  L  S     C  E
 Z E R O   D I A L O G U E
   N  T  E  K     N  C
   C H A R G E   D R E W
```

511

```
 S  A  S  I   A P R O N
 T E S T T U B E   O  N
 A  T  A  E   Y I E L D
 C R O C K E R Y   G  O
 K  N  E  I   U N I O N
    S  S   T A B   A  K
 B U C K L E   R A N G E R
   I  E   E R A   T  R
 S T Y L E   E S S   S  A
   C  E   R A S P U T I N
 H A S T Y   G I O   I
    S  O   B A N K R U P T A
 B E A N O   N   E  T  A
```

508

```
 B L I N D M A N S B U F F
 O  S  R  V        N     R
 A V A R I C E   P L A N E
    A  P  N     E  W     E
 L O C H   J U N K M A I L
 E  H     E  I  R        A
 T E A P O T   I N T E R N
 H  L  A  W        G     C
 A U S T R I A N   Y A L E
 R  O  S  F        P     M
 G O R S E   F A L S I F Y
 I  A     L        O     E
 C O N S C I E N T I O U S
```

512

```
 E     O  T           C  S  A
 J O S P I N   E A R W I G
 E  T  T  A     S     O  O
 C A R C A S S   S P O O N
 T  I  N  S     O     N  Y
 E A C H   J U I C Y
 D  H  L  R     K  R     R
       M I L A N   V A L E
 S  B  B  N     C  M     M
 C H O I R   C A L Y P S O
 O  A  A  E     W  A     R
 W A R C R Y   C Y P R U S
 L  D  Y        D  T     E
```

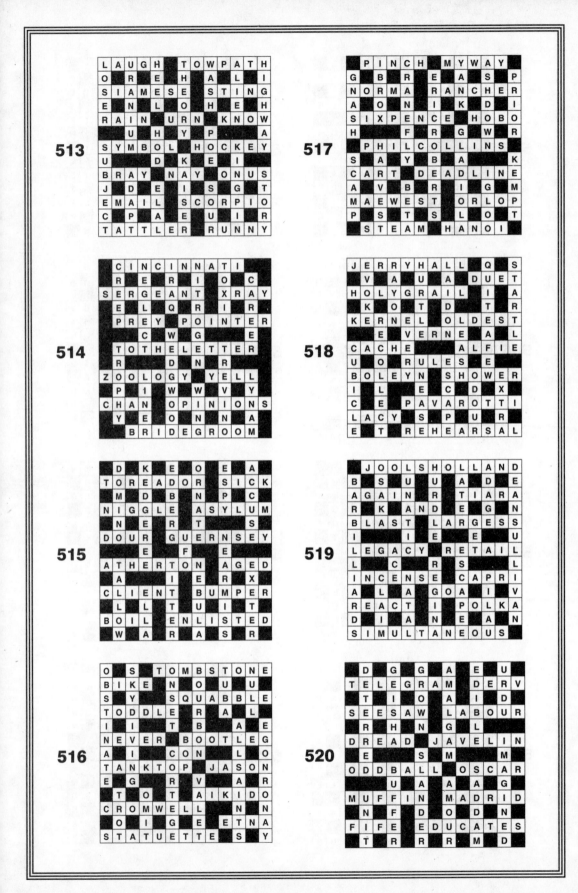

513

514

515

516

517

518

519

520

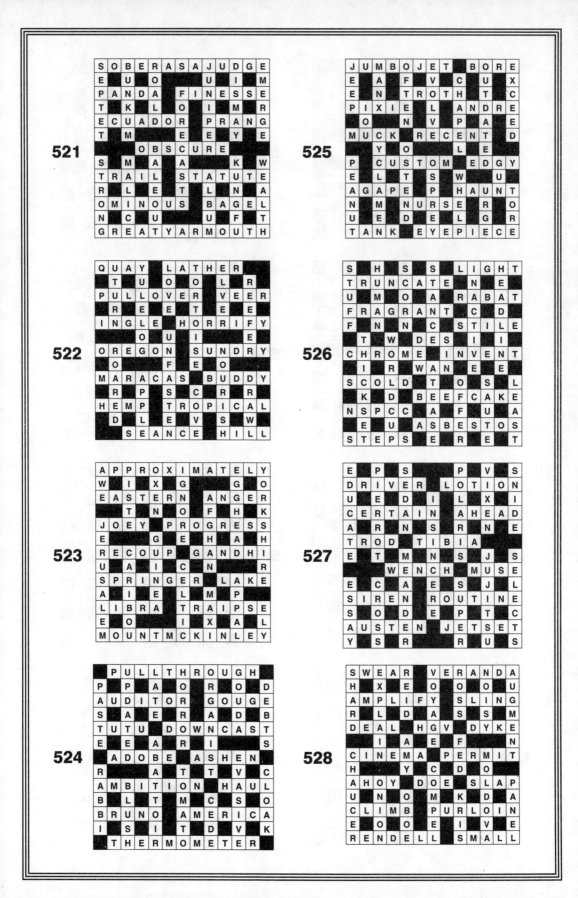

521

```
S O B E R A S A J U D G E
E   U   O       U   I   M
P A N D A   F I N E S S E
T   K   L   O   I   M   R
E C U A D O R   P R A N G
T   M       E   E   Y   E
        O B S C U R E
S   M   A   A       K   W
T R A I L   S T A T U T E
R   L   E   T   L   N   A
O M I N O U S   B A G E L
N   C   U       U   F   T
G R E A T Y A R M O U T H
```

522

```
Q U A Y   L A T H E R
  T   U   O   O   L   R
P U L L O V E R   V E E R
  R   E   E   T   E   E
I N G L E   H O R R I F Y
  O   U   I       E
O R E G O N   S U N D R Y
  O   F   E   O
M A R A C A S   B U D D Y
  R   P   S   C   R   R
H E M P   T R O P I C A L
  D   L   E   V   S   W
    S E A N C E   H I L L
```

523

```
A P P R O X I M A T E L Y
W   I   X   G       G   O
E A S T E R N   A N G E R
    T   N   O   F   H   K
J O E Y   P R O G R E S S
E   G   E   H   A   H
R E C O U P   G A N D H I
U   A   I   C   N   R
S P R I N G E R   L A K E
A   I   E   L   M   P
L I B R A   T R A I P S E
E   O   I   X   A   L
M O U N T M C K I N L E Y
```

524

```
  P U L L T H R O U G H
P   P   A   O   R   O   D
A U D I T O R   G O U G E
S   A   E   R   A   D   B
T U T U   D O W N C A S T
E   E   A   R   I   S
  A D O B E   A S H E N
R   A   T   T   V   C
A M B I T I O N   H A U L
B   L   T   M   C   S   O
B R U N O   A M E R I C A
I   S   I   T   D   V   K
  T H E R M O M E T E R
```

525

```
J U M B O J E T   B O R E
E   A   F   V   C   U   X
E N   T R O T H   T   C
P I X I E   L   A N D R E
  O   N   V   P   A   E
M U C K   R E C E N T   D
    Y   O       L   E
P   C U S T O M   E D G Y
E   L   T   S   W   U
A G A P E   P   H A U N T
N   M   N U R S E   R   O
U   E   D   E   L   G   R
T A N K   E Y E P I E C E
```

526

```
S   H   S   S   L I G H T
T R U N C A T E   N   E
U   M   O   A   R A B A T
F R A G R A N T   C   D
F   N   N   C   S T I L E
  T   W   D E S   I   I
C H R O M E   I N V E N T
I   R   W A N   E   E
S C O L D   T   O   S   L
K   D   B E E F C A K E
N S P C C   A   F   U   A
E   U   A S B E S T O S
S T E P S   E   R   E T
```

527

```
E   P   S       P   V   S
D R I V E R   L O T I O N
U   E   D   I   L   X   I
C E R T A I N   A H E A D
A   R   N   S   R   N   E
T R O D   T I B I A
E   T   M   N   S   J   S
        W E N C H   M U S E
E   C   A   E   S   J   L
S I R E N   R O U T I N E
S   O   D   E   P   T   C
A U S T E N   J E T S E T
Y   S   R       R   U   S
```

528

```
S W E A R   V E R A N D A
H   X   E   O   O   O   U
A M P L I F Y   S L I N G
R   L   D   A   S   S   M
D E A L   H G V   D Y K E
    I   A   E   F       N
C I N E M A   P E R M I T
H   Y   C   D   O
A H O Y   D O E   S L A P
U   N   O   M   K   D   A
C L I M B   P U R L O I N
E   O   O   O   E   I V E
R E N D E L L   S M A L L
```

529

```
E L D E R B E R R Y . .
B . E . O . L . I . A .
R O U L E T T E . N A S H
N . A . A . V . G . C .
Y O Y O . H A N O V E R
. E . . . C . T . . N .
R A D I O L O G I S T .
. E . . . N . R . M .
T A B A S C O . R A I D
. S . W . E . F . G . R
S O L O . I D O L I S E D
. N . K . V . R . N . G
. R E L E N T L E S S .
```

530

```
. C . E . F . A . W . S
F A S T F O O D . A S T I
. S . H . R . V . F . E
S T R I P E . E N T I R E
. R . O . G . R . . E .
S O U P . O N T H E D O T
. I . . . E . N . . . .
T O M A H A W K . C A R E
. B . . . R . A . U . A
M E D I U M . S U M M I T
. Y . O . A . P . B . D
D E A N . D I A M E T E R
. D . A . A . R . . R .
```

531

```
O . D . A M A R Y L L I S
S N U B . I . U . O . N
T . M . R E S O U R C E
R A B B I T . T . T . H
A . F . H . L . P . O
C R O O N . Y E L T S I N
I . U . C A R . E . T
S Y N O N Y M . B R U S H
E . D . A . A . D . E
. R . T . N . R E F O R M
N I N E P I N S . N . E
. C . A . D . O . H Y M N
C H I L T E R N S . M . D
```

532

```
. J O N A H . P I L O T
S . L . B . B . N . R . C
C H I P S . R E C O V E R
U . V . E . O . E . I . A
B I E N N I A L . S L U M
A . . T . D . G . L . P
. S U P E R M A R K E T
I . N . E . I . A . . A
S O C K . S N A T C H E D
S . O . J . D . E . A . D
U K U L E L E . F A R C E
E . T . E . D . U . E . R
. S H I R K . P L U M B
```

533

```
B R E A K D O W N . C . R
. O . U . A . A . M A R E
G U E R R I L L A . F . D
. T . A . N . T . E . U
P E L L E T . E R O T I C
. I . L Y C R A . E . E
P I Z Z A . . L U R I D
I . T . N E W E L . I .
C L A U D E . G Y R A T E
T . Y . Y . B . E . R .
U . L . H O N E Y M O O N
R O O F . R . R . I . U
E . R . D E S T I T U T E
```

534

```
. R E F R I G E R A T O R
C . R . O . R . E . U . E
A L A M O . E . A R T I C
R . S . S E E . D . O . I
T R E N T . D A Y T R I P
O . . E . Y . A . . R .
G O K A R T . T U X E D O
R . L . N . L . . . C .
A L G E B R A . Y U C C A
P . R . A . S O S . R . T
H A I T I . S . S U E D E
E . L . R . A . E . W . S
R E L I N Q U I S H E S .
```

535

```
. A D A M S . S . S . .
R U S E D S K I . P A P A
. T . T . T . C . R . A
S O L A C E . H E A R T S
. B . C . R . A . I . .
B A T H E . T E E N A G E
. H . . . H . L . . L .
A N T I Q U E . S O Y U Z
. . . G . S . A . P . T
G A N N E T . B E A U T Y
. K . I . L . B . Q . O
L I F T . E L O Q U E N T
. N . E . D . T . E . Y
```

536

```
P I E R C E B R O S N A N
A . N . R . . A . E . U
S W I P E . S E R P E N T
T . G . E T . S . S . M
R A M B L E R . M O O S E
Y . A . A . . A . N . G
. . . D E S T I N Y . . .
A . J . V . E . . B . B
T B O N E . G E S T U R E
T . V . R . I . A . T . A
I D I O T I C . L E A P T
L . A . O . . V . N . E
A T L A N T I C O C E A N
```

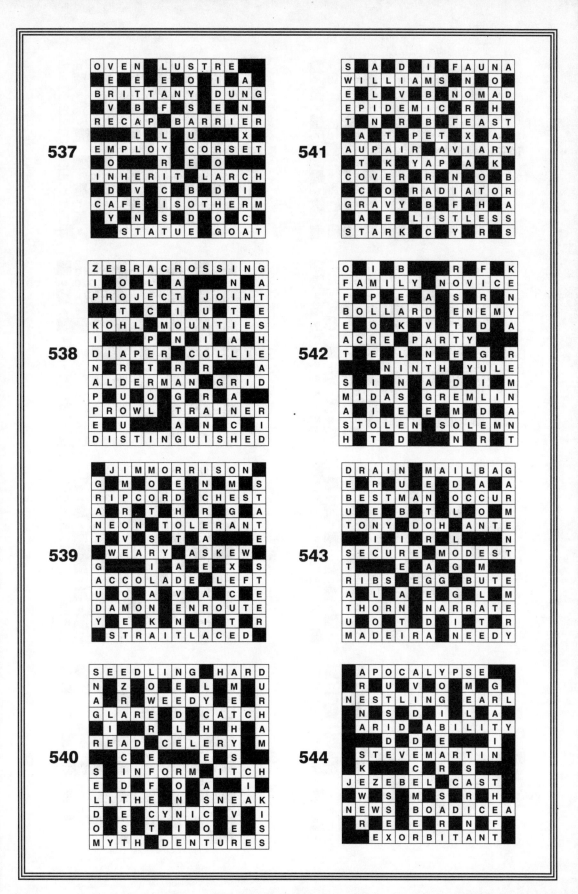

545

```
  M A B S   B T
P I E D M O N T   R O U T
L   J   G   I   E R
A L P A C A   F I D G E T
E   C   R   L   E
B R A E   T H E B R O N X
    N   O       E
H A S T I N G S   C U B E
    N   A   I   E R
E N D E A R   G I N G E R
    U   P   R   N T T
R A V E   O V E R L O O K
    L   E   W   T Y N
```

549

```
  C O M P L I M E N T E D
A   R   U   N   M   E   I
R E B E L   V   B U R N S
T   I   S K I   E   S   C
F A T W A   T O R P E D O
U   T   E       A   T   N
L E T T E R   V I R G I N
D       I   R   L       E
O B S C E N E   L O G I C
D   O   A   F B I   U   T
G E N U S   U   C A S T E
E   I   E   T   I   T   D
R E C O L L E C T I O N
```

546

```
B   O   T A R A N T I N O
L O F T   P   S   O   E
E   F   A L S A T I A N
A N S W E R   U   E   T
S   P   T   R   D   A
D I R T Y   M E G R Y A N
A   I   S O D   S   N
L E N I E N T   A M P L E
E   G   O   S   E   F
  L   C   W   H E L P E R
  U   L   O   E D I O N
P R O M E N A D E   A K
```

547

```
  T E P E E   M A G I C
O   V   L   T   R   D
C R A V E   A P O L O G Y
T   D   N P   M   N   F
T E L E C T I O N   F A R E
T   U   F   R   G   D
  P A R A P H R A S E S
S   B   L   O   K   F
P O S H   A N C E S T O R
I   T   S   O   I W   I
C H A T E A U   T R I A L
E   I   M   R   I N   L
  A N T I C   A N G E L
```

550

```
  S   T   I   A   H   H
S A L E S M A N   E G O N
  T   A   P   I   B   N
B U B B L E   S T R E E P
  R   A   L   E   E
B A D G E   N E T W O R K
  T   A   D       I
N E S T E G G   S T A F F
    A   I   P   A   F
G A M B O L   R E V E R E
  L   L   I   U   E   A
C O R E   T E N E R I F E
  E   T   Y   E   N   F
```

548

```
L O N D O N Z O O   C   E
  M   E   E Y   B O O M
F A U L T L E S S   N   I
  H   H   S   T   T   N
C A S I N O   E N D U R E
    C   A N G R Y   S   N
V I O L A       M O I S T
I   O   F E D U P   O
A L B E I T   S H A N T Y
D   Y   H   E   C   R
U   D   M A Y F L O W E R
C L O T   N   U   R   S
T   O   R E P L E N I S H
```

551

```
W E I G H T L I F T I N G
A   N   A       U   T   R
R O S E S   C O R S A G E
S   I   T   A   N   L   A
A D D R E S S   A L I A S
W   E   T   C   C   E
    C I T I Z E N
C   G   N   G       G   R
R O A C H   A U S T E R E
I   T   A   T   P   N   M
T R E M B L E   O P E R A
I   A   I       U   V   R
C O U N T E R A T T A C K
```

552

```
M A S H   E X T E N D
  L   O   X   H   O   P
S O F T W A R E   D A U B
  F   L   M   H   D   T
S T R I P   L A N Y A R D
    N   A   G       I
M E T E O R   U G A N D A
  Y       G   E   L
S E L L O U T   B I N G O
  L   A   M   S   B   R
P E S T   E M U L A T E D
  T   H   N   R   B   E
  B E R T I E   A U R A
```

553

```
B A S I C I N S T I N C T
A W U O . . . . U . . . R
T R A C T O R . M E L B A
. R . E . M . A . L . V .
E M M Y . L A D Y L I K E
N . . R . N . H . F . L .
D I S P E L . J E K Y L L
E . C . A . S . M . . . E
A N E C D O T E . S P A R
V . P . E . U . M . L . .
O T T E R . P R E T E X T
U . I . . . I . N . A . O
R I C H A R D B U R T O N
```

554

```
. R U N N I N G L A T E .
F . P . A . O . A . R . S
A R R I V E D . B L A C K
L . I . E . O . O . I . I
S A G A . A F L U T T E R
E . H . S . F . R . T . .
. O T H E R . P E T E R .
R . . D . M . R . R . E .
I M P R I S O N . C R U X
G . A . M . R . K . A . P
H A L V E . T H E A T R E
T . M . N . A . P . I . L
. M A N T E L P I E C E .
```

555

```
N E L L G W Y N . V A R Y
O . I . U . E . S . V . E
W . I V O R Y . S N E E R
T W E E D . V . I . T . Y
. E . . E . I . T . M . L
H E S S . C L U E D O . .
. . P . C . . . M . R . .
M . U P R O A R . F E E D
I . R . A . D . A . L . .
D A I L Y . M . G N O M E
G . O . O U I J A . A . M
E . U . N . . . R . T . I
T O S H . D E T E C T O R
```

556

```
S . S . D . U . S T R A P
C H L O R I N E . R . P .
O . O . I . I . D A L E K
R U T H L E S S . V . R .
E . H . L . O . M O T I F
. W . F . A N T . L . T .
B E H I N D . O X T A I L
. L . R . O B E . A . F .
F L O S S . A . S . F . S
. T . T . B R A C E L E T
L O Y A L . T . R . O . U
. D . I . R E P A I R E D
M O O D Y . R . M . A . Y
```

557

```
S . R . K . . . C . V . P
W O E F U L . C H O I C E
A . G . D . M . E . C . P
P I A N O L A . D I A R Y
P . L . S . H . D . R . S
E D I T . J A P A N . . .
D . A . A . R . R . H . B
. . . B R E A D . W E I R
T . S . C . J . K . X . I
W E L C H . A B R E A S T
A . I . A . H . O . G . T
I M P A I R . S N O O Z E
N . S . C . . . E . . . N
```

558

```
P O U C H . S A V E L O Y
O . M . A . T . E . A . A
S U B L I M E . T R U S S
E . R . L . F . O . R . H
R E A M . R A W . W A R M
. . G . E . N . W . . . A
T W E L V E . S H R I E K
O . . E . R . Y . V . . .
B A N G . O U T . W A I T
A . I . A . S . Z . N . .
C H E S S . S T E P H E N
C . C . I . E . U . O . G
O V E R A C T . S E E D Y
```

559

```
. U N C L E R E M U S . .
. T . O . X . N . N . A .
U T E N S I L S . D E B T
. E . F . T . C . E . S .
. R A I L . L O U R D E S
. . . D . A . N . . . N .
. I N E F F I C I E N T .
. R . F . E . Q . . . . .
T R I P O L I . Q U I T .
. U . A . U . M . A . R .
S P U R . E L E C T R I C
. T . K . N . M . O . K .
. E A S T B O U R N E . .
```

560

```
. S . S . R . U . E . O .
I N N O C E N T . D E F T
. E . N . V . O . G . F .
B E S I D E . P R E A C H
. Z . N . R . I . U . . .
H E L L . T R A V E S T Y
. A . . . U . T . . . . .
E N T W I N E D . E M M A
. O . . . I . E . R . Y .
F R O L I C . M I N I O N
. M . E . K . A . I . P .
V A S E . E I N S T E I N
. L . R . L . D . Y . C .
```

561

```
O E . C O N F L I C T S
F O X Y . P . U . D . A
F . C . R E S O L U T E
T R A U M A . S . E . E
H . L . H . P . S . A .
E M I L Y . J O S T L E D
P . B . P O T . I . V .
E Q U E R R Y . T O N N E
G . R . O . M . G . N .
. D . I . R . O U T S E T
C O X S W A I N . H . U
. D . I . T . T . R O A R
M O U S T A C H E . T . E
```

565

```
. L . P . A . A . I . E
V I L L A G E S . M I M E
. F . A . R . P . P . I
D E V I C E . H E A R T Y
. T . C . E . A . C .
F I D E L . B L A T A N T
. M . I . T . . . O .
D E S C E N D . J A U N T
. Y . S . A . U . S .
N O U G H T . C O B W E B
. P . N . E . R . U . N
C A P E . A P I A R I S T
. L . T . D . D . N . E
```

562

```
. T H Y M E . M O T E L
S . O . E . M . A . G . U
T R U S T . A C T I O N S
O . S . A . R . S . T . H
C H E A P E S T . P I P E
K . H . H . A . S . R .
. A C C O M M O D A T E
S . H . R . A . R . P
H O A X . A L L I A N C E
R . M . C . L . A . E . A
E M B A R G O . T O P E R
W . E . A . W . I . A . L
. T R I B E . S C A L E
```

566

```
J U S T I F I C A T I O N
O . H . N . L . C . U .
S N I F F . C R A V I N G
T . N . E . E . D . C . G
L A T E R A L . D E L V E
E . Y . E . I . E . T .
. . I K E B A N A . . .
T . L . I . R . A . P
R O Y A L . A D M I R A L
A . C . D . T . E . M . E
G R E N A D E . D I A N A
I . U . R . . . I . N . S
C O M M E R C I A L I S E
```

563

```
P I R O U E T T E . S . S
. N . F . R . R . D U C T
B E E F E A T E R . N . A
. R . A . S . M . F . R
A T T L E E . O U T L E T
. E . A D O R N . O . E
V I S O R . C O W E R
I . T . T W I R L . E
T A I C H I . H E A R S E
A . M . L . O . L . L
L . O . G L A D I A T O R
L O N G . I . E . I . P
Y . Y . P E R S O N N E L
```

567

```
S T I R . E I T H E R
. W . E . N . U . X . C
D I S C O V E R . T A L C
. C . L . Y . N . O . O
R E L A X . F O O L I S H
. I . I . V . . . E .
S E R M O N . E Q U A T E
. L . S . R . N .
B A C K O U T . A D L I B
. T . E . L . W . R . B
J E S T . A C A D E M I C
. D . C . T . G . S . Z
. C H E E S E . S N A P
```

564

```
. I N H O S P I T A B L E
P . I . N . R . Y . O . X
E I G H T . I . S T O A T
R . H . A P E . O . S . R
A L T E R . S I N A T R A
M . I . T . G . . . V .
B A L L O T . A L A S K A
U . E . G . U . . . G
L E A T H E R . C O C O A
A . T . Y . O U I . E . N
T I T L E . U . F E L T Z
O . I . N . N . E . L
R I C H A R D P R Y O R
```

568

```
J U L I O I G L E S I A S
A . I . H . I . M . E
B E L G I U M . L E M U R
. A . O . L . E . E . V
O U C H . H E L S I N K I
N . D . T . T . S . E
S O R B E T . D E T E C T
L . E . N . S . R . T
A P P R O A C H . C A N E
U . L . T . A . G . T
G U I S E . M E A S L E S
H . C . P . L . A . I
T R A N Q U I L L I S E R
```

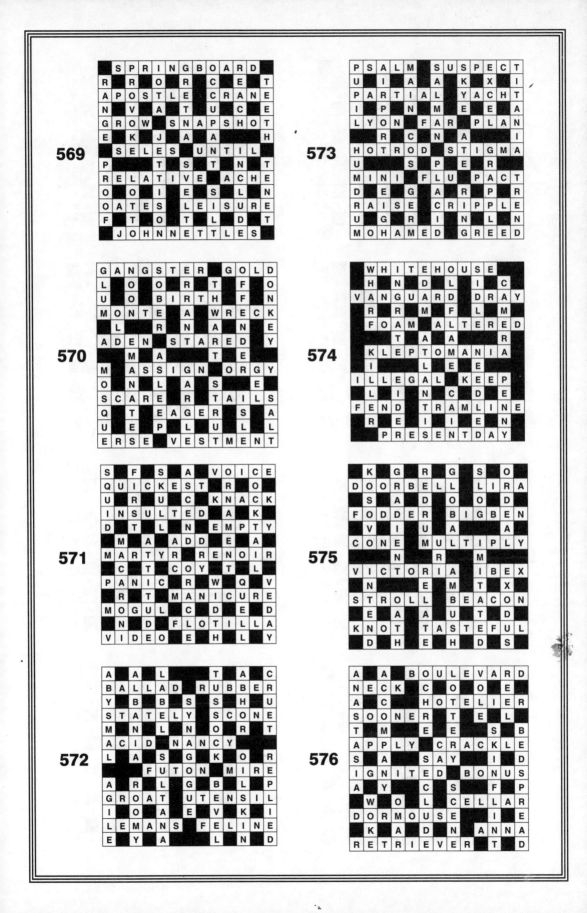

569 570 571 572 573 574 575 576

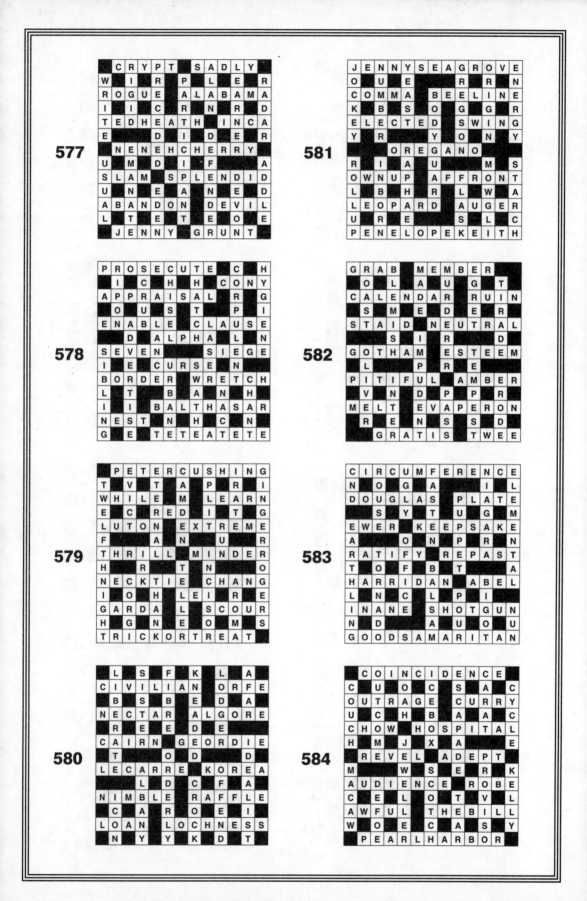

577

581

578

582

579

583

580

584